Flavor Chemistry

A symposium sponsored by the
Division of Agricultural and
Food Chemistry at the 149th
Meeting of the American
Chemical Society, Detroit,
Mich., April 6–7, 1965.

Irwin Hornstein, *Symposium Chairman*

ADVANCES IN CHEMISTRY SERIES **56**

AMERICAN CHEMICAL SOCIETY

WASHINGTON, D.C.   1966

Library of Congress Catalog Card 66-27216

PRINTED IN THE UNITED STATES OF AMERICA

Advances in Chemistry Series

Robert F. Gould, *Editor*

AMERICAN CHEMICAL SOCIETY PUBLICATIONS

1-3367 - dupont Am Chemautyre. 8.00 - £1X.

56776

FOREWORD

ADVANCES IN CHEMISTRY SERIES was founded in 1949 by the American Chemical Society as an outlet for symposia and collections of data in special areas of topical interest that could not be accommodated in the Society's journals. It provides a medium for symposia that would otherwise be fragmented, their papers distributed among several journals or not published at all. Papers are refereed critically according to ACS editorial standards and receive the careful attention and processing characteristic of ACS publications. Papers published in ADVANCES IN CHEMISTRY SERIES are original contributions not published elsewhere in whole or major part and include reports of research as well as reviews since symposia may embrace both types of presentation.

CONTENTS

Preface   vii

1. Chemical Excitation of Taste and Odor Receptors   1
   Lloyd M. Beidler, Florida State University, Tallahassee, Fla.

2. Current Status of Odor Theories   29
   Andrew Dravnieks, IIT Research Institute, Chicago, Ill.

3. Objective Approaches to Odor Measurement   53
   Henri L. Rosano, City University of New York, New York, N. Y.,
   and Herman H. Friedman, General Foods Corp., Tarrytown, N. Y.

4. Sensory Evaluation of Food Flavor   64
   Amihud Kramer, University of Maryland, College Park, Md.

5. Progress and Limitations in the Identification of Flavor Components   70
   William S. Ryder, General Foods Corp., Tarrytown, N. Y.

6. Role of Milk Lipids in Flavors of Dairy Products   94
   Edgar A. Day, Oregon State University, Corvallis, Ore.

7. Advances in Fruit Flavor Chemistry   121
   Roy Teranishi, U. S. Department of Agriculture, Albany, Calif.

8. Separation and Characterization of Flavor Components from Vegetables   131
   Richard A. Bernhard, University of California, Davis, Calif.

9. Chemistry of Bread Flavor   153
   John A. Johnson, Lloyd Rooney, and Ali Salem, Kansas State University, Manhattan, Kan.

10. Beverage Flavors   174
    Kurt S. Konigsbacher and Mary Ellen Donworth, Evans Research
    and Development Corp., New York, N. Y.

11. Flavor of Flesh Foods   190
    H. L. A. Tarr, Fisheries Research Board of Canada, Vancouver,
    B. C., Canada

12. Advances in Spice Flavor and Oleoresin Chemistry   203
    J. A. Rogers, Fritzsche Brothers, Inc., New York, N. Y.

13. Irradiation Damage in Lipids   225
    Charles Merritt, Jr., Pio Angelini, M. L. Bazinet, and D. J. McAdoo,
    U. S. Army Natick Laboratories, Natick, Mass.

14. **Flavor and Biochemistry of Volatile Banana Components** 241
     Emily L. Wick, Alice I. McCarthy, Marshall Myers, Edwina
     Murray, Harry Nursten, and Phillip Issenberg, Massachusetts Insti-
     tute of Technology, Cambridge, Mass.

15. **Recent Studies of 5′-Nucleotides as New Flavor Enhancers** 261
     Akira Kuninaka, Massachusetts Institute of Technology, Cam-
     bridge, Mass.

Index 275

PREFACE

The factor which has the greatest influence on flavor is odor. If a food has no odor, its "flavor" is gone and it is experienced primarily in terms of bitter, sweet, sour, and salt. The happy circumstance that odor is basic to flavor and that instrumental techniques for the analysis of trace amounts of volatiles have been perfected to a degree undreamed of only 10 years ago has enabled the flavor chemist to accumulate data on the volatile odor constituents of flavors at an ever-increasing rate.

Surprisingly, this steadily increasing accumulation of factual information has not provided the breakthrough that seemed imminent just a short time ago. True, much valuable information has been gained. Useful imitation flavors have been created. The quality control of raw materials going into processed foods has been improved. The flavor quality of foods available to the consumer has been upgraded. But this accumulation of data has not led to any better understanding of how we experience flavor, to the development of any objective methods for the evaluation of flavor, or to the duplication of a naturally occurring flavor.

The identification of literally hundreds of compounds present in the volatiles of desirable and undesirable flavors is an impressive tribute to the skill and ingenuity of the analytical chemist. A flavor investigation approached solely as an analytical problem requires that the chemist track down and determine the concentration of all the compounds that can be sensed by taste or smell. Then, and only then, can he hope to duplicate successfully all the nuances of taste and odor that characterize a naturally occurring flavor. The enormity of the analytical task is self-evident. The sampling procedure is, in itself, a source of difficulty. Head space analysis of volatiles may ignore the contributions to flavor of higher boiling materials. Extraction and concentration techniques may destroy flavor components or create flavor artifacts. And even assuming that the operational procedures produce no flavor alterations, the compounds to be identified may be many, their concentration vanishingly small, and their stability fleeting.

The highly sophisticated flavor work currently being done is well illustrated in a recent paper by Day and Libby (1). A programmed temperature capillary column gas chromatographic pattern of a Cheddar cheese concentrate revealed approximately 130 components. Mass spectrometry was used to identify at least 46 of these compounds. This chromatographic pattern of 130 compounds was, however, still considered incomplete since highly polar compounds were retained by the column and low boiling volatiles were probably lost during solvent removal. Despite the identification of the major components, the authors added this note of caution. "Since the unidentified compounds in low concentration may also have significant aroma-contributing qualities, conclusions on the significance of various compounds are forbidden at this point."

It is this task—to evaluate the significance of the data—that is the biggest problem facing the flavor chemist today. Detection and identification of volatile compounds are essential, but the correlation of chemical findings with organoleptic quality is equally important, and progress in this direction has been slow. Emphasizing this problem of data evaluation is the interesting pattern that has emerged from much of the flavor research on the volatile compounds produced from foods prepared by dry heating or boiling in water. Similar low boiling aldehydes, ketones, alcohols, sulfides, and thiols are found in the volatiles of meat, bread, cooked vegetables, and presumably in the volatiles of other foods where nonvolatile precursors react to form volatile flavors. These questions arise—Are these rather simple compounds the characteristic flavor compounds? Do quantitative differences result in the qualitative flavor differences we experience? or, Do these compounds provide a common background note and the trace amounts of higher boiling volatiles that have been detected but not identified in all of these products provide the characteristic flavor? Again the flavor chemist is faced with evaluation problems that he cannot solve.

Another problem facing the flavor chemist, and this too results from the inability to establish meaningful flavor correlation, is the absence of a coherent nomenclature with which to describe flavor experiences. Terms such as floral, ethereal, pungent, rancid, oxidized, etc., may mean very different things to different observers, and this inability to communicate intelligently hampers attempts to correlate flavor and structure based on results obtained in different laboratories. The ability of the flavor chemist, thanks in a large degree to advances in instrumentation, to identify flavor compounds has outstripped the efforts of those trying to correlate structure and odor as well as those trying to elucidate the mechanism of odor detection. A comprehensive flavor theory is still to be formulated. The mechanism by which odors are perceived is still unclear. The relationship between chemical structure and flavor is essentially unknown. As a result, the type of information essential to the establishment of criteria for objective flavor evaluations is still meager.

I have emphasized the problems that the flavor chemist faces; the following papers emphasize the tremendous progress that has been made in spite of the enormous experimental difficulties characteristic of this area of research.

The purpose of this symposium is not only to present recent advances in flavor chemistry but also to bring together current thoughts concerning the mechanism of taste and odor reception, odor theories, and approaches to flavor evaluation. The hope is that this exchange of ideas will open new approaches to flavor evaluation.

Literature Cited

(1) Day, E. A., Libby, M., *J. Food Sci.* **29**, 576 (1964).

IRWIN HORNSTEIN

Market Quality Research Division
Agricultural Research Service, USDA
Beltsville, Md.
April 1965

Chemical Excitation of Taste and Odor Receptors

LLOYD M. BEIDLER

Department of Biological Sciences, Florida State University, Tallahassee, Fla.

The mechanisms of chemical excitation of taste and olfactory receptors are similar, both depending upon adsorption of the stimulus molecules to the receptor surfaces. The plausibility of relations between molecular structure and odor thresholds depends greatly upon the reliability of experimental data. Present theoretical concepts of chemoreceptor stimulation may serve as a basis for prediction and design of experiments in flavor research.

The flavor of an exquisite food is as satisfying as the beauty of a sculptured Venus. It is said that beauty is in the mind of the observer. The reaction of man to the sculpture is complex and depends not only upon the beauty of the object but also on past experiences and their emotional content. This is rather similar to the delight obtained from an unusually fine food prepared by an outstanding chef. His is also a rare art that cannot easily be explained in scientific terms. It is difficult to describe a Venus or a fine food in terms of the language we have at our command. We have a tendency to use a series of words such as sweet, sour, and fruity in describing a flavor, but we are never able to convey a satisfactory description of a particular food to another person. This is not surprising, since in describing Venus we convey little impression by telling how light or dark the statue is, and whether it is straight or round at any given point. The only way we can convey the impression of Venus is to make a similar statue or take a picture of the original. We have not yet appreciated the fact that a flavor may approach the complexity of a visual image.

Taste Qualities

The scientist who studies the basis of flavor finds the problem so complex that he makes a simplification and redefines flavor in terms of the stimulation of taste and odor receptors. Then he may ask, how many different tastes can we perceive? Miller (*33*) has shown that when someone tries to categorize sensations such as those of pitch, loudness, and odors, he usually obtains about 7 ± 2 categories. A limit on our capacity for processing information is related to our inability to comprehend more than about 7 to 9 such categories at any given time. When one categorizes taste, about seven different types are also found. We may start with the so-called primary tastes—sour, bitter, salty, and sweet—but when pressed, we usually add a few others such as metallic, alkaline or soapy, and astringent. In reading the history of our present development of taste qualities, one is impressed with the agreement about sour, bitter, salty, and sweet, and the fact that each investigator adds a few more qualities to describe such things as soap or the fullness of monosodium glutamate. We talk about four primary taste qualities because it was thought that the taste buds, the organs of taste, respond only to these four types of substances and that the other qualities, such as metallic, are due to stimulation of free nerve endings on the surface of the tongue. As taste categorization is simplified, the description of a real flavor becomes more difficult. Most taste scientists use the concept of four taste qualities but do not for a moment believe that four can completely describe all tastes.

Taste and odor should be compared to visual images on the retina. That is, we should consider not only which specific receptors are stimulated but also where they are located on the tongue surface and when they are stimulated. The tongue is organized with certain areas more sensitive to a given taste substance than others. For example, the anterior of the tongue is more sensitive to sweet than the posterior; the posterior is more sensitive to bitter. Thus, the flavor of a substance depends very greatly upon which part of the tongue is stimulated. This is utilized by the youngster who, when taking a bitter medicine, swallows quickly to avoid stimulating the back of the tongue. On the other hand, a child tends to lick a lollipop with the tip of the tongue. A wine taster slowly moves the wine from the tip of the tongue to the sides and finally to the back in order to obtain a full appreciation of the flavor. There are temporal differences in the response of receptors to a given stimulus. For example, receptors respond to salty substances much faster than to bitter. The taste of malic acid builds up more slowly than that of citric acid but persists longer.

If there are but four primary taste qualities, it should be possible to mix compounds representing these qualities to duplicate the taste of any given natural substance or food. This was tried by von Skramlik (*49*), who used quinine, sodium chloride, tartaric acid, and glucose as compounds he thought elicited one pure taste quality. In many cases he was able to duplicate the taste of other inorganic salts. However, it is impossible to make such taste duplications of more complex substances.

Flavor and Information Theory

Information theory allows us to make a quantitative comparison of the complexity of the auditory, visual, gustatory, and olfactory systems. We can obtain a measure of the maximum informational capacity of a sensory system by simply multiplying the number of available sensory receptor units by the maximum frequency of nerve impulses that can be sent from each of these units toward the central nervous system. (It is assumed that each nerve fiber carries one bit of information for each nerve impulse transmitted.) For example, in man there are about ten million olfactory receptors, each of which can conduct a maximum of about ten nerve impulses per second over its neural extension. Thus, the informational capacity of the olfactory receptor system is about 10^8 bits per second. This compares favorably with the 10^6 optic nerve fibers, each of which carries 300 nerve impulses per second to produce an information capacity of 3×10^8 bits per second (*1*). If one considers the taste nerves, as well as other sensory nerves of man which are stimulated by foods taken into the mouth, one can estimate that there are 10^4 taste buds (*42*), each of which is innervated by 2 to 10 nerve fibers and there are more than 10^4 other sensory fibers subserving tactile, temperature, pain, etc., each of which has a maximum impulse frequency of 200 per second. Thus, the informational capacity is about 10^7 to 10^8 bits per second. This means that the gustatory and olfactory systems may be capable of handling information almost as complex as that utilized by the visual system.

The above calculations of the informational capacities were based on ideal anatomical and physiological considerations. What capacities are found when psychophysical data are considered? One measure may be obtained from a knowledge of the number of intensities (JND's) and qualities of sensations that can be discriminated by a given sensory system. In audition, for example, Stevens and Davis (*51*) conclude that the average person can discriminate 1500 different pitches, each with an average of 227 different loudnesses, or a total of 340,000 distinguishable tones. It has been estimated (*22*) that some observers can distinguish as high as 10,000 different odor qualities and that for each odor quality they can distinguish about 20 different levels of intensity. This indicates that the informational capacity of the olfactory system for this type of discrimination is of the order of magnitude of that of the human ear. The number of different qualities of taste that can be discriminated is difficult to determine, but it is clear that although we think of sugars as all being sweet, each one tastes slightly different and can be discriminated. Most of the taste substances studied have 20 to 30 different intensities of taste that can be distinguished by the average human. It is not unlikely that the informational content of taste is similar to that of olfaction as measured by behavioral responses. The number of distinguishable colors is similar to the magnitude of discriminability of the ear, according to Stevens and Davis (51), which in turn we have shown to be similar to that of the nose.

Engen and Pfaffmann (17, 18) obtained another measure of the information capacity of the olfactory system using absolute judgments. They concluded that the informational capacity obtained by this method is far less than the above calculations would indicate but is still comparable to that of the other sense modalities as determined by similar experimentation (33). They state, ". . .given some practise, the human's ability to judge odor intensity approaches his ability to judge auditory and visual stimuli. His ability to identify odor quality is not phenomenal but falls within the range of his ability to identify multidimensional stimuli in other sense modalities." We may therefore conclude that the flavor of a food may be very complicated, and we are capable of making as complex decisions concerning flavor as concerning art or music. Many simplifying assumptions have been made in the above calculations (28), but they probably do not change the overall argument.

It is often useful to capture enough information associated with a given sensation so that we can transfer it to another person at some distant place and have him receive the satisfaction he would have if he had experienced the original sensation. Such is the case with television, where visual experiences are brought into the home using a television channel with an informational capacity of about 10^7 bits per second (1). The problem with flavor imitation is similar. Imitating strawberry flavor will be difficult because the odors and taste associated with the flavor are not released simultaneously as one eats a strawberry. In addition, the tactile and other receptors of the tongue contribute greatly to the over-all flavor. Even color plays a large role in flavor determination. One would not like to eat purple mashed potatoes, even though the purple coloring may not have any taste or odor. The role of color in identifying flavor is particularly important when one asks a child to identify various fruity Popsickles or Kool-Ade in the dark. This is a difficult task even for an adult. In conclusion, one must agree that flavor is a very complex phenomenon, and although the taste scientist must simplify such a complex system, we should realize that after we understand something about the simple system, we are far from understanding the real system itself—namely, the flavor of fine foods.

Coding of Taste Messages

It is often thought that there exist taste buds responsive only to sugars, others to salts, others to bitters, and others to sours. This is commonly stated in textbooks today, although it was proved wrong many years ago. Since one is able, with electrophysiological methods, to tap in on the neural messages being sent from the taste bud to the brain, it is

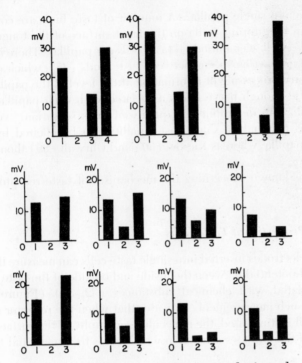

Figure 1. Change in resting potential of single
cells of taste buds in response to chemical stimulation

1. 0.1M NaCl
2. 0.5M sucrose
3. 0.02M quinine hydrochloride
4. 0.05M HCl

possible to study some of the properties of taste coding. Most single
nerve fibers respond to not just one of the four simplified taste qualities,
but to many (44). In addition, if microelectrodes are placed in the individual cells of the taste bud, it is found that these cells also respond to a
variety of stimuli and not just to stimuli of one quality (31, 32) (see
Figure 1). In fact, it looks as if each receptor is a little different from its
neighbor, so that we do not have highly specific receptors, nor receptors
that are all alike. This means that the coding of information concerning
taste quality is much more complex than we normally like to think.
Pfaffmann (41, 42) addressed himself to this problem several times and
concluded that the pattern of nerve activity coming from many different
taste cells determines the taste quality.

Although both single taste nerve fibers and single taste receptors
within a taste bud respond to stimuli of more than one taste quality, it is
not certain how much information related to taste quality sensation is

obtained from a single papilla. A number of taste buds are contained in each human fungiform papilla on the front surface of the tongue. Thus, there may be well over a hundred taste cells per papilla. There is evidence that neural interactions occur between taste buds (45), which could lead to preliminary processing of information at the level of the papilla. There appear to be enough nerve fibers associated with each papilla so that a single papilla can determine the quality of taste sensation. von Bekesy (10) claims that only a single taste quality can be elicited by a single fungiform papilla, whereas Kiesow (30) and Öhrwall (39) thought otherwise.

What is known concerning the mechanism of taste receptor stimulation?

Electrical Properties of Taste Cells

Microelectrodes inserted into single taste cells can measure the change in electrical potential between the inside and outside of the taste cell when it is stimulated with chemical substances (32, 53) (Figure 2). An analysis of such measurements indicates that when the receptor surface of the taste cell is stimulated, the molecular geography of the surface changes slightly and this initiates a reaction which leads to a small and temporary

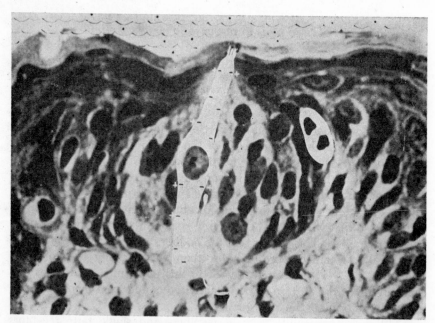

Figure 2. Taste bud with single taste cell shown as electrically charged Notice cell undergoing mitotic division near periphery of taste bud. Daughter cell may enter taste bud to become a taste cell.

breakdown in the portion of the taste cell membrane near the associated nerve axon. This breakdown allows the potassium ions, which are in high concentration inside the cell, to escape. This results in a change in the electrical potential across the cell membrane, which in turn initiates electrical nerve impulses that are transmitted to the brain. These impulses are of only a few milliseconds' duration and may be sent along the nerve with a frequency of as high as 100 or 200 per second. It is the frequency of these impulses and the number of nerve fibers activated that signal to the brain the intensity of the taste stimulation. The energy to initiate the nerve impulses does not arise from the stimulus. In fact, the energy associated with the electrical potential across the surface of the taste cell is due to the difference in ion concentration between the inside and outside of the cell, which is maintained by cellular metabolism.

Mechanism of Receptor Stimulation

The magnitude of electrical neural response emanating from the taste receptors can be recorded electronically and measured quantitatively (Figure 3). The response magnitude increases at a declining rate with concentration until a point is reached where further increases in concentration no longer increase response. A quantitative analysis of such response-concentration functions led Beidler (7) to derive a mathematical equation that describes the relation between magnitude of steady-state response and concentration:

$$\frac{C}{R} = \frac{C}{R_s} + \frac{1}{KR_s}$$

where C is the concentration of the stimulus, R is the magnitude of electrical response, R_s is the maximum magnitude of electrical response at saturation level, and K is the equilibrium constant of the reaction between the stimulus and the receptor. The chemist will readily note that this equation is similar to the Langmuir adsorption isotherm, and the biochemist will notice a similarity with the equation he uses to describe enzyme-substrate reactions. In fact, such a hyperbolic equation can describe a large number of physical processes that may be unrelated to any chemical or biological function. The equation describes a sigmoid curve when plotted on a semilogarithmic basis (R vs. log C). The middle range of this curve can be approximated to a logarithmic relation between the magnitude of response and concentration, but such an approximation fails at high and low concentrations. Thus, one concludes that agreement of data with a given equation is not alone sufficient to prove that the theory leading to the equation is correct. Additional experiments with taste receptors led Beidler (8) to conclude that the chemical stimulus is weakly adsorbed to the surface of the taste receptors. The equilibrium constant for many substances is between 5 and 15, although with a stimulus such as sodium saccharinate it can be greater than 1500.

The similarity between the taste equation and that describing enzyme-substrate reactions led Duncan (*16*) to conclude that the initial reaction of taste stimulation is an enzymatic process. He postulated that enzymes in the surface of the receptor react with the stimulus substrate—for example, sodium chloride— to catalyze some unspecified reaction. Such a

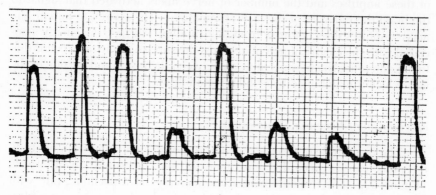

Figure 3. Summated response of electrical neural activity from rat taste nerve in response to 0.1M concentrations of NH₄Cl, LiCl, NaCl, KCl, NaCl, RbCl, CsCl, and NaCl, applied to surface of tongue
Time scale. 1 large division = 20 seconds

concept is difficult to accept, particularly since experimental evidence has not been forthcoming to support such a theory. Enzymes are proteins which are very pH-dependent, yet the response of taste receptors to sodium chloride, for example, is rather independent of pH between 3 and 11. Furthermore, if the enzymatic processes were reasonably specific, one would have to postulate a very large number of enzymes to take care of the tens of thousands of different taste stimuli.

The fact that the initial mechanism is not enzymatically controlled does not mean that other processes in the cell that either directly or indirectly affect the taste response are not enzymatically controlled. The metabolism of the cell involves many different enzymes. However, when enzymatic inhibitors are used in taste studies to determine whether the initial mechanism is enzymatically controlled or not, it must be remembered that the taste response may occur within 25 milliseconds after the stimulus is applied to the receptor. If enzymatic inhibitors were applied to the receptor over a period of many minutes or an hour, one would expect many changes in the normal function of the entire cell. This would have little bearing on the importance of enzymes in the initial reaction which occurs well within 20 or 30 milliseconds. Thus, we must conclude that until additional evidence is found, the concept that the taste chemical is weakly adsorbed to the surface of the cell, which in turn creates a disturbance in the molecular geography of that surface and allows an interchange of ions across the surface is a useful one. An electrical depolarization of the taste receptor follows the ion interchange, and a nerve impulse is initiated.

Equilibrium constants may be determined from the above taste equation only if equilibrium values of the magnitude of the response of the taste receptors to the stimulus are utilized. Actually, the response of the taste receptor may decline rapidly during the first second or two of stimulation and then approach a steady level of response. The initial transient response cannot be utilized in the taste equation, but the steady level has been shown to be useful in characterizing the response of such receptors. Since the magnitude of the equilibrium constant is a measure of the force of attraction between the stimulus and receptor, utilization of the taste equation is useful in describing the efficiency of various taste stimuli.

Properties of Taste Molecules

The surface of most cells is thought to consist of a double layer of protein and phospholipid molecules. The exterior and interior surfaces of the cell membrane are made up of tangentially oriented protein molecules with a double layer of radially oriented phospholipid molecules sandwiched in between to form a membrane about 75 A. thick. Such descriptions of cell surfaces have been obtained from the study of many types of cells found in different species of animals. This is a simplification of the structure of the surface, but it does characterize many of the cell's properties. It is reasonable to assume that the surface of the taste receptor is similar to that of many other different types of cells. The exact nature of the protein, however, is not known.

Table I.   Substitutions in Saccharin (*14*)

SWEET   SWEET

SWEET   BITTER   SWEET

In most biological systems, the efficiency of the adsorption reaction depends upon the geometry of the adsorbed molecule. Such appears to be the case in taste. Let us consider one of the common artificial sweeteners. Saccharin has a sweet threshold at a concentration one five-hundredth that of sugar. Now, if a methyl group or a chloride is added in the para position, this molecule is half as sweet as saccharin (Table I). *m*-Nitrosaccharin is very bitter, very much like quinine. If the structure of a sweet compound is changed, the new product may be very bitter. *p*-Aminosaccharin is also very sweet. *N*-Methylsaccharin, *N*-ethylsaccharin, and *N*-bromoethylsaccharin are all tasteless, whereas sodium saccharin (crystallose) is very sweet (Table II).

Table II.   Substitutions in Saccharin (*14*)

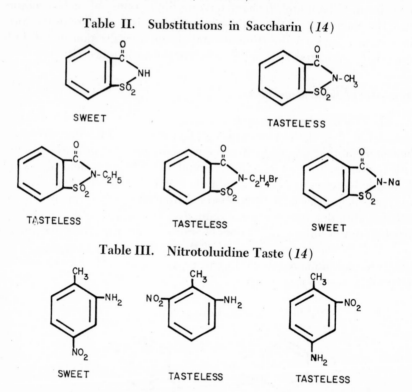

Table III.   Nitrotoluidine Taste (*14*)

5-Nitro-*o*-toluidine is a rather sweet substance. If the nitro groups are rearranged as 3-nitro-*o*-toluidine or 3-nitro-*p*-toluidine, both compounds become tasteless (Table III).

Isomers of the same molecule may have different tastes (Table IV). With the four molecules indicated, taste may change with substitution from ortho to meta to para positions. Again we see how a sweet compound may turn to a bitter one with just a small change in molecular structure. Do stereoisomers differ in taste? It has been known for a long

Table IV. Taste of Isomers (*34*)

		o	*m*	*p*
Nitrobenzoic acid	NO_2—C_6H_4—$COOH$	V. sweet	Sl. sweet	Bitter
Oxybenzamide	NH_2—CO—C_6H_4—OH	Tasteless	Bitter	—
Sodium cresotic acid	$NaCO_2$—C_6H_3 (with OH and CH₃ branches)	V. sweet	Sl. sweet	Bitter
Dioxybenzole	OH—C_6H_4—OH	Bitter	Sweet	Sl. sweet

Table V. Tastes of Stereoisomers (*11*)

Amino Acid	*Taste of L Isomer*	*Taste of D Isomer*
Asparagine	Insipid	Sweet
Glutamic acid	Unique	Almost tasteless
Phenylalanine	Faintly bitter	Sweet with bitter aftertaste
Leucine	Flat, faintly bitter	Strikingly sweet
Valine	Slightly sweet, yet bitter	Strikingly sweet
Serine	Faintly sweet, stale aftertaste	Strikingly sweet
Histidine	Tasteless to bitter	Sweet
Isoleucine	Bitter	Sweet
Methionine	Flat	Sweet

Table VI. Anomers of Mannose (*50*)

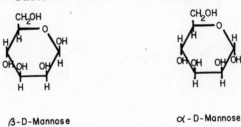

β-D-Mannose   α-D-Mannose

BITTER   SWEET

time (Table V) that many of the stereoisomers, D and L forms of amino acids, have different tastes. L-Glucose is not sweet but has a slightly salty taste, whereas D-glucose is sweet (*13*). Similarly, there is a difference in taste between D- and L-mannose. In fact, the two anomers of D-mannose possess different tastes (*50*). α-D-mannose is sweet like sucrose, whereas β-D-mannose is bitter like quinine (Table VI). These differences in taste due to very slight differences in molecular structure indicate that the receptor sites on the surface of the taste receptor can be specific. This is not unexpected, because there are many such examples in the biological literature.

Genetics of Taste

If one studies the type of structures that elicit a sweet taste, such as sucrose, beryllium chloride, saccharin, and glycine, one must conclude that different receptor sites exist on the same receptor cell and must be genetically related. The receptor cell that responds to many of these sweet substances may also respond to salts, acids, and many bitter compounds. Perhaps it is only the relative number of these different types of receptor sites that codes the information for the central nervous system regarding over-all taste quality.

The genetic basis of taste is not known for most compounds. It has been well studied with phenylthiourea (PTC), which about 25% of most populations do not taste, or at least at high concentrations only, whereas it is bitter at very low concentrations for the other 75%. The nontasting characteristic is, in all probability, a recessive gene. The question then arises: Why should any animal possess a genetic determination of a substance that does not occur naturally in nature? All of these bitter-like substances possess one thing in common—the —C—N moiety (*see* Table VII).

Table VII.   Genetic Determination of Certain Substances (23)

   A.   Molecules by which tasters and nontasters may be differentiated
B.   Similar molecules by which tasters and nontasters fail to be differentiated

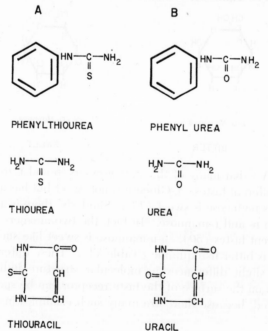

A	B
PHENYLTHIOUREA	PHENYL UREA
THIOUREA	UREA
THIOURACIL	URACIL

Recently a substance with the same moiety has been isolated from turnips and cabbages—1-5-vinyl-2-thio-oxazolidone (*12*). The ability to taste this compound parallels the ability to taste PTC. Many substances containing $-C-N$ are classified as antithyroid drugs. A similar basis for the genetic

$$\underset{S}{\overset{\|}{}}$$

determination of PTC taste has been found in the chimpanzee, which indicates that the genetic factor has existed in man for a very long time, the reason doubtless being that the heterozygote had some advantage over the homozygote (*19*). The percentage of the population of nontasters depends upon racial characteristics, so that anthropologists can use the taste testing of PTC as an indication of origin of a given group of people.

Taste Inhibitors and Potentiators

Since taste stimulation depends upon the weak adsorption of the taste stimulus to specific sites on the receptor cell surface, one would expect that certain compounds can also be adsorbed to those sites but when adsorbed, change the cell surface very little, so that taste is not stimulated. Furthermore, if there exist taste cells that respond to sweet substances predominantly, one might expect that these same cells can be interfered with by certain molecules, do not function as well, and are thus inhibited. Inhibitors are a common characteristic of any biological system, and of the taste receptors. The leaf of an Indian plant containing gymnemic acid, after being chewed for a minute or two, will completely abolish the sweet sensation. This inhibition slowly decays in an hour or two (Table VIII). After the leaf of this plant has been chewed, table

Table VIII. Inhibition of Taste (29)

Saccharin Threshold

C_t	Before G.A. application
$50\ C_t$	50 min. after application
$25\ C_t$	60 min. after application
$12.5\ C_t$	80 min. after application
$5\ C_t$	100 min. after application
$2.5\ C_t$	130 min. after application

sugar tastes like sand—it has no sweet taste and is only gritty. Bitter sensations may also decline, but the salty and sour are untouched.

The berry (miracle fruit) of another plant found in Nigeria tends to abolish the sour sensation after being chewed for a few minutes (*27*); the taste of a sour lemon is similar to that of a sweet orange. Many other types of inhibitors must exist, but since taste inhibition has been little studied, they still remain unknown. Application of the fundamental taste equation is useful in designing an experiment to discover new inhibitors.

One would expect certain tasteless substances with a high equilibrium constant to make good taste inhibitors.

The potentiation of taste is also little known but may be rather directly related to the problem of inhibition. The action of monosodium glutamate (MSG) on taste receptors is still uncertain. Beidler (6), using electrophysiological methods, found no MSG enhancement of receptor response to various taste stimuli. Sato and Akaike (46) using similar electrophysiological techniques, showed a large enhancement of response to L-MSG when small amounts of 5′-GMP (sodium 5′-guanylate) or 5′-IMP (sodium 5′-inosinate) were added (Figure 4). The action of certain nucleotides on the taste receptors is not understood. However,

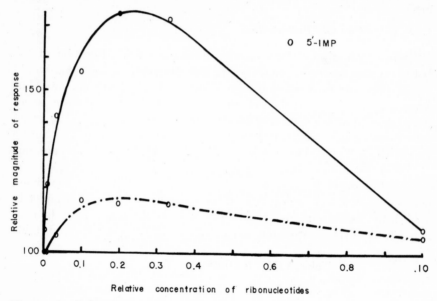

Figure 4. *Relative magnitude of electrical neural activity of rat taste nerve*

In response to 0.9 g./100 ml. L-MSG in 0.1% NaCl (lower curve) applied to surface of tongue. Upper curve indicates response to above solution when 5-IMP is substituted for equivalent amount of L-MSG. (Sato, 1965)

Beidler (7) concluded from binding studies to taste receptor surfaces that ". . . the reacting anionic groups of the molecules of the chemoreceptors are strong acidic radicals. . . . The phosphate and sulfate radicals of such natural polyelectrolytes as nucleic acids and certain polysaccharides are able to bind cations in a manner consistent with the properties of taste receptors as described above.

"Recent evidence indicates that nucleic acid may be found in cellular membranes. It has also been demonstrated that calf thymus deoxypentose nucleic acid binds cations predominantly over anions and that the extent of binding does not change with depolymerization."

5′-GMP and 5′-IMP, which Frieden and Alles (20) showed are strong chelators, may play a role in unmasking certain receptor sites and allow them to contribute to stimulus adsorption and taste receptor stimulation.

The recording of Sato and Akaike (46) from the taste nerve of the rat shows that the response to the nucleotides is as fast as to normal taste stimuli. This suggests that the action of these nucleotides is at the receptor surface and the nucleotides need not enter the cell and react with enzymatic systems bearing little direct relation to the initial taste receptor mechanism.

There has been much effort to recreate artificial flavors by synthesizing compounds that have tastes and odors similar to that of a natural product. Casual observation would indicate, however, that it might be better to spend some time searching for inhibitors and potentiators to increase the natural flavor of a product.

Naturally Occurring Odorous Molecules

Odors play a prominent role in most flavors although the identity and source of odors in a complex food are still not too well understood. The flavor of an apple, for example, may be complicated, since the odorous substances are not uniformly distributed throughout the body of the apple. Certainly the peel is different from the remainder of the apple but does contribute to the over-all flavor. The apple, like all other biological products, is made up of highly organized material. Even a simple cell has a complex organization. We know that the cell contains a cell wall if it is part of a plant, an external membrane, mitochondria, microsomes, Golgi apparatus, and so forth, all of which have been studied separately and shown to have different functions. Each component is made up of different types of molecules. It is important, for example, that the enzymes be separated from their substrates in some way, so that they can be brought together when their reaction is necessary to serve a particular cellular function. A cell cannot be considered homogeneous as far as its chemical components are concerned. As cells are put together to form a complex plant, it becomes even more obvious that molecular homogeneity does not exist.

Some odorous molecules may exist within a fruit structure and be released upon eating. Since the fruit is not homogeneous, flavor can vary from one bite to another, to give a variety of subflavors which make up the characteristic flavor of the particular fruit. On the other hand, there may be some flavorous molecules which are not initially present within the fruit but are made during the process of eating, when the various previously separated components of the fruit are brought together and synthesize a new odor (26).

If we agree that many natural products, such as the example of the fruit above are very complex as an odor source, then if we grind up a fruit and chemically assay the various odorous components, we may not reconstitute the original aroma by merely placing these components together in a homogeneous mixture. We may, however, determine some of the high notes of the aroma, reproduce them, and obtain an aroma which we associate with a given product. For example, we can make artificial orange odors which have some semblance to a real orange, but it does not take an expert to tell the difference between the two. Natural aroma can be more accurately approached if a number of odors are combined in the proper amounts to enhance the body. Such methods are used in the perfume industry and make up the art of perfumery.

Since it is difficult to isolate, identify, synthesize, and recombine odors to resemble the natural aroma, we may better turn our attention to enhancing or inhibiting wanted or unwanted odors within a natural product without affecting most of the complex odors that remain. Odor inhibitors are poorly understood, and the basic science of their action has not been studied too thoroughly. Recently more attention has been given to taste potentiators such as monosodium glutamate or the 5'—nucleotides. The real value of inhibitors and potentiators lies in the fact that most of the properties of a complex aroma of a natural product remain unchanged and the few objectionable qualities can be inhibited or the more acceptable qualities accentuated. The addition of enzymes (flavorases) to natural food to accelerate the formation of preferred aromas is an interesting approach to this difficult problem. Since odors may be concentrated in certain cell regions, such as aqueous *vs.* lipid, or even on the surfaces rather than in bulk, the use of detergents or specific solvents should be considered as a possibility for odor enhancement or depression.

Odor and Behavior

Odor is used in a variety of ways in the normal behavior of many animals. Odor associated with sex may be important in an insect's locating its mate and culminating reproduction. Many animals use odors as signals to communicate. Ants, for example, form odor trails which may be followed by other ants or read to recognize an ant colony. Odors are commonly related to reproduction even in mammals. If the odor of a strange male mouse is brought into the environment of a recently pregnant female mouse, the pregnancy may be inhibited and the egg not implanted in the uterus. Fish depend greatly upon odors. It is thought that salmon recognize a particular stream by its characteristic plant odors. The salmon also has a very unusual sensitivity to the amino acid, serine. Fishermen know that the odor of gasoline or of amino acids given off by a man's skin may alarm fish. To man, odor is of greatest importance in food flavors and the regulation of the air we breathe.

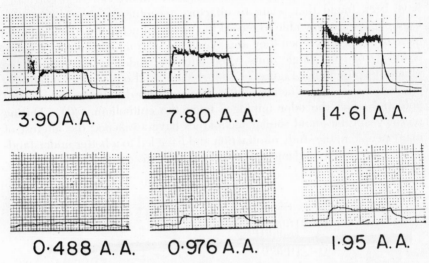

3·90 A.A.   7·80 A.A.   14·61 A.A.

0·488 A.A.   0·976 A.A.   1·95 A.A.

Figure 5. Summated response of electrical neural activity from olfactory rabbit nerve in response to successive inspirations of above micromolar concentrations of amyl acetate odor

Time scale. 1 large division = 20 seconds

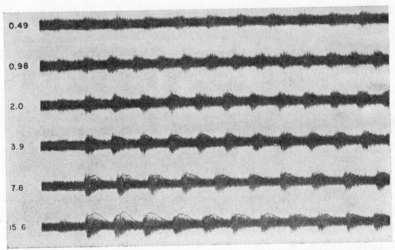

Figure 6. Electrical neural activity of olfactory nerve of rabbit during successive inspirations of various amyl acetate micromolar concentrations shown (Kimura, 1962)

Quantitative Measurements

In the past decade there have been many advances in technique that allow us to obtain objective and quantitative information concerning the interaction of odors with olfactory receptors. Many electrical correlates have been found that relate to olfactory receptor response (36). For example, we are now able to record the electrical nerve impulses from the olfactory receptors when they are stimulated with an odor (56) (Figures 5 and 6) or from single units when microelectrodes are thrust into the olfactory epithelium (Figure 7) (48). We can also place two electrodes on the surface of the olfactory epithelium and record a change in electrical potential when the odor impinges upon the epithelium (40). During recent years these and similar techniques have awakened the interest of many people in the study of olfaction and have led to a better understanding of some of the fundamental properties of the receptors.

AMYL ACETATE

FLORIDA ORANGE

LAVENDER

$$\rsb{500\ \mu v}$$

|1 sec|

Figure 7. Electrical response of receptor unit in olfactory epithelium of tortoise (Gopherus polyphemus) in response to odors as recorded with microelectrodes (Shibuya, 1964)

If the electrical activity of the olfactory nerve is recorded while a rabbit breathes normally, the amount of neural activity is seen to increase greatly during each inspiration of an odor and decline during each expira-

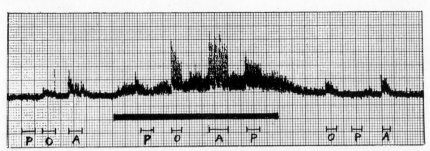

Figure 8. Electrical activity of rabbit olfactory nerve in response to phenylethyl alcohol, orange, and amyl acetate odors before, during, and after stimulation of cervical sympathetic nerve

Time scale. 1 large division = 20 seconds

tion. The magnitude of this increased activity is related to the concentration of the odor. Little decline in magnitude of response is seen in successive inspirations of low and medium odor concentration. With high odor concentration, the activity during successive inspirations may decrease in magnitude, so that adaptation is easily seen (Figure 5). Adrian (2) has shown, however, that if one records the neural activity from the olfactory bulb of the brain, adaptation may also be seen at low and medium odor concentrations. Thus, adaptation may be more closely related to properties of the central nervous system than to properties of the peripheral olfactory receptors.

Odor Flow Rate

The magnitude of olfactory receptor response to a given odor depends not only upon the odor concentration but also its flow rate through the nasal passage, which in turn can be regulated by the sympathetic or involuntary nervous system. Tucker and Beidler (57) have shown that when the sympathetic nerves innervating the nose of the rabbit are stimulated, the blood vessels constrict, and more odor can flow back to the olfactory receptors (Figure 8). Thus, odor thresholds can be changed by a factor of 100 or more merely by stimulating the sympathetic nervous system. Since the amount of activity along the sympathetic nerve depends greatly upon the emotional state of an individual, one can easily understand why thresholds may vary in the same individual from day to day or even during the same day.

Olfactory Receptor Sensitivity

The sensitivity of olfactory receptors is well known. If the threshold concentration of a mercaptan is measured with dogs, it can be calculated that there are not enough mercaptan molecules in a single sniff to make available an average of one molecule for each olfactory receptor (52). Such calculations indicate that the receptor may possibly respond when a few or even one odorous molecule is adsorbed to its surface. Since not much is known by physicists or chemists concerning reactions with such minute quantities, it is not hard to understand why those studying olfaction find the subject both intriguing and difficult. Certain insects can respond to specific sex odors in concentrations of less than $10^{-17}M$ (47). Eels can respond to a fraction of a drop of β-phenylethyl alcohol dissolved in an entire lake or reservoir (54). However, the sensitivity to many other odors is not nearly as high. Furthermore, other biological functions can also be affected by stimuli of low concentrations. For example, lysergic acid diethylamide (LSD) may affect heart function at 10^{-16} to $10^{-15}M$ concentrations.

Odor and Molecular Properties

In order for an odor to be smelled, the odorous molecule must be transported to the olfactory receptors. This implies a reasonable degree of volatility. In studying the olfactory functions of mammals, the volatility is best expressed as the vapor pressure of the odorous substances at thermodynamic equilibrium at 37° C. Concentration of the odor may then be expressed as a fraction of this vapor pressure, or the molar concentration may be calculated. Most olfactometers generate a saturated vapor of the odor and dilute it by a known amount of clean air in order to obtain any given odor concentration. In such cases, unusual care must be taken, so that one is initially assured of a saturated vapor pressure.

It is most desirable to know the actual concentration of the odorous molecules in contact with the olfactory receptors. This is difficult in the case of man, as appreciable concentrations of certain odors can be lost to nonolfactory tissue during the passage of the odor through the nose. This severely limits the reliability of subjective olfactory thresholds in determining a mechanism of olfactory stimulation. Tucker (55), using intact animals, solved this problem by cannulating the nose and passing the odor directly to the olfactory epithelium. Other experimenters, such as Ottoson (40), surgically exposed the olfactory epithelium of the frog and eliminated the possibility of previous adsorption of the odor.

Since many odors can be smelled at extremely low concentrations, the possibility of contaminants remains as a deterrent to a good reliability of odor threshold measurements. As more zone-refined chemicals are used and are checked for contaminants by mass spectrometry, the reliability of olfactory measurements may increase. Most of the above considerations have been neglected in a number of olfactory studies, although some, such as those of Mullins (37), show great care in the preparation of odorous stimulants. The argument that specification of the above stimulus parameters in olfactory experimentation is so formidable that it is better to ignore them altogether is regrettable and only leads to results of doubtful utility. Much of the literature relating molecular structure to odor quality has been based upon rather casual observations, and this must be kept in mind when one tries to relate molecular structure to olfactory receptor stimulation.

The structure of an odorous molecule determines all its properties, physical, chemical, and physiological. How an odor interacts with an olfactory receptor depends on not only the molecular structure of the odor but also the structure of the interacting site on the surface of the olfactory receptor. Since the latter is unknown and there may be many different types of receptor sites on each receptor surface, one is left with the question: Can one, by studying the similarities in molecular structure of various odors eliciting the same odor quality, determine which properties of molecules best determine the stimulus-receptor interaction? This problem is even more difficult if different receptor sites are genetically related such that they always exist together in the same receptor cell. Another way of saying this is that two odors giving forth the same odor quality may be unrelated structurally since they interact with two different types of receptor sites on the surface of the olfactory receptor. Such odorous molecules can best be studied by using inhibitors that selectively interfere with one receptor site but not the other or by studying certain anosmics in which the subject can smell odors from one group of molecules but not the other.

Various saturated fatty hydrocarbons may have different odors depending upon chain length. For example, methane is odorless, hexane is easily noticeable, and octane has a powerful gasoline odor. The amount of saturation of the molecule also determines odor quality, since ethane is almost odorless, whereas ethylene is ethereal. Isomers may also have different odors; 2,4-xylen-l-ol has a faint odor, 3,5-xylen-l-ol has a strong cresolic odor, 3,4-xylen-l-ol has a musty odor, and 2,6-xylen-l-ol has a wintergreen odor (*34*).

Esters are known for their fruity odors. The characteristic fruit depends, however, upon a particular ester—for example, propyl ester smells like pears, ethyl butyrate like pineapple, and octyl acetate like orange.

D and L stereoisomers also are reported to have differences in odor quality and odor strength. Although such differences have been reported many times, the results must be considered carefully since traces of impurity play a very large role. Naves (*38*) showed that the two optical antipodes of α-ionone have the same threshold concentration and the same odor quality.

There appears to be general agreement in the literature that the initial mechanism of olfactory receptor stimulation depends upon the adsorption of the stimulus molecule to the receptor surface. This adsorption depends upon the shape of the molecule as well as the character of functional groups. Such a molecular approach to olfaction has recently been reviewed by Beets (5). However, the conclusions of studies relating molecular structure to olfactory sensitivity are only as good as the experimental data upon which they are based.

Odor Quality Classification

The classification of an odor quality is an old pastime. Again we see the appearance of Miller's magical number, 7 ± 2. Odors have been most recently classified by Amoore (3), who empirically correlated chemical structure and odor quality. His classification is based on about 600 published experimental observations primarily found in Moncrieff (34) and Beilstein's Handbuch (9) on the odors of newly synthesized chemicals. The odorants were arranged in lists dependent upon their odor quality. By comparing the recurrences of various odor qualities in the lists he formulated, he concluded there are about seven primary odors for man—camphoraceous, pungent, ethereal, floral, pepperminty, musty, and putrid (Table IX).

Table IX.   Primary Odors for Man (3)

Camphoraceous	*Pungent*	*Ethereal*
Borneol	Allyl alcohol	Acetylene
tert-Butyl alcohol	Cyanogen	Carbon tetrachloride
d-Camphor	Formaldehyde	Chloroform
Cineol	Formic acid	Ethylene dichloride
Pentamethyl ethyl alcohol	Methyl isothiocyanate	Propyl alcohol

Floral	*Peppermint*	*Musky*
Benzyl acetate	*tert*-Butylcarbinol	Androstan-3α-ol (strong)
Geraniol	Cyclohexanone	Cyclohexadecanone
α-Ionone	Menthone	Ethylene sebacate
Phenylethyl alcohol	Piperitol	17-Methylandrostan-3α-ol
Terpineol	1,1,3-Trimethylcyclo-5-hexanone	Pentadecanolactone

Putrid

Amylmercaptan
Cadaverine
Hydrogen sulfide
Indole (when concentrated; floral when dilute)
Skatole

Many times odor classifications are thought to be related to similar primary events in the receptor mechanism. However, as Pfaffmann (41, 43) has pointed out, such relations are based upon dangerous assumptions and phenomenology may have little to do with receptor organization. As the number of odors studied has increased, one is usually forced either to increase the number of classifications or else broaden each classification so there is little separation from one to another.

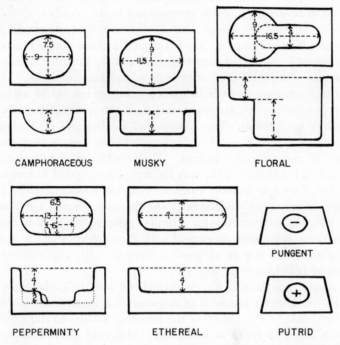

CAMPHORACEOUS   MUSKY   FLORAL

PEPPERMINTY   ETHEREAL   PUNGENT   PUTRID

Figure 9.   Olfactory receptor sites as hypothesized by Amoore

Amoore empirically related the odor quality to the size, shape, and electronic status of a molecule. He formulated the dimensions of hypothetical receptor sites whose size, shape, and electronic status were complementary to the properties of similar odors (Figure 9). The over-all size and shape of the molecule were found to be the determining factors for the camphoraceous, musty, floral, pepperminty, and ethereal sites, whereas the electrophilic properties of the pungent and putrid receptor sites were most determining.

Mechanism of Stimulation

Quantitative data indicate that the probable mechanism of stimulation is very similar to that of taste—that is, the odorous molecules adsorb on the surface of the olfactory receptor and eventually elicit an electrical depolarization of the olfactory cell which initiates nerve impulses in its axonal extension.   The taste equation devised by Beidler (7) can be applied to quantitative olfactory responses with success (56).   The equilibrium constants involved in these reactions are high compared with those normally found in taste.   At near threshold concentrations it may be necessary to make additional assumptions.   Beidler had assumed that magnitude of response is merely proportional to the number of molecules adsorbed to the receptor, irrespective of where they are adsorbed.   Davies and Taylor (15), on the other hand, assumed a given number of odorous molecules must be adsorbed onto a small area of the receptor membrane in order to cause a depolarization at near threshold concentrations.   This is a reasonable assumption, but whether it is accurate or not we do not know.

Only a few theories are concerned with the quantitative aspects of the olfactory mechanism.   The approach of Beidler and of Tucker (56) depends upon applying an adsorption equation to known magnitudes of responses of the olfactory system.   This results in a rather accurate mathematical description of the way the receptors respond to various substances but does not include much speculation concerning the role of molecular structure in stimulation.   On the other hand, the theory of Davies, which is concerned with a similar process but at near threshold concentrations, is strongly concerned with the properties of the molecule, but his results are not in as good agreement with experimental data [Figure 4 of (15)].

Most olfactory theories are concerned not with an explanation of the generation of a given intensity of response but more with quality discrimination—that is, the ability of the olfactory system to distinguish between two different types of molecules.   Molecule discrimination is an age-old problem in biology that has not been solved for the vast majority of systems.   The reason for this is very obvious.   Even in the simplest system, the structure of the stimulus may be known, but the structure of the receptor site is hidden.   Most theories of olfaction start with an assumption that olfactory receptor cells exist that are specific to but one group of molecules and that others exist for other types of molecules.   In this way, coding of odor quality would consist of the relative stimulation of different types of receptor cells in a manner similar to that proposed by theories of color vision.   Unfortunately, when one records from a single receptor cell of the olfactory epithelium, one is usually astonished to find a lack of high odor specificity (21).   In fact, most receptors so far studied respond to a variety of stimuli.   This is similar to the properties of taste receptors, which indicates that neural coding is not as simple as once thought.   This does not mean, however, that the receptor sites of the olfactory surface are not highly specific, nor that sensation of odor quality cannot be grouped into highly specific categories.   There is a great need at the present time for a cross-fertilization between chemists and physicists interested in olfactory theories and psychologists, physiologists, and biophysicists who study the properties of the olfactory system, usually using precise electrophysiological techniques.

Emotional Content of Odors

Although we have excellent techniques for measuring the olfactory receptor response, such measurements tell us little of the appreciation that an animal may have for a given odor. There need not be any relation between the magnitude of olfactory response to an odor and how the odor is liked or disliked. A number of studies in our laboratory have shown that an animal may respond intensively to a given odor, as shown by a change in his respiration or pulse beat, and yet there may be only a small change in the magnitude of the response of the olfactory receptors (35). The lack of relation between magnitude of response and the effect of odor on behavior should not be too surprising if we consider the fact that many odors of high emotional content, such as those in perfumes, need not be smelled at high odor intensities. The relation between odors and emotion is not well understood, but it is realized that the olfactory system is unusual in its ability to recall very specific events when a given odor is detected. This may be related to the fact that the olfactory system is very primitive and evolved earlier than other major sensory systems.

Taste, Odor, and Food Acceptance

Taste and odor determine the food habits of many animals. The common housefly, for example, has receptors on the tarsi or feet that respond to sweet substances such as sugar. When these receptors are stimulated, the fly puts down its mouth part to imbibe the sugar. When other receptors are stimulated by bitter or salty substances, the fly does not put down its mouth part. Throughout nature there seems to be some relation between substances that taste sweet, which are related to energy sources, and substances that taste bitter, which are related to a number of natural poisons, particularly alkaloids. Babies prefer sweet things to bitter at a very early age although they can be trained to reverse their preference. As the baby grows, it acquires new tastes not related to any metabolic need.

In adult man there is no simple relation among taste, odor, and food acceptance. Generalities can be formed, but it is difficult to determine beforehand what types of substances will be highly acceptable to a given population. Unfortunately, the economy of commercial enterprises may depend greatly upon such knowledge. Recently, Hess (24, 25) showed that the magnitude of interest in a number of visual images presented to a boy or girl can be measured quantitatively merely by observing the pupil size, and that pupil size can also be used as a criterion of acceptability of various orange drinks. These preliminary experiments allow one to speculate on the possibility of quantitative measures of certain human preferences.

Future Possibilities

The study of the function of taste and odor receptors is essentially a study of the interaction of molecules with structures within biological cells. Since modern methods have been developed which enable us to study the response of the taste and odor receptors in a quantitative and objective manner, our knowledge concerning molecular interaction should increase rapidly. The spin off benefits should be apparent in seemingly distant fields such as pharmacology. In addition, the fact that the cells of the taste buds undergo differentiation, which is presumably related to neural innervation, make it possible to study the most important problem of cell differentiation in a more quantitative manner in the taste cells than in any other known system.

The economic value of basic research concerning taste and odor will no doubt increase as the fundamental principles are applied to practical flavor problems. Greater understanding of the relation between molecular structure of the stimulus and the receptor site on the gustatory and olfactory receptors should allow us to design flavors at will. Inhibitors and potentiators should make a rapid contribution to the enhancement of natural flavors and enable us to remove unwanted tastes from various products.

The amount of current basic research in this country concerning taste and smell is very limited and primarly supported by federal agencies. Such research should be accelerated and supported by industries which might in the future make use of the information obtained from these studies, to obtain a better understanding not only of molecular interactions but also of the responses of various animals to food. Possibly the greatest need in research at the present time is for individuals to bridge the gap between laboratories now studying basic problems in taste and olfaction and industrial laboratories studying applied problems concerned with flavor.

There is an increased awareness of the importance of the chemical senses not only in the behavior of man but also in the behavior of most other animals. Fortunately, research in this area is accelerating, particularly in relation to odor attractants and repellents of insects.

It will take the combined efforts of biologists, chemists, physicists, psychologists, and engineers to solve many of these problems. The application of such knowledge to practical problems in animal behavior must be undertaken by psychologists well grounded in modern techniques.

Literature Cited

(1) Ackerman, Eugene, "Biophysical Science," Prentice-Hall, Englewood Cliffs, N. J., 1962.
(2) Adrian, E. D., *Electroencephalog. Clin. Neurophysiol.* **2**, 377 (1950).
(3) Amoore, J. E., *Proc. Sci. Sec., Toilet Goods Assc.*, Suppl. **37**, 1 (1962).
(4) Amoore, J. E., Johnston, J. W., Rubin, M., *Sci. Am.* **210**, 42 (1964).
(5) Beets, M. J. G., "Molecular Pharmacology," Vol. II, E. J. Ariens, ed., Academic Press, New York, 1964.
(6) Beidler, L. M., "Chemistry of Natural Food Flavors," J. A. Mitchell and N. J. Leinen, eds., p. 7, Quartermaster Food and Container Institute, Chicago, 1957.
(7) Beidler, L. M., *J. Gen. Physiol.* **38**, 133 (1954).
(8) Beidler, L. M., "Progress in Biophysics and Biophysical Chemistry," p. 107, Pergamon Press, London, 1961.
(9) Beilstein, "Handbuch der organischen Chemie," 4th ed., Julius Springer, Berlin, 1918.
(10) Bekesy, G. von, *J. Appl. Physiol.* **21**, 1 (1966).
(11) Berg, C., *Physiol. Rev.* **33**, 145 (1953).
(12) Boyd, W. C., *Science* **112**, 153 (1950).
(13) *Ibid.*, **137**, 669 (1962).
(14) Cohn, G., "Die organischen Geschmacksstoffe," Franz Siemenroth, Berlin, 1914.
(15) Davies, J. T., Taylor, F. H., *Biol. Bull.* **117**, 222 (1959).
(16) Duncan, C., *J. Theoret. Biol.* **5**, 114 (1963).
(17) Engen, T., Pfaffmann, C., *J. Exptl. Psychol.* **58**, 23 (1959).
(18) *Ibid.*, **59**, 214 (1960).
(19) Fisher, R. A., Ford, E. D., Huxley, J. S., *Nature* **144**, 750 (1939).
(20) Frieden, E., Alles, J., *J. Biol. Chem.* **230**, 797 (1958).
(21) Gesteland, R. C., *et al.*, "Olfaction and Taste," Y. Zotterman, ed., p. 19, Pergamon Press, London, 1963.
(22) Hainer, R. M., Emslie, A. G., Jacobson, Ada, *Ann. N. Y. Acad. Sci.* **58**, 158 (1954).
(23) Harris, H., "Introduction to Human Biochemical Genetics," p. 69, Cambridge University Press, Cambridge, 1953.
(24) Hess, E. H., *Science* **143**, 1190 (1964).
(25) Hess, E. H., *Sci. Am.* **212**, 46 (1965).
(26) Hewett, E. J., Mackay, D. A. M., Konigsbacher, K. S., "Chemistry of Natural Food Flavors," J. A. Mitchell and N. J. Leinen, eds., p. 86, Quartermaster Food and Container Institute, Chicago, 1957.
(27) Inglett, G. E., Dowling, B., Albrecht, J. J., Hoglan, F. A., *J. Agr. Food Chem.* **13**, 284 (1965).
(28) Jacobson, Homer, *Science* **112**, 143 (1950).
(29) Kiesow, F., *Phil. Studien.* **9**, 510 (1894).
(30) *Ibid.*, **14**, 591 (1898).
(31) Kimura, K., Dept. of Biological Sciences, Florida State University, private communication, 1962.
(32) Kimura, K., Beidler, L. M., *J. Cell. Comp. Physiol.* **58**, 131 (1961).
(33) Miller, G. A., *Psychol. Rev.* **63**, 81 (1956).
(34) Moncrieff, R. W., "The Chemical Senses," Leonard Hill, London, 1951.
(35) Moulton, D. G., Dept. of Biological Sciences, Florida State University, private communication, 1965.
(36) Moulton, D. G., Tucker, D., *Ann. N. Y. Acad. Sci.* **116**, 380 (1964).
(37) Mullins, L. J., *Ibid.*, **62**, 247 (1955).
(38) Naves, Y. R., *Helv. Chim. Acta* **30**, 769 (1947).
(39) Öhrwall, H., *Skand. Arch. Physiol.* **2**, 1 (1894).
(40) Ottoson, D., *Acta Physiol. Scand.* **35**, Suppl. **122**, 1 (1956).
(41) Pfaffmann, C., *Am. Psychol.* **14**, 226 (1959).

(42) Pfaffmann, C., *Am. Scientist* **52**, 187 (1964).
(43) Pfaffmann, C., *Ann. Rev. Psychol.* **7**, 391 (1956).
(44) Pfaffmann, C., *J. Cell. Comp. Physiol.* **17**, 243 (1941).
(45) Rapuzzi, G., Casella, C., *J. Neurophysiol.* **28**, 154 (1965).
(46) Sato, M., Akaike, N., *Japan J. Physiol.* **15**, 53 (1965).
(47) Schneider, D., "Olfaction and Taste," Y. Zotterman, ed. p. 85, Pergamon Press, London, 1963.
(48) Shibuya, T., Dept. of Biological Sciences, Florida State University, private communication, 1964.
(49) Skramlik, E. von, *Z. Psychol. Physiol. Sinnes Abt. II Z. Sinnes* **53**, 219 (1922).
(50) Steinhardt, R. G., Calvin, A. D., Dodd, E. A., *Science* **135**, 367 (1962).
(51) Stevens, S. S., Davis, H., "Hearing," Wiley, New York, 1938.
(52) Stuiver, M., "Biophysics of the Sense of Smell," University of Groningen, Germany, 1958.
(53) Tateda, H., Beidler, L. M., *J. Gen. Physiol.* **47**, 479 (1964).
(54) Teichmann, H., *Z. Vergleich. Physiol.* **42**, 206 (1959).
(55) Tucker, D., Dept. of Biological Sciences, Florida State University private communication, 1965.
(56) Tucker, D., *J. Gen. Physiol.* **46**, 453 (1963).
(57) Tucker, D., Beidler, L. M., *Federation Proc.* **15**, 613 (1956).

RECEIVED June 3, 1965. Work supported in part by National Science Foundation Grants GB-1491 and G-14334 and U. S. Public Health Service Grant NB 01083-09.

Current Status of Odor Theories

ANDREW DRAVNIEKS

Chemistry Research Division, IIT Research Institute, Chicago, Ill.

Odor theories deal with odorivector properties that correlate with odor quality and threshold and processes that convert the presence or arrival of odorivectors into a change in electrical neural activity. Both aspects relate to how odorivector molecules interact with sensors. Among the molecular properties related loosely and not always consistently to odor quality and threshold are: size, shape, peripheral functional groups, electrophilic and nucleophilic characteristics, and some far-infrared frequencies. The number of molecules per sensor at the threshold is very small; this seems to rule out odorivector-sensor interaction as the active signal source. However, a triggering effect or a passive mode of operation could be involved. Superficially, different theories seem to conflict, but eventually they reduce to molecular energetics and may supplement each other.

A complete odor theory must describe the correlation between the odor and some other property of the odorivector, and also the mechanism operating in the olfactory sensor. These must be mutually consistent. In other words, the theory must explain, on the basis of relevant physicochemical properties, why one odorivector stimulates certain sensors but not others.

A rational classification of odors and an explanation of odor thresholds and odor mixing phenomena will result as side products in developing odor theory.

The development of a complete odor theory is still a task for the future, and progress toward it is slow. Only dim contours appear in seemingly disconnected theories and hypotheses, which sometimes at first conflict with each other but later may be found to be several aspects of the same phenomenon.

The present paper reviews existing theories with attention to their inherent physicochemical meaning when possible. The review is organized along three aspects: odor types, thresholds, and olfaction mechanisms. Some theories deal with two or three of these aspects and hence are referred to in several places. The theories are not described in detail, so that the reference material should be consulted for details. Several books dealing with chemical senses summarize various aspects of odor theories (*43, 81, 86, 113, 127*).

Odors and Odorivector Characteristics

The principal olfactory characteristics of an odorivector are its detection threshold, quality (type), and intensity. Only the threshold is measurable quantitatively. Quality and intensity are heavily weighted psychologically and can be expressed quantitatively only in subjective terms of degree of similarity or dissimilarity. Most of the research effort so far has been in the direction of odor quality and threshold.

The physicochemical properties of odorivectors can be divided in two major groups, molecular and bulk. The molecular properties include size and shape of molecules; dipoles; type, number, and distribution of functional groups; and molecular spectra. The bulk properties include vapor pressure, solubility, and adsorptivity at the oil-water interface. They are secondary since they result from intermolecular interactions and hence are derived from the molecular characteristics.

Correlations with molecular properties are more rewarding as they can guide research in odors and flavors. Correlations with bulk properties, however, can serve as useful shortcuts. For example, relations (*42, 55, 93*) between the olfactory thresholds and the saturation vapor pressures may assist in estimating the threshold, even though the vapor pressure cannot be calculated from the available molecular parameters (except for the simplest molecules).

Correlations between the odor and the other properties of an odorivector constitute the oldest subject in the study of olfaction. Unfortunately, until recently experimental information for developing these correlations has been deficient, since before the advent of gas chromatography it was difficult to examine the chemical purity of odorivector samples. The fact that minor constituents easily change the quality and the threshold of an odorivector (*70*) has plagued comparisons of odors of optical stereoisomers (*94, 96*). The report that skatole, which for decades rated as a substance with an extremely low odor threshold, does not exhibit the unpleasant odor after zone refining (*22*) is a particularly striking warning against the use of older data. Another deficiency has been that the true concentrations of odorivectors in air were not measured. In well-designed continuous-flow systems, dilution factor and saturation vapor pressure can suffice for calculating the concentration, but in experiments in which the odorivector is sniffed in solution in an odorless or a low-odor solvent, the concentration of vapor in air depends not only on the concentration in the solvent but also on the intermolecular interactions between the solvent and the odorivector (66). Molecular properties of the solvent and its purity then become additional complicating factors. The possibility of biasing or otherwise influencing odor observations by the method of selecting and operating the panel also should be taken into account (41, 128).

It is possible that much of the older literature used extensively in recent papers on odor theories contains erroneous data, not only on thresholds but also on the degree of similarity or dissimilarity of odors. Developing adequate theories depends on the accuracy of the data. The preferable course in olfactory work is to verify data before discarding or modifying a theory. A dire need exists for obtaining new data on odorivectors whose chemical purity has been determined by gas chromatography analysis (68, 70).

Odor Types and Molecular Properties

The question of the number of odor types is still unsolved. "Odor types" implies that there may be different types of olfactory sensors. It does not imply that pure odor types must exist, since it is always possible that no substance stimulates only one type of sensor. It is also possible that instead of more-or-less definite sensor types, there is a sensor continuum, with a gradual change of specificity from sensor to sensor.

Odor Classifications. Humans can distinguish in excess of 10,000 odors. According to the information theory (62), 13 types of sensors can provide for this capability if each reports on a "yes or no" basis, but over 20 might be required to respond quickly and with little error (127). Simpler odor classifications utilize four (32), six (63), or nine (134) primary odors. The literature on odors of organic compounds uses 14 descriptive names, according to Amoore (3, 4, 6, 7). His theory of stereochemical sites thus far considered seven of these to correspond approximately to the primary odors. Recent results with subjective organoleptic categories suggest a larger number; Johnston (67) believes that 15 to 21 subjective categories may be involved and that the nucleophilic and electrophilic characteristics postulated by Amoore (pungent and putrid types) plus a neutral characteristic superimpose across five to seven stereochemical types. Cross-adaptation experiments by Köster (74) also do not support the stereochemical theory based on seven simple primaries.

Statistical factor analyses of panel tests on chemicals representing a broad spectrum of odor qualities indicate the existence of at least eight to nine factors (112, 130). Many odors can be consistently described by panels on the basis of similarity or dissimilarity with odors of this number of selected chemicals. For a refined characterization of a complex food aroma, much more complex descriptions of coexisting odor notes, including hedonistic terms, are required. Such descriptions coupled with simultaneous taste sensations are frequently termed "flavor profiles" (29). No indication exists of how many factors represent all known profiles and which are semantic artifacts stemming from the language structure.

Another school of thought (35, 56), strongly supported by electrophysiologists and sensory psychologists, suggests that sensors differ only in degree of their sensitivity or accessibility to any kind of odorivector and that there are no highly specialized types of sensors in humans. The existence of highly specific sensors for sex attractants in insects has been demonstrated convincingly (110). Then odorivectors differ in their ability to interact with sensors, and the quality of odor is perceived in terms of the spatial and temporal pattern of sensor response (1) in much the same way as perception of many visual shapes is possible through a small number of optical sensor types. Some (99) doubt that complex odors consisting of many odorivectors can in principle be simulated by a mixture selected from a set of definite odor types, especially in view of psychological filters at the higher neural processing level (79).

Since the number and mutual boundaries of odor types are still poorly defined, correlations with the molecular properties are possible only in limited areas. The importance of the size, shape, and functional groups of odorivector molecules is now generally recognized. None of these characteristics alone is sufficient to explain the similarities and dissimilarities in odors (15, 16, 17). The old concept of osmophoric groups (86, 107) that impart the odor quality has gradually grown to include consideration of molecular shape and the positions of the functional groups.

Profile Functional Group Theory. Beets (15, 16, 17), in his profile functional group theory, proposed that the functional group with the highest tendency to interact with a receptor (high solvation tendency) orients toward the receptor and that similarities in the profile of the rest of the molecule determine similarities in odor. "Similar profile, similar odor" would then explain why different molecules with different functional groups in many cases have similar odors (compare the bitter almond odor of benzaldehyde, cyanobenzene, and nitrobenzene with the vanilla odor of these same compounds when the $-OCH_3$ group is in the meta and the $-OH$ group is in the para position). Beets' theory was limited to a demonstration of some structural effects and did not develop into a comprehensive system.

Stereochemical Site Theory. Amoore (6, 7, 43) advanced a classification of odors on the basis of molecular shape and size. A few specific types of intermolecular interactions—electrophilic, nucleophilic, and hydrogen-bonding—were involved for some odor types. The shape and size factors are described in terms of match into a shaped site; hence the name stereochemical theory of odor (Figure 1). The functional groups are significant only when they give strong electrophilic or nucleophilic character, as in the pungent and putrid types, where the molecular shape and size do not matter. In the case of pepperminty odor, he supplements the shape and size specifications by a weak nucleophilic function in a certain position on the molecule. Since the electrophilic and nucleophilic functions can coexist on one molecule and a molecule can partially match several steric sites, Amoore's classification is equivalent to the description of odors of single substances in terms of up to seven coordinates.

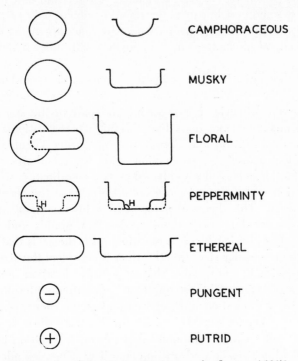

CAMPHORACEOUS

MUSKY

FLORAL

PEPPERMINTY

ETHEREAL

PUNGENT

PUTRID

Figure 1.   Odor types in Amoore's theory (1952, 1962)

Left. View of sites from above
Right. Cross-section of sites

Amoore's theory with its seven odor types is the first to bring an indication of order into the correlations between odor and molecular properties, although recent evidence (67) indicates that the number of types is too low. Particularly impressive is his demonstration of size- and shape-fitting for 21 molecules having camphoraceous odor. Among these are compounds containing two to eight carbon atoms with eight different functional groups in various arrangements (3).

Other workers (*68, 106, 109*) have reported observations in reasonable agreement with some aspects of Amoore's theory. The theory has also been criticized by Amoore himself and others (*80*). Some small molecules do not fulfill the size requirements unless two molecules are taken; dimerization by hydrogen-bonding or dipole interaction must be assumed to explain this effect (*2*). About 10 molecules have odors not fitting their shape (*2*). Some classes of compounds—e.g., glycols—fit sites but have no odor (*2*). The number of primary odors, seven, is too small to explain the total number of odors that can be discriminated by humans (*129*). Observations (*5, 60, 61, 77, 127*) on partial anosmia and olfactory fatigue revealed that some people can differentiate or detect only certain classes from among several musks (a primary odor by Amoore's theory) belonging to different chemical classes; this is in conflict with other panel tests (*67, 68*).

The last three criticisms are probably the most serious, and only further olfactory experiments will be able to clarify the issue. The assumed existence of seven primaries is not an integral part of the stereochemical theory, and some odors may not satisfy this initial classification.

Interface Adsorption and Membrane-Puncturing Theory. Recently Davies (*34*) proposed, in connection with his membrane-puncturing theory of olfaction, a classification based on two coordinates: the molecular cross section, and the free energies of adsorption at the oil-water interface (Figure 2). This theory developed from his treatment of olfactory thresholds, discussed in more detail under "Thresholds and Molecular Properties." The physicochemical meaning of his theory is that it first accounts for the molecular size directly; then it considers the size again, in combination with the molecular shape, polarity, location, and type of functional groups, since all these parameters determine intermolecular interactions with hydrocarbon and water and hence the energy of adsorption at the interface. Davies has no provision for singularly discrete odor types. The odor note of a single compound depends on its position in the two-coordinate field of sizes and adsorption energies. Complex odors consisting of many odorivectors would intermix through a complex olfactory sensor-neural network system. It will take time to assess the scope of usefulness and validity of Davies' classification. Tentatively, it appears to open an attractive semiempirical shortcut to correlations with molecular parameters and to interlock nicely with the membrane-puncturing mechanisms of olfaction proposed by him and discussed in more detail under "Mechanisms of Olfaction."

Vibrational Theories. In other attempts to relate the quality of odor to molecular characteristics, correlations with quantized energy transitions in odorivector molecules were proposed. The theory that some electromagnetic radiation—e.g., infrared—from an odorivector or absorption

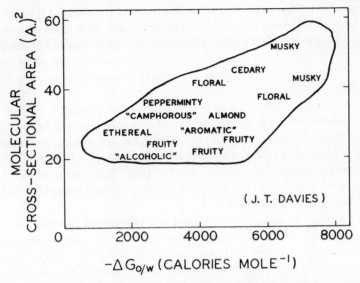

Figure 2. Odor types in Davies' theory (1965)

of radiation by odorivectors is the sensing mechanism (*13, 14*) has been shown by theoretical and experimental methods (*15, 118*) to be untenable. However, correlations between quantitized energy transitions and odor may result through some other mechanism. The question really is: Do such correlations exist?

Dyson (*49, 51*) originally proposed that the olfactorily significant frequency range, in wave number, is 1500 to 3500 cm.$^{-1}$, and he assigned osmic frequency ranges to certain odors. This system did not work. Wright (*122*) argued that at body temperature the population density of the excited states is significant only for the transitions corresponding to lower frequencies, and he tried to demonstrate correlations with spectra below 700 cm.$^{-1}$ and down to 50 cm.$^{-1}$. His and other work (*25, 121, 123, 124, 125, 130, 132*) indicated that limited correlations can be observed, but inconsistencies occur.

Several arguments have been advanced against this hypothesis, known as the vibrational theory of odors. One is that the olfactory receptors cannot operate as infrared or Raman spectrographs. However, the theory claims correlations only between odor and frequencies and does not propose that the frequencies interact with the receptors. Another argument is that substances with similar spectra do not have similar odors (*117*). The theory does not propose that all parts of the spectrum are significant (*127*), and a statistical factor analysis (*130*) shows correlations that are not obvious from visual inspection of spectra. Still another argument is that some simple molecules have no energy levels in the low-frequency range.

The counter argument assumes that the reaction products of the molecules may have the appropriate levels. The argument that isotopic molecules differ in frequencies but not in odors does not apply to the low-frequency range for complex molecules. Optical stereoisomers do not differ in spectra, and the evidence that they may differ significantly in odor is waning (94).

The strongest argument against the vibrational theory is that for some sets of substances with similar odors no common features in the spectra can be found by present methods. Examples are musks, if macrocyclic musks are included (126), and camphoraceous odors, which fit nicely into the Amoore theory but whose spectra have little in common (126). Future work will decide the range of validity of the Dyson-Wright vibrational theory or its variations.

Basically, the stereochemical and the vibrational theories are not in opposition. The molecular energy transitions in the range corresponding to wave numbers below 500 cm.$^{-1}$ originate from intramolecular movements involving groups of carbon or heavier atoms (50, 64, 102). For instance, the vibrations that involve bond stretching require three or more carbon atoms if the frequency is to be low enough, or else heavy halogen atoms or other groupings are necessary. If enough atoms participate, bond-bending vibrations fall into the range proposed by Wright. These skeletal bendings tend to have characteristics unique to the molecule as a whole. Low-frequency spectra may appear when hindered rotations within the molecule lead to the existence of rotational isomers; they describe the relative resistance of the atomic chains in the molecule to kinking. Finally, the rotational spectra of molecules are in the far-infrared and through the microwave range (below 1 cm.$^{-1}$); they describe the shape and the size of molecules in terms of their momenta of inertia. Thus, although the low-frequency spectra are not unique descriptions of the shapes and the sizes of odorivector molecules, a relation between the spectra and stereochemistry exists, and the correlations between the odor and the spectra are perhaps just another way of expressing the correlations between the odor and the shapes, the sizes, and the functional groups.

The term "vibrational" implies that the phenomenon of intramolecular vibrations (to include bending, wagging, and some types of rotation as well) is involved in producing the olfactory signal. Only a working hypothesis for a mechanism based on the vibrational effect has been proposed. It is discussed under "Mechanisms of Olfaction."

The Raman frequencies describe structural characteristics similarly to the infrared. However, infrared frequencies appear only when the dipole moment changes in vibration while Raman frequencies appear when the vibration changes the polarizability. Either spectrum in the low-frequency range tends to describe the molecule as a whole, even if in somewhat different terms.

Thresholds and Molecular Properties

The phenomenon of olfactory threshold, the concentration below which an odorivector is not detectable, is another starting point for odor theories. The concept of threshold can leave open the question of the existence of primary odor types, but some threshold theories allow for the mechanisms of odor discrimination. Studies based on temporary changes of the threshold after fatiguing the olfactory sensor with another odorivector (*31, 74*) present a good tool for investigating odor similarities and dissimilarities.

Thresholds expressed in relative concentrations

$$A_{olf} = \frac{\text{concentration at threshold}}{\text{concentration at saturated vapor pressure}} \qquad (1)$$

vary among odorivectors much less than thresholds expressed in absolute concentrations, molecules per cubic centimeter (*42, 55, 93*). Physicochemically, this indicates that the interaction between the odorivector and the sensor at the threshold is somewhat stronger than that between molecules of the odorivector in the condensed state (*45*).

Consequently, threshold theories implicitly deal with correlations to some interaction parameter. The theories differ in the selection of the parameter. The purpose is usually to show that either the value of A_{olf} or the absolute threshold is a simple function of the selected parameter and conforms to some postulated mechanism.

Surface Adsorption. Beck (*12*) assumes that one of the factors determining the threshold is the "dynamic area" of the odorivector molecule. This in his definition is the area swept by a molecule in the adsorbed state and depends on the volume, shape, and the axis around which the molecule rotates. A functional group anchored at a receptor site produces an axis for rotation. Beck concludes, on the basis of older and in parts questionable literature data, that for a series of homologs the product of the dynamic area times the surface concentration of the odorivector on the active receptor surface is approximately constant. The surface concentration is inferred to be proportional to the cube root of the threshold, and several unorthodox assumptions about the dynamics of adsorbed molecules are used to demonstrate the constancy of such products.

Although Beck's argument and supporting data can be disputed at length, a tenuous correlation does appear to exist between threshold and molecular size, at least within an individual series of some homologs. The need to introduce a coefficient that is a function of the type and the location of the functional group again stresses the significance of functionality in addition to shape and size of the molecule. First-odor proportionality between the concentration in air and at the receptor surface, proposed by DeVries and Stuiver (*44*), results in poorer correlation, according to Beck.

Solution in Membrane. Two other theories in essence relate olfactory threshold to the distribution coefficient of the odorivector between the sensing phase and air. The sensing phase is assumed to be a cell membrane.

Mullins (93) employs the ratios of threshold to the saturation concentration of the odorivector in air, as has been done earlier in narcosis theories, and assumes the existence of sensing membranes with different abilities to dissolve odorivectors. His concepts translated into conventional thermodynamics are as follows. The solubility of an odorivector in a membrane may be normal (conforming to the law of ideal solutions), low, or high (58). Mullins considers the first two cases only. Hence he excludes the notion of specific sites or specific interactions, which lead to higher solubility because of hydrogen bonding, charge-transfer complex formation, chemical compound formation, or a particularly fortunate match of size and shape. In the absence of specific interactions, solubility is highest when the solution is ideal. At equilibrium, the mole fraction in the odorivector in the membrane is proportional to its partial pressure outside the membrane.

In most solutions, however, the differences in the molecular sizes and the existence of nonspecific van der Waals interactions between the components of the solution result in lower solubility than that of ideal solutions. These solutions are termed regular (65, 103), since no specific interactions enter. The principal factor that determines the extent of the decrease in the solubility is the excess free energy of mixing,

$$F^E{}_{mix} = (\delta_1 - \delta_2)^2 \, V \times \phi_1\phi_2 \tag{2}$$

Here $\delta_1 = \left(\dfrac{\Delta E_1}{V_1}\right)^{1/2}$ and is the cohesive energy density, known also as the solubility parameter for species i; V is the molal volume of solution; ϕ is the volume fraction; subscripts 1 and 2 refer to the odorivector and the membrane for the present case; ΔE is the energy of vaporization, approximately equal to $\Delta H - RT$, where H is the heat of vaporization, R is the gas constant, and T is the absolute temperature; and V_1 and V_2 are the molal volumes of the pure components. $F^E{}_{mix}$ disappears when $\delta_1 = \delta_2$. In any other regular solution, it is positive and depresses the solubility.

Mullins proposes that a range of membranes with different δ_2 values exist. A membrane with a given δ_2 dissolves best the odorivectors with δ_1 equal to δ_2. The free energy term and consequently $(\delta_1 - \delta_2)^2$ enter the solubility equation exponentially. Hence small differences between δ_1 and δ_2 result in a large change in the solubility of the odorivector in the membrane.

Mullins' theory has several advantages. It explains easily many variations of thresholds with molecular size for a homologous series of odorivectors. It also can account eventually for the size- and shape-dependence of odor quality if the reasoning is extended to the thermodynamics of polymer solutions. However, specific intermolecular interactions between the odorivector and the sensor cannot be described by the simple δ-related expressions. Hence the significance of functional groups and their positions or nucleophilic or electrophilic characteristics evades description by the simple form of this theory.

Interface Adsorption and Membrane Puncturing. Davies and Taylor (*33, 35, 37–40*), in their initial membrane-puncturing theory, relate threshold, irrespective of the odor quality, to the size of the odorivector molecule and to the ability of the odorivector to accelerate hemolysis of red blood cells by saponin. Their thesis is that odorivector molecules assist in the destruction of the cell walls by promoting dislocations in the wall membrane or, as Davies proposed more recently (*34*), by permitting ionic current flow when they desorb from the membrane. Red blood cells were chosen as a convenient experimental model. The properties (size, polarity, etc.) of the odorivector molecule determine, through adsorption energies, its concentration at the lipid–aqueous phase interface, which is in equilibrium with some given concentration in air.

In essence, the Davies-Taylor theory is an extension of Mullins' theory by introducing specific interactions of peripheral functional groups with an aqueous phase (one end of molecule dissolves in oil, the other in water). The size further determines how many odorivector molecules have to be copresent within a small dislocation-susceptible area of the membrane to initiate dislocation. One large molecule—e.g., ionone—may be sufficient, but several small molecules may need to cooperate.

Davies and Taylor obtained adsorption constants empirically for adsorption at petroleum ether–water interfaces. They employed assumptions on the number of molecules of strong and weak odorants needed per sensitive region. They also employed the Poisson distribution formula to estimate the probability of finding the smaller molecules close to each other. They further assumed that the dislocating power of the molecules is a linear function of the cross-sectional area of the molecules.

Davies and Taylor derived the threshold equation:

$$\log (\text{O.T.}) + \log K_{LA} = \frac{\log n}{P} - \log \alpha d + \frac{\log P!}{P} \qquad (3)$$

Here O.T. is the olfactory threshold, molecules per cubic centimeter of air; K_{LA} is the adsorption constant at the oil-water interface; n is the number of sensing regions per one olfactory sensor cell; P is the number of odorivector molecules per region necessary to initiate puncture; α is the area of one sensing region; and d is the thickness (10 A.) of the region and is assumed to convert the K_{LA} value to the volume units.

The relation between the cross-sectional area of the molecule, A_0, and the dislocating power, $1/P$, is obtained from $P = 1$ for ionone and $P = \infty$ for water:

$$\frac{1}{P} = \frac{A_0}{47} - 0.2 \tag{4}$$

With these assumptions, an approximately linear relation is obtained between the logarithm of the calculated thresholds (Equation 3) and the logarithm of the literature thresholds (probably not too reliable) essentially from log O.T. $= 8$ to log O.T. $= 16$.

Close analysis of the Davies-Taylor equation indicates that the only significant parameters are the size factors, A_0, and the empirical constant, K_{LA}. This is apparent from transcription of the combined equations:

$$\log (\text{O.T.}) = -\log K_{LA} - (\log n) \left(\frac{A_0}{47} - 0.2 \right) - \log \alpha d + \frac{\log P!}{P} \tag{5}$$

With Davies' $\log n = 4.64$, $\log \alpha d = 21.2$, and P between 1 and 24, this simplifies to:

$$\log (\text{O.T.}) = -\log K_{LA} - 0.1 A_0 + (22.13 \pm 0.5) \tag{6}$$

According to Davies, $\log K_{LA}$ can vary from 6 to 8.4. The value of A_0 for molecules is 10 to 60 (A.)^2, giving a range for $0.1 A_0$ between 1 and 6. Hence, the size factor has the highest leverage, with the adsorption constant supplying additional leverage. The term in parentheses was in essence derived from the observed O.T. and the empirical K_{LA} values, and the correctness of the physical meaning of its component terms (n, α, d, P) is disputable. The scatter in the log-log plot of observed O.T. vs. calculated O.T. is frequently ± 1 logarithmic unit and sometimes as much as ± 2.5 units.

Thus the mathematical treatment of threshold by Davies and Taylor indicates principally the significance of the molecular size and probably of the interactions of odorivector molecules with an oil (perhaps lipid)-water interface. A more recent development is an extension by Davies of these principles to classification of odors of single compounds, already discussed under "Odor Types and Molecular Properties."

The other experimental finding by Davies and Taylor stands by itself. Odorivectors with lower thresholds were found to accelerate hemolysis of erythrocyte wall membranes more than those with higher thresholds. A linear relation with some scatter exists between the logarithm of the accelerating power, A, and the logarithm of the olfactory threshold for threshold values from 10^8 to 10^{16} molecules per cc. The slope of a plot of $\log A / \log (\text{O.T.})$ is approximately 0.38. The plot is strong evidence that odorivectors interact with the cell walls, and it gives stronger support to the puncturing theory than the mathematical correlation of Equation 3. No claim is made that olfaction involves attack on erythrocytes; these were used as a convenient model.

Davies and Taylor in their initial theory avoided postulating the existence of different olfactory sensor units and suggested that differences in odors originate from spatial and temporal differences in the response of sensor membranes. Our interpretation of this is that odorivector concentrations build up to threshold values with different rates at different locations on sensors or in the olfactory region. This concept is related to Stuiver's (114) hypothesis that the rate of absorption is the measure of the olfactory stimulus. However, in Davies' more recent theory (34), differentiation of the membrane walls is proposed. The membrane walls differ in their fluidity; some are more resistant to penetration by odorivectors than others.

The concept of poorly differentiated sensors is in favor with electrophysiologists and sensory psychologists, who observed diffuse specificities in experiments on animals (19, 21, 57, 90, 91, 119). An analysis of electrophysiological and sensory perception studies is outside the scope of the present survey and can be found elsewhere (19, 21, 133).

One of the concepts appears to be as follows. Perhaps 20 or more somewhat specifically reacting sites exist. Each sensor (neuron) carries many or all types of sites in multiple, but the sensors differ in distribution or in the relative occupancy by the various specific sites (58). Hence there is some differentiation in response. There may be further discrimination on the basis of the rate with which different odorivectors reach sensors in different areas of the olfactory region.

Other Correlations with Odorivector Properties

Other characteristics of odorivectors have received limited attention. Rosano, Hartman, and others (82, 104) suggested that the oxidizability or some other related parameter, such as adsorbability at electrodes, can be important. Earlier, Ruzicka (108) proposed that the significant factor is the ease of consumption by enzymes. Alexander (2), Thompson (118), and Kistiakowski (72) modified this to suggest that odorivectors differ in their ability to interfere with enzymatic reactions. Other theories (52, 85, 88, 94, 95, 98) represent precursors of the theories of shape matching and intermolecular interactions discussed above.

Interrelationship of Molecular Properties Theories

The theories on correlations between odor or its threshold and the molecular or other properties of odorivectors differ in classifications of odors and in selection of the properties. Close examination, however, reveals that the differences are less than they appear to be initially. Certain unifying concepts underlie the structures of the seemingly different theories but are clouded by the scientific idioms used by their authors.

The unifying concepts are best understood by beginning with Beets' (16) formulation:

$$\text{Odorivector} + \text{receptor} \rightarrow \text{``sensing state''} \tag{7}$$

The formation of the sensing state may include matching into a site, interaction through matched intermolecular force matrices, solution in a membrane, and adsorption at an interface. The differences between these terms are nearly semantic.

Except for a few highly reactive odorivectors, chemical consumption, or strong chemisorption, of the odorivector is unlikely (45, 115). Hence, formally the process is that of distribution of the odorivector between the gaseous phase (air) and the sensing phase, probably in most cases without major chemical changes of the odorivector. The question of the mechanism by which the formation of the sensing state might be converted to a neural signal is discussed below.

In forming the sensing states, the odorivectors can be characterized by differences in the rates of formation, the equilibria reached, or both. One of the obvious rate factors is the rate of diffusion to the sensing phase. Barrier media (air, mucus, membrane coatings, etc.) must be transversed before the sensing phase is reached. The rate of diffusion toward the sensing phase depends on the mobility of the odorivector molecules and their solubility in the barrier phases. The mobility is a function of the molecular size of the odorivector and the viscosity of the barrier phase. If the barrier phase is polymeric, the diffusion paths may consist of preferred adsorption sites, and the distance between the sites also becomes a factor in mobility. The solubility depends on intermolecular interactions between the odorivector molecule and the barrier medium. The solubility is an equilibrium function, and its treatment is the same as that for the interaction of the odorivector with the sensing plate.

Dravnieks (45) has estimated that the rate of diffusion of odorivectors to olfactory cilia is consistent with the rate of olfactory response. Whether rate factors alone can account for most of the specificity is highly questionable. Perhaps they serve as temporal modifiers in the sense used by Adrian (1), Beidler (18), Ottoson (97), and Mozell and Pfaffman (92).

The equilibrium factors determine the ultimate concentration of the sensing state in the sensing phase. This concentration is probably never fully reached since the odorivectors continue to diffuse into adjoining tissues.

In the sensor, the odorivector molecule is in the force field of the molecular interactions of the sensing phase. Statistical and quantum mechanics provide an insight into the parameters that determine the distribution of the odorivector molecule between the gas phase (air) and a captive state (sensing state). A detailed discussion of the relations is beyond the scope of this paper.

Symbolically, the principal relations are:

$$n_c = n_g \times A \times \underbrace{\frac{1}{m^{3/2}} \times \frac{Z_c \, Z_{ic}}{Z_r \, Z_{ig}}}_{B} \times \underbrace{\exp\left(\frac{\Delta u}{kT}\right)}_{C} . \qquad (8)$$

Here n_c and n_g are the volume concentrations of the odorivector in the condensed and the gas phases, respectively; A is a coefficient encompassing several fundamental constants; m is the mass of the odorivector molecule; the Z's are the quantum-mechanical partition functions for the odorivector molecule; Z_c is for all external molecular motions in the captive state and may include bouncing and wobbling in a limited volume (highly limited translations, oscillations, and rotations); Z_r is for rotation in the gas phase; Z_{ic} is for internal motions of the molecule (intramolecular rotations, skeletal vibrations, etc.) in the captive state; and Z_{ig} is for similar intramolecular motions in the gas state. Z_{ic} may not be similar to Z_{ig} because of the restrictive action of the sensing phase, especially in larger, flexible molecules. The exponential factor represents the partition function for the potential energy and contains Δu, which is the potential energy increment caused by intermolecular interactions between the odorivector and the sensing state in excess of the interactions of the odorivector with the gas phase; Δu is basically the heat of solution or adsorption (or sorption) at $0°$K., if the interactions of the odorivector molecule with air are considered negligible.

Equation 8 contains, in principle, all the relations proposed by various odor theories. The exponential factor, C, accounts for size and for functional groups. The intermolecular interactions include van der Waals–London dispersion forces, which depend on the size and shape of the molecule and their match into some fitted site or cavity in the sensing phase. The forces further include hydrogen-bonding, dipole interactions, quadrupole interactions, and bonding through formation of electron donor-acceptor (charge-transfer) complexes. Thus the functionality is also important and includes ring structures, conjugation, etc. With an increase in size, the relative significance of the dispersion forces increases, and the significance of most types of the functionality decreases. This relation is consistent with observations on the relation of shape, size, and odor (53, 95).

Size and shape factors also enter through the factor B. In particular, the rotational partition function in the gas phase is shape-dependent:

$$Z_r = \frac{\pi^{1/2} \, (8\pi^2 kT)^{3/2}}{\sigma \, h^3} \times (I_x I_y I_z)^{1/2} \qquad (9)$$

Here k is Boltzmann's constant; h is Planck's constant; σ is the symmetry factor for the molecule ($\sigma = 1$ for a completely unsymmetrical molecule); and I_x, I_y, and I_z are the rotational moments of inertia for the molecule. For a flat molecule, one of the I's is small. For a long, thin molecule, two of the I's are small. Hence the shape, at the same mass, influences B strongly. For a large, flexible molecule, Z_{ic} may also be very different from Z_{ig}.

Equations 8 and 9 hint at the significance of shape, size, and functional groups in the distribution of odorivectors among sensors with various characteristics, thus hinting at a relation of odor to solubility in membranes or at interfaces (Mullins, Davies) or to shape and size (Amoore and others). The relation to spectral characteristics (Dyson, Wright) is much looser. However, the momenta of inertia and the skeletal vibrations are among the spectra-producing and modifying features, and at the same time, enter Equation 8 through Z_r, Z_{ig}, and Z_{ic}. Oxidizability [Rosano (104); Hartman (120)] may enter through Δu. Adsorptivity at the oil-water or other interface [Davies, Eaton (75, 76); Tanyolac (116)] is in principle similar, except that Δu then consists of two interactions, one with one phase on one end of the molecule and another with another phase on the other end of the molecule (36). Hence the shape of the molecule and the location of polar and other functional groups on the periphery of the molecule also relate to the odor, as in Beets' and Beck's theories.

Thus it appears plausible that all theories on relations between odor and molecular properties are inherently related to the same common origins and are not really in conflict. Of course, a tremendous amount of work is required to clarify quantitatively the actual significance of each parameter for all groups of odorivectors.

Physiological and Psychological Mechanisms

It is not the intent of this paper to elaborate on the physiological and psychological factors that complicate the perception of odors. However, if pitfalls in reasoning are to be avoided, it is necessary at least to name the effects that must be considered in collecting experimental data on threshold and odor quality.

Evidence increases that several substances at subthreshold concentrations can build up to a joint threshold concentration (9, 105). Addition of similar odors contributes in a complex way to the joint intensity (69). Addition of different odors can result in suppressing or intensifying the various components or in developing a blend odor different from the odor of the components (70, 83). Fatiguing of the olfactory organs by one substance raises the threshold for the same and related substances but can leave the threshold for others uninfluenced (31, 93).

Adaptation and cross adaptation can occur in the higher neural network rather than in the receptor (*1, 18, 74, 97*). There is interaction through the higher network between contralateral olfactory regions (*59, 71*). Thus cross influences between chemically pure odorivectors occur in accordance with complex and largely unknown laws at both the receptor and the neural network levels.

Mechanisms of Olfaction

The arrival of an odorivector or the formation of the sensing state is converted to a neural impulse through the mechanism of olfaction. The nature of the impulse, the meaning of its shape and frequency, and its processing in the neural network are subjects for electrophysiology and neurology research (*19, 21, 133*) and are outside the scope of this paper.

Stereochemical theories (Moncrieff, Beets, Amoore, Johnston) do not discuss the mechanism of impulse formation. None of the mechanisms proposed by other theories for impulse initiation has been sufficiently proved to attain textbook maturity. Most are still in the stage of blissful speculation, and their review should stimulate further development of ideas and experiments.

The proposed mechanisms of olfaction can be loosely classified as follows.

The signal can be derived from an energy or potential change contributed directly by the odorivector, as in the enzymatic oxidation or adsorption potential theories.

An impulse can result from triggering an energy-rich process, as in the membrane-puncturing or pigment-de-excitation theories.

The odorivector can merely steer a biochemical process, as in the enzyme theories.

The receptor can serve as a passive bioelectric circuit element merely modifying the temporal pattern (frequency spectrum) of the electro-neural activity, which receives its energy from an independent metabolic mechanism.

Since a few molecules suffice to generate an impulse, objections exist against any theory in which the energy of adsorption or dissolution is the prime source of the impulse energy. Hence theories such as Beck's (*12*), in which the energy exchange between the adsorbed layer and the inner phase of the sensor is taken as the source of the impulse, seem to be untenable energetically. This objection does not negate the relation between molecular parameters of odorivectors pointed out by Beck. Similarly, although interactions between cephaline and odorivectors have been demonstrated by Friedman *et al.* (*54*), their direct energetic relation to impulse generation is questionable.

Ehrensvard (*52*), Eaton and Tanyolac (*75, 76, 116*), Moncrieff (*87*), and Chapman (*30*) have pointed out the possibility that adsorption and the corresponding contact potential or surface tension changes may be a part of the olfaction mechanism, but again a mechanism of impulse generation is not proposed. The surface potential changes that can result from low-level surface coverage (46, 48) are insufficient to influence the membrane potentials significantly.

The ideas advanced in the membrane-puncturing, pigment, and enzyme theories are more plausible energetically, since in these theories the odorivector merely triggers or otherwise steers higher-energy processes. In the same category and speculative is Dravnieks' (47) proposal that the chemosensor is a biochemical ferroelectric element that produces an electric pulse during the ferroelectric transition triggered by the odorivector. This hypothesis is based on indications that ferroelectrically active substances are found in living tissues (8).

The simplest and most straightforward theory on the mechanism of olfaction is the membrane-puncturing theory of Davies, Taylor (33, 34, 35, 37, 38, 39, 40), and Mullins (93). The odorivectors dissolve in the lipid layer or a similar structure of the membrane wall of the olfactory neuron endings, and either by disordering its structure (35) or by leaving a hole that does not close instantaneously upon desorption (34) cause a collapse of the potential that exists across the wall of an operating neuron. This initiates the ionic flow and the electrical impulse, which propagates along the neuron in a usual fashion while the cell wall repairs and the metabolic processes restore the membrane potential.

Davies initially advocated the theory that the sensing membrane phase is essentially the same in all olfactory sensors and that differentiation of odors comes from a mild differentiation of sensors plus their spatial arrangement in various regions of the olfactory area. More recently, Davis (34) proposed that differentiated receptors do exist; some receptor wall membranes can dissolve odorivectors more easily, healing of the holes upon the desorption of the odorivector can occur with different rates, etc. Mullins' theory is based on ranges of differentiated sensors.

It may well be that both factors are important. Possibly differentiation in the sensing phase combines with differentiation in some barrier phase. The barrier could determine the rate with which various odorivectors reach particular sensors. If the rate is too low, the signal disappears in the noise level of the neural network. Mullins' observation that adaptation to paraffinic vapors does not influence the threshold for alcohols, and Cheesman's (31) observation that cyclopentanone adaptation has little influence on cyclopentanol threshold are easier to explain by a distinct differentiation in the sensors than by spatial and temporal differentiation only.

In the pigment theories of Briggs and Duncan (25) and Wright (127, 131), it is assumed that the olfactory receptors act like the photon receptors in the eye (24). Recently Köster (74) has pointed out the resemblance of the recovery curve for olfaction after self-adaptation with the recovery curve for rod and cone adaptation in vision. In photo-receptors, however, the large energy of the photon can electronically excite a biochemical assembly—e.g., a charge-transfer complex. In olfaction, the number of molecules that reach the receptor is extremely small (35, 45), and hence the energy package available per receptor is also much smaller than in vision. Therefore the theories resort to some triggering mechanism.

For instance, it has been proposed that exchange of energy between the odorivector and a carotene-protein complex may cause isomerization of the carotene and change the properties of the complex (25). Whether carotenes are present in the olfactory regions of all mammals is still not clear (26, 89). In Wright's theory (126), an easily excitable pigment molecule has such quantal characteristics that it tends to stay in a polar excited state. An odorivector molecule with similar internal vibrational levels couples with the pigment molecule, induces the discharge of the excited state with a loss of polarity, and an impulse results. Wright's hypothesis was advanced to match the elusive relations between the infrared or the Raman spectral characteristics and odor. The pigment theories have not yet been developed into workable models, and their experimental basis so far appears weak.

Other theories attempt to postulate mechanisms based on specific interaction of odorivectors with specialized biochemical systems. Enzyme processes may be influenced by the presence of odorivectors (2, 72, 108) and be changed in such a way that the impulse is triggered. Localization of various enzymes in the olfactory regions has been well established, and in some cases pigments also have been found (10, 11, 23–28, 84, 89, 100, 101). An attempt has been made to link alkaline phosphatase to a sensing mechanism (11).

There are many valid arguments against enzyme systems as the primary sensing elements. Molecules with similar shape but totally different functionalities may have the same odor. The electrophysiological response to an odorivector is relatively independent of ionic strength and pH in the olfactory region (119), whereas enzyme systems are usually sensitive to changes in chemistry and pH (20). A large number of odor types would require many enzyme systems, which seems unlikely (115, 118). This objection holds regardless of whether odorivectors are assumed to be chemically changed by enzymes or to inhibit or catalyze enzyme reactions. Findings that cyclic hormonal changes have a strong effect on thresholds (73, 78, 111) suggest that sensors could be nonfixed, biochemically adaptable elements. In some enzyme theories the sensor monitors the level of a regulatory chemical and the concentration of the chemical is changed by the odorivector.

Another possibility is that the olfactory sensor does not produce the impulse signal—that is, no net energy is derived from the sensor. The sensor can serve as a passive circuit element, merely changing its electrical state when the odorivector is present. The neural pulses in this case may be generated elsewhere or in the sensor but do not depend directly on the odorivector detection mechanism. The sensor then merely modifies the pulsing frequency or pulse shape.

It has been proposed (45) that the sensor can act as a nonlinear circuit element and intermodulate two inquiring frequencies. The attachment of the odorivector can change the degree of nonlinearity toward either more or less linear behavior. Thus it modifies the spectrum of the mixed frequencies and yields information on the presence of the odorivector. The sensor acts, then, as a device that respaces the temporal distribution of the supplied a.c. pulses. The inquiring signals may originate from an independent mechanism put into action by the arrival of an odorivector or by aerodynamic stimulation, obtaining its energy independently from a nonspecific biochemical process. Such a system allows for a convenient steering of the sensitivity of the sensor by electrical effects such as d.c. potential bias directed from the higher levels of the neural system.

Conclusions

A review and comparison of existing theories on the relation of odor quality and odor threshold to physicochemically accessible properties of odorivectors indicate that all theories are interrelated. None has reached a state such that odor can be predicted from independently measured or calculated molecular or bulk characteristics. Odor thresholds probably can be predicted within one or two orders of magnitude from the saturation vapor pressures of odorivectors.

For smaller molecules the odor quality depends more on functionality; for larger molecules the shape and the size are more important. Whether distinct primary odors exist is still unresolved; the tendency among the proponents of their existence is toward a larger number of types. The current trend is to consider that olfactory receptors are poorly differentiated and that complex physiological and psychological factors participate heavily in characterizing odor.

From the large selection of the theories on the mechanism of olfaction, the membrane-puncturing theory of Davies and Taylor can be singled out as the most advanced, plausible, and promising. It also proposes explanations for odor quality and threshold. Other odor quality theories emphasize additional molecular properties and perhaps can usefully modify the simple form of the Davies-Taylor theory. Proofs and further evolution of this theory will probably be among the most significant directions in the development of odor science in coming years.

Literature Cited

(1) Adrian, E. D., *Electroencel. Clin. Neurophysics* **2**, 377 (1950).
(2) Alexandar, Jerome, *Proc. Sci. Sect. Toilet Goods Assoc.*, No. **16** (1951).
(3) Amoore, J. E., *Ann. N.Y. Acad. Sci.* **116**, 457 (1964).
(4) Amoore, J. E., *Nature* **198**, 271 (1963).
(5) Amoore, J. E., *Ibid.*, **199**, 912 (1963) (in answer to B. Fullman).
(6) Amoore, J. E., *Perfumery Essent. Oil Record* **43**, 321 (1952).
(7) Amoore, J. E., *Proc. Sci. Sect. Toilet Goods Assoc.*, Suppl. to No. 37, 1 (1962).
(8) Athestaedt, H., *Naturwissenschaften* **47**(19), 13 (1960).
(9) Baker, R. A., *Ann. N.Y. Acad. Sci.* **116**, 495 (1964).
(10) Baradi, A. F., Bourne, G. H., *Nature* **168**, 977 (1951).
(11) Baradi, A. F., Bourne, G. H., *Science* **113**, 660 (1951).
(12) Beck, L. H., *Ann. N. Y. Acad. Sci.* **116**, 228 (1964).
(13) Beck, L. H., Miles, W. R., *Proc. Natl. Acad. Sci.* **35**, 292 (1949).
(14) Beck, L. H., Miles, W. R., *Science* **106**, 511 (1947).
(15) Beets, M. G. J., *Am. Perfumer Aromat.* **76** (6), 54 (1961).
(16) Beets, M. G. J., in Stoll, M., *et al*, "Molecular Structure and Organoleptic Quality," Monograph 1, Society of Chemical Industry, London, 1957.
(17) Beets, M. G. J., *Parfum. Cosmet. Savons* **5**(4), 1 (1962).
(18) Beidler, L. M., *Ann. N. Y. Acad. Sci.* **58**, 52 (1954).
(19) Beidler, L. M., ADVAN. CHEM. SER. **56**, 1 (1966).
(20) Beidler, L. M., *Ibid.*, p. 8.
(21) Benjamin, R. M., Halpern, B. P., Moulton, D. G., Mozell, M. M., *Ann. Rev. Psychol.* **16**, 381 (1965).
(22) Beynon, J. H., Saunders, P. A., *Brit. J. Appl. Phys.* **11**, 128 (1960).
(23) Bourne, G. H., *Nature* **161**, 445 (1948).
(24) Briggs, M. H., Duncan, R. B., *Arch. Otolaryngol.* **67**, 116 (1962).
(25) Briggs, M. H., Duncan, R. B., *Nature* **191**, 1310 (1961).
(26) *Ibid.*, **195**, 1313 (1962).
(27) Bronshtein, A. A., *Dokl. Akad. Nauk SSSR* **142**, 936 (1962).
(28) Bronshtein, A. A., *Tsitologiya* **2**, 194 (1960).
(29) Caul, J. F., Cairncross, S. F., Sjostrom, L. B., *Perfumery Essent. Oil Record* **49**, 130 (1958).
(30) Chapman, C. R., "Electrical Potential Changes at Surfaces as Means of Measuring Odorous Atmospheric Contamination," Ph.D. thesis, Purdue Univ., 1955; Doct. Dissert. Series Publ. No. 14, 384, Univ. Microfilms, Ann Arbor, Mich.
(31) Cheesman, G. H., *Proc. Roy. Australian Chem. Inst.* 70 (1960).
(32) Crocker, E. C., Henderson, L. F., *Perfumery Essent. Oil Record* **22**, 325 (1927).
(33) Davies, J. T., *Intern. Perfumer* **3**, 17 (1953).
(34) Davies, J. T., *J. Theoret. Biol.* **8**, 1 (1965).
(35) Davies, J. T., *Symp. Soc. Exptl. Biol.* **16**, 170 (1962).
(36) Davies, J. T., Rideal, E. K., "Interfacial Phenomena," pp. 158–63, Academic Press, New York, 1961.
(37) Davies, J. T., Taylor, F. H., *Biol. Bull. Woods Hole* **117**, 222 (1959).
(38) Davies, J. T., Taylor, F. H., *Nature* **174**, 693 (1954).
(39) Davies, J. T., Taylor, F. H., *Perfumery Essent. Oil Record* **46**, No. 1 (1955).

(40) Davies, J. T., Taylor, F. H., *Proc. 2nd Intern. Congress Surface Activity* **4**, 329 (1957).
(41) Deryam, D. R., *Food Technol.* **12**, 231 (1958).
(42) Dethier, V. G., *Ann. N. Y. Acad. Sci.* **58**, 139 (1954).
(43) Dethier, V. G., "The Physiology of Insect Senses," Wiley, New York, 1963.
(44) DeVries, H., Stuiver, M., in W. A. Rosenblith, Edit., "Sensory Communications," Wiley, New York, 1961.
(45) Dravnieks, A., *Ann. N. Y. Acad. Sci.*, **116**, 429 (1964).
(46) Dravnieks, A., "Contact Potentials in Detection of Airborne Vapors," in "Surface Effects in Detection," Spartan Books and Macmillan, New York, 1965.
(47) Dravnieks, A., *Nature* **194**, 245 (1962).
(48) Dravnieks, A., Weber, H. S., "Sensitivity Limitations in the Detection of Airborne Vapors by Surface-Related Effects," in "Surface Effects in Detection," Spartan Book, and Macmillan, New York, 1965.
(49) Dyson, G. M., *Chem. Ind. (London)* **16**, 647 (1938).
(50) Dyson, G. M., *Nature* **173**, 831 (1954).
(51) Dyson, G. M., *Perfumery Essent. Oil Record* **28**, 13 (1937).
(52) Ehrensvard, G., *Acta Phys. Scand.* **3**, Suppl. 9, 1 (1942).
(53) Engen, T., *Ann. N.Y. Acad. Sci.* **116**, 504 (1964).
(54) Friedman, H. H., Mackay, D. A., Rosano, H. L., *Ibid.*, **116**, 602 (1964).
(55) Gavanadan, P., Poussel, H., Brebion, G., Schutzenberger, M. P., *Compt. Rend.* **226**, (1948).
(56) Gesteland, R. C., *Ann. N.Y. Acad. Sci.* **116**, 440 (1964).
(57) Gesteland, R. C., Lettvin, J. Y., Pitts, W. H., Rojas, A., in Y. Zotterman, ed., "Olfaction and Taste," p. 19, Pergaman Press, Oxford, 1963.
(58) Glasstone, S., "Textbook of Physical Chemistry," pp. 711–13, Van Nostrand, New York, 1946.
(59) Green, J. D., Mancia, M., van Baumgarten, R., *J. Neurophysiol.* **25**, 467 (1962).
(60) Guillot, M., *Compt. Rend.* **226**, 1307 (1948).
(61) Guillot, M., *Compt. Rend. Soc. Biol.* **142**, 161 (1948).
(62) Hainer, R. M., Emsile, A. G., Jacobson, A., *Ann. N.Y. Acad. Sci.* **58**, 158 1964).
(63) Henning, H., *Z. Psychol.* **73**, 161 (1915).
(64) Herzberg, G., "Molecular Spectra. Infrared and Raman Spectra of Polyatomic Molecules," Van Nostrand, Princeton, N.J., 1945.
(65) Hildebrandt, J. H., Scott, R. L., "Regular Solutions," Prentice-Hall, New York, 1962.
(66) Jelinek, J. S., *Ann. N. Y. Acad. Sci.* **116**, 725 (1964).
(67) Johnston, J. W., personal communication, April 1965.
(68) Johnston, J. W., Sandoval, A., *Proc. Sci. Sect. Toilet Goods Assoc.*, Suppl. to No. **37**, 34 (1962).
(69) Jones, F. N., Woskow, H. M., *Ann. N. Y. Acad. Sci.* **116**, 484 (1964).
(70) Kendall, D. A., Neilson, A. J., *Ibid.* **116**, 567 (1964).
(71) Kerr, D. I. B., *Australian J. Exptl. Biol. Med. Sci.* **38**, 29 (1960).
(72) Kistiakowski, G. B., *Science* **112**, 154 (1950).
(73) Köster, E. P., *Intern. Rhinol.* **3**, 57 (1965).
(74) Köster, E. P., personal communication, March 1965.
(75) Kopplin, J. O., Eaton, J. R., Christian, J. E., *J. Am. Pharm. Assoc. Sci. Ed.* **48**, 427 (1959).
(76) *Ibid.*, p. 521.
(77) LeMagnen, J., *Compt. Revol. Soc. Biol.* **226**, 753 (1948).
(78) LeMagnen, J., *Arch. Sci. Physiol*, **6**, 125 (1952).
(79) LeMagnen, J., in Y. Zotterman, "Olfaction and Taste," p. 237 Pergamon Press, Oxford, 1963.
(80) McCartney, W., *Soap, Perfumery Cosmetics* **36**, 33 (1963).
(81) McCord, C. P., Witheridge, W. N., "Odors, Physiology, and Control," McGraw-Hill, New York, 1949.

(82) McLeod, P., Cavoy, A., *J. Physiol. (Paris)* **52**, 158 (1960).
(83) Matteson, J. F., *Ann. N.Y. Acad. Sci.* **58**, 83 (1954).
(84) Milas, N. A., Postman, W. H., Heggie, R., *J. Am. Chem. Soc.* **61**, 1929 (1939).
(85) Moncrieff, R. W., *A. Perfumer* **54**, 453 (1949).
(86) Moncrieff, R. W., "Chemical Senses," Leonard Hill, London, 1951. Ed. I (1944), Ed. II (1951).
(87) Moncrieff, R. W., *Ind. Water Wastes* **6**, 107 (1961).
(88) Moncrieff, R. W., *Perfumer Essent. Oil Record* **40**, 279 (1949).
(89) Moulton, D. G., *Nature* **195**, 1312 (1962).
(90) Moulton, D. G., in Y. Zotterman, ed., "Olfaction and Taste," p. 71 Pergaman Press, Oxford, 1963.
(91) Moulton, D. G., Tucker, D., *Ann. N.Y. Acad. Sci.* **116**, 380 (1964).
(92) Mozell, M. M., Pfaffman, C., *Ann. N.Y. Acad. Sci.* **58**, 96 (1954).
(93) Mullins, L. J., *Ibid.*, **62**, 249 (1955).
(94) Naves, Y.-R., in Stoll, M., *et al*, "Molecular Structure and Organoleptic Quality," Society of Chemical Industry Monograph 1, London, 1957.
(95) Nerdel, F., Spaeth, I., *Angew. Chem.* **63**, 545 (1951).
(96) Niccolini, P., Riv. Ital. Essenze Profumi Piante offic. Oli. Vegetali Saponi, **38**,
(97) Ottoson, D., in Y. Zotterman, ed., "Olfaction and Taste," p. 35, Pergamon Press, Oxford, 1963.
(98) Pauling, L., *Chem. Eng. News* **24**, 1064 (1946).
(99) Pfaffman, C., in "Flavor Research and Food Acceptance," p. 29, Reinhold, New York, 1958.
(100) Philippot, E., Gerbetzoff, M. A., *J. Physiol. Paris* **48**, 683 (1956).
(101) *Ibid.*, **50**, 451 (1958).
(102) Phillips, J. P., "Spectra-Structure Correlations," p. 11 Academic Press, New York, 1964.
(103) Pitzer, K. S., Brewer, L., "Lewis-Randall Thermodynamics," p. 289, McGraw-Hill, New York, 1961.
(104) Rosano, H. L., Scheps, S. Q., *Ann. N. Y. Acad. Sci.* **116**, 590 (1964).
(105) Rosen, A. A., Peter, J. B., Middleton, F. M., *J. Water Pollution Control Federation* **34**, 7 (1962).
(106) Rubin, M., Apotheker, D., Lutmer, R., *Proc. Sci. Sect. Toilet Goods Assoc.*, Spec. Suppl. to No. **37**, 24 (1962).
(107) Rupe, H., von Majewski, K., *Ber. Deut. Chem. Ges.* **33**, 3401 (1900).
(108) Ruzicka, L., in Stoll, M., *et al.*, "Molecular Structure and Organoleptic Quality," Soc. Chem. Ind. Monograph No. 1, London, 1957.
(109) Saunders, H. C., *Proc. Sci. Sect. Toilet Goods Assoc.*, Spec. Suppl. to No. **37**, 46 (1962).
(110) Schneider, D., in Y. Zotterman, ed., "Olfaction and Taste," p. 85, Pergamon Press, Oxford, 1963.
(111) Schneider, R. A., Wolf, S., *J. Appl. Physiol* **8**, 337 (1955).
(112) Schutz, H. G., *Ann. N.Y. Acad. Sci.* **116**, 517 (1964).
(113) Stoll, M., *et al.*, "Molecular Structure and Organoleptic Quality," Monograph 1, Society of Chemical Industry, London, 1957.
(114) Stuiver, M., "Biophysics of the Sense of Smell," doctoral thesis, Rijks University, Groningen, Holland, 1958.
(115) Sumner, J. B., *Ann. N.Y. Acad. Sci.* **58**, 68 (1954).
(116) Tanyolac, N. N., Eaton, J. R., *J. Am. Pharm. Assoc. Sci. Ed.* **39**, 565 (1950).
(117) Thompson, H. W., Williams, R. L., *Trans. Faraday Soc.* **48**, 1 (1952).
(118) Thompson, H. W., in Stoll, M., *et al.*, "Molecular Structure and Organoleptic Quality," Monograph 1, Society of Chemical Industry, London, 1957.
(119) Tucker, D., in Y. Zotterman, ed., "Olfaction and Taste," p. 45, Pergamon Press, Oxford, 1963.
(120) Wilkens, W. F., Hartman, J. D., *Ann. N.Y. Acad. Sci.* **116**, 608 (1964).

(121) Wright, R. H., *Ibid.*, **116**, 552 (1963).
(122) Wright, R. H., *J. Appl. Chem.* **4**, 611 (1954).
(123) Wright, R. H., in Stoll, M., *et al.*, "Molecular Structure and Organoleptic Quality," Monograph 1, Society of Chemical Industry, London, 1957.
(124) Wright, R. H., *Nature* **173**, 831 (1954).
(125) *Ibid.*, **178**, 638 (1956).
(126) Wright, R. H., personal communication, November 1964.
(127) Wright, R. H., "Science of Smell," Basic Books, New York, 1964.
(128) *Ibid.*, p. 133.
(129) *Ibid.*, p. 137.
(130) Wright, R. H., Michels, K. M., *Ann. N.Y. Acad. Sci.* **116**, 535 (1964).
(131) Wright, R. H., Reid, C., Evans, H. G. V., *Chem. Ind.*, No. 37, 973 (1956).
(132) Wright, R. H., Serenius, R. S. E., *J. Appl. Chem.* **4**, 615 (1954).
(133) Zotterman, Y., ed., "Olfaction and Taste," Pergamon Press, Oxford, 1963.
(134) Zwaardemaker, H., "The Physiology of Smell," Barth, Leipzig, 1924.

RECEIVED May 10, 1965.

Objective Approaches to Odor Measurement

HENRI L. ROSANO

The City College, City University of New York, New York, N. Y.

HERMAN H. FRIEDMAN

Maxwell House Division, General Foods Corp., Tarrytown, N. Y.

A method of objective odor measurement has been developed in terms of a possible theory of olfaction. Starting from accepted ideas concerning the structure and composition of the nerve cell membrane and the composition of the mucus, possible mechanisms of olfaction are advanced. Any odor-carrying substance must make physical contact with the interior part of the nose. Whether the mucous membrane is "punctured" by the odoriferous substance, or absorption by the mucus produces a change in the state of polarization of the membrane and induces firing, is still open to experimental verification. The authors review current theories of olfaction and some physical models of the olfactory apparatus.

Among man's senses, his ability to detect odors has been most neglected by scientists. Microanalytical methods (chromatography, mass spectrometry, radiochemistry, etc.) have been employed to detect minute concentrations of substances. Unfortunately, these methods are not always selective and their responses do not correspond to that of the human nose. The nose can distinguish, for example, various qualities of odor, whereas the machine cannot. The main reason is that the machine response has no connection with the mechanism of smelling or olfaction.

To develop a valid method for an objective odor measurement, a minimum theoretical understanding of the mechanism of olfaction is necessary—i.e., to build an airplane one does not have to duplicate a bird's flight, but one cannot avoid recognizing the basic principles of aerodynamics. While advancing a hypothesis of the mechanism of olfaction, we would like to review current ideas concerning the structure and composition of nerve cell membranes and the modern theories of the mechanism of the nerve impulse, then to examine a few theories of olfaction and study some physical models of the olfactory apparatus.

Structure and Composition of Nerve Cell Membranes

Most living cells are composed of membranes which separate biological solutions that are different in nature and ionic concentrations. The unequal distribution of the ions appears to play a major role in propagating a nerve impulse. This phenomenon was demonstrated after the Second World War in particular by Hodgkin, Huxley, and Keynes (11). They showed, by using radiotracers, that the nerve membrane is selectively permeable to certain ions. Membranes of human cells are more permeable to potassium ions than sodium ions. During the transmission of a nerve impulse, the permeability of the membrane increases, and the potential decreases and sometimes changes sign. This is called action potential. Sodium ions penetrate the cell when the potential is increasing while potassium ions leave the cell when the potential is returning to its resting potential—the influx of sodium ions precedes the outflow of potassium ions. The change in the sign of a decrease in the concentration of extracellular sodium suppresses this effect. These changes in potential at sites on the membrane are associated with local electrical currents which lead to propagation of the nerve impulse. However, this explanation does not take into consideration the precise role played by the membrane itself, nor does it consider the other substances present in the fluids bathing the nerve fiber.

Because of technical difficulties in isolating individual nerve cells, the precise chemical composition and physical structure of the cell membrane are imperfectly known. Nevertheless, certain experimental facts allow us to speculate on its probable composition and organization. Electron micrographs of nerve tissue have shown that nerve membranes are composed of bimolecular leaflets. Robertson (21) has even hypothesized that the bimolecular leaflet is the fundamental biological unit rather than the cell. Van Deenen and coworkers have analyzed brain, liver, and heart of a vertebrate for fatty acid content (30). They found that the composition and distribution of fatty acids from these different organs were identical while there were differences in the fatty acids extracted from the phospholipid fraction. If we accept Robertson's hypothesis of a fundamental bimolecular leaflet, some of the differences between living cells depend on the different concentrations of phospholipids in these cells. Thus, the nerve membrane can be thought of as a leaflet (65 to 70 A. thick) composed of two oriented monomolecular layers analogous to a phospholipid-protein film. Significantly, when phospholipids are added to water, they produce liquid crystals called myelenic figures. Electron micrograph examination of these artificial myelenic figures shows that they are similar to the neurilemma (*28, 29*). Oparin (*20*) reviews a great number of references dealing with the formation and composition of living matter.

Inversion of Emulsions

The membrane of the nerve cell probably has a pseudo-liquid structure; under these conditions, it may be logical to think that certain molecules or groups can rotate and so allow an ionic exchange. This molecular overturning has been observed. Alkaline soaps produce preferentially oil in water emulsions while earth-alkaline soaps produce water in oil emulsions. In the case of a mixture of soaps the type of the emulsion will depend on the Na^+/Ca^{+2} ratio. Biological solutions surrounding the lipoprotein membrane contain calcium and magnesium ions in addition to sodium and potassium ions. These ions are bound, to a greater or lesser degree, to the membrane or to the proteins surrounding it.

It is natural to ask, what will be the effect of a sudden release of acetylcholine on the permeability of the membrane. In addition to the effect on the charge of the membrane, we must also consider the effect on the Na^+/Ca^{+2} and K^+/Mg^{+2} ratios. It has been shown that acetylcholine, $(CH_3COOCH(CH_2)_2N(CH_3)_3Cl^-)$, is responsible for the variations in permeability following the transmission of nerve impulses across the synapse (space between two nerve cells) and across the neuro-muscular junction. Nachmansohn (*19*) has suggested that acetylcholine is also responsible for the changes in permeability along the fiber. This hypothesis has created a lot of controversy. Finally, molecular overturning has also been observed in the case of built-up monolayers (*13*).

Role of Phospholipids in Nerve Sheath

By using a physicochemical model of the phospholipid sheath found in nervous tissue, Schulman, Rosano, and coworkers studied (*22, 23, 25, 26, 27*) the mechanism involved in nerve activity. By using different physiological components, they devised a simple system which stimulates the complexity of the actual membrane of nerve tissues. A liquid membrane is used for studying the selective flux of various salts through short-chain alkyl alcohols.

The system consists of a nonaqueous (oil) liquid membrane floating on two aqueous solutions. In the presence of a phospholipid (or a long-chain ionized compound) in the oil membrane interface, ions such as potassium, sodium, and chlorine are able to migrate against their concentration gradients through an ionic exchange that takes place at the oil-water interface (*26*). Calcium ions can block the ionic exchange of cephalin and therefore calcium may play an important role with respect to the change of permeability. Physicochemical studies are under way to measure the influence of physiological or odoriferous substances in repelling or removing calcium ions from the solid calcium cephalin film, leading to the unblocking of the phospholipid molecule, which is then able to perform its ionic exchange role. It is also possible that odorant molecules may "penetrate" the membrane and "liquefy" its structure, just as soap scum dispersant is able to prevent the formation of "solid" calcium soap by forming a mixed monolayer. Finally, the odorant molecule can also modify the amount of bound ions, thereby shifting the sodium-calcium balance, which in turn may drastically affect the structure and therefore the permeability of the nerve membrane.

Theories of Olfaction

In recent years it has been generally accepted that any odor-carrying substance must make physical contact with the interior part of the nose. However, it is not basically agreed as to which part of the nose is involved in the adsorption. Moncrieff (*14–18*) postulated that the olfactory receptors possess "receptor sites" of molecular dimensions. If the air-borne molecules were of a suitable size and shape, they might be able to lodge on and adhere to the receptor site. This lodgement of an odorant molecule on the receptor site was considered to be the primary stimulus to the receptor, giving rise to a nerve impulse. According to Moncrieff's idea, therefore the two prerequisites for odor are: (1) volatility and (2) a molecular configuration that is complementary to certain sites on the receptor system.

Recently, a small booklet was published on Amoore's stereochemical theory of olfaction. Unfortunately, the conclusions are based, not on quantitative results, but on qualitative experiments wherein the human nose was the primary instrument. This tends to limit the scope of the conclusions since there is no standard reference. In addition, although phenylethyl alcohol and geraniol "smell like a rose" and propylthioaldehyde and propyl disulfide "smell like an onion," the chemical structures within the pairs are different. In addition, the shape of the odorifereous molecule depends upon its environment. Therefore a steric theory of odor can be, at its best, only approximate.

Davies and Taylor (*6*) have attempted to relate the olfactory threshold to the free energy of adsorption at the oil-water interface. They conclude that the olfactory threshold for different odorants depends quantitatively on: (1) the adsorption energies in passing from air to lipid aqueous surfaces of the olfactory membranes, and (2) the sizes and shapes of the odorant molecules.

Davies and Taylor tried to verify their theory by utilizing published values of the olfactory threshold, but the results are questionable. Furthermore, the free energy of a substance passing from water to air was also obtained mostly from published data on the partial pressure of aqueous solutions. Their results were clouds of points through which straight lines were traced. This is not surprising in view of their experimental sources. Recently, Davies (5) conceived a purely chemical hypothesis on the mechanism of olfaction. He explained the interaction of molecules and nerve cells in the olfactory epithelium in terms of energy of adsorption of the osmogenic molecules to the lipid-water interface of the cell membrane. The odorant molecule, if adsorbed with sufficient strength, penetrates the lipid cell membrane, which results in an exchange between potassium ions in the cell and sodium ions outside the cell. This process initiates an impulse in the olfactory nerve. Davies discusses a theory of the quality of odors. The concept of primary odors is based on his assumption of "puncturing." After a time, the molecule desorbs, the hole in the cell membrane "heals," K^+-Na^+ interchange ceases, and the nerve cell is ready to produce another impulse. Odor quality is determined by such factors as molecular cross-sectional area and the energy of desorption from the lipid-water interface into water.

It is difficult to disprove these quantitative theories since values of olfactory thresholds for identical substances vary so widely. In addition to all the factors already mentioned, Davies, Taylor, and others have neglected a basic phenomenon occurring at the level of the nose membrane: probable enzymatic interaction of the odoriferous molecules with the mucus. Bronshtein (4) has shown that cholinesterase, phosphotase, succinic dihydrogenase, and cytochrome oxidase are present in the olfactory organs of rabbits, guinea pigs, and cats. Jackson (12) extracted phospholipids from olfactory tissue of various animals. This is why, although we agree with the concept of adsorption of the odorant molecules, we also believe that primary enzymatic interaction must be taken into consideration during the adsorption of the odorant on the surface of the mucous layer in the nose, since direct interaction between odorant material and receptor site would be eventually inhibited by the mucus, one of whose functions is to prevent foreign materials (dust, nonpathogenic bacteria, etc.) from reaching the interior parts of the nose.

Mucus is essentially equivalent to an enzymatic aqueous solution containing ions—i.e., Na^+, Cl^-, Ca^{+2}—more or less bound to the protein. Any absorption by the mucus of a foreign substance—i.e., odoriferous molecules—which would modify the ionic distribution in the mucus will in turn change the state of polarization of the nerve endings and induce firing. This hypothesis is basically different from that of Davies and Taylor (6) of direct "puncturing" of the nerve membrane by the odoriferous molecules, although not completely in disagreement with the stereochemical theory of Amoore (1)—since enzymatic reaction can be stereospecific. In view of the nature of the enzymes found in mucus, it appears to us that this interaction between the odoriferous molecules and the mucus could be oxidative. Angeli and Polverini (2), in the case of coumarin and seven of its homologs, have found a direct relationship between oxidation and presence of odor.

Furthermore, the stimulation of olfactory receptors has also been investigated by neurophysiologists, who agree that the stimulation is a result of odoriferous molecules on the surface of the neuroepithelium (19). In summary, the olfactory epithelium lies under a thin sheet of mucus and is recessed from the main respiratory air stream. The mucus constitutes the "outside" aqueous solution containing mostly water, Na^+, Cl^-, and Ca^{+2} ions in addition to enzymes whose primary role is to protect us against nonpathogenic bacteria and foreign bodies. An electrical potential exists between the inside and the outside of the olfactory nerve cell endings. When these cells are fired, Na^+ and K^+ ions probably migrate through the cell membrane. The dimensions of the cell membrane indicate that each face can be identified with an oriented monolayer in contact with a substrate containing a ratio of sodium to calcium ions around 50–100 to 1. From monolayer studies, we can draw an analogy between the surface of the nerve cell ending and a lipoprotein monolayer at the borderline between a gel to sol two-dimensional transformation (22). The effect of an odorant molecule coming into contact with the inside of the nasal cavity can be twofold: penetration into the cell membrane and "liquefying" it or interaction with the enzymes to alter primarily the ratio of free to bound sodium.

Before reviewing some analogs of the human nose, we would like to describe the authors' concept of smell, represented schematically in the diagram below.

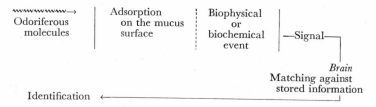

Authors' Concept of Smell

An odor entering the nose adsorbs on the mucus and a bio- or physicochemical event produces a signal. This signal is matched in the brain against known information. At the start of their research the authors attempted to construct an analog of the schema. The first attempt (8) was to study the interaction between odoriferous molecules interacting with a monolayer of cephalin. No simple correlation between odor and variation of surface pressure of the cephalin monolayer was found. Next the interaction of odoriferous vapors and cephalin-coated thermistors was investigated (8). Unfortunately, the analysis of the profiles of the curves indicated that we were measuring essentially the heat of adsorption and desorption of the odoriferous molecules on cephalin, so far no simple relationship to odor has been found.

In addition, to see if any correlation existed between ease of oxidation and smell, an electrochemical cell made up of an exposed electrode/an oxidizing electrolyte (nitrochromic mixture)/immersed electrode was used. Vapors of odoriferous substances were introduced into a nitrogen carrier steam penetrating into the cell. The vapors entering the cell interacted with the exposed electrode wetted by the nitrochromic solution. The response of the cell was a function of the ease of oxidation. Nevertheless, no direct relationship between cell response and odor was found. So far, the authors have not found a valid analog of the human nose. Research is now centered on the effect of odoriferous molecules on ion binding to proteins.

Analogs of the Human Nose

Physical Models of Olfactory Apparatus. As we have explained, the process of smelling involves adsorption of the odoriferous material onto the mucus surface, occurrence of biochemical events not well understood, and production of a nerve impulse which is sent to the brain. Therefore, a physicochemical analog should take into consideration the sequence of the three events: adsorption of a vapor, a physical or chemical event, and an electrical signal.

Let us now examine several recent physical models that are used to detect odors.

MONCRIEFF'S MODEL. All substances that are appreciably volatile are also odorous (*14–19*), provided that:

They are not already present in the olfactory system, as water and air are (because it is only change that produces sensation).

They are not very difficult to adsorb, as are the light gases, which are also difficult to liquefy.

Ignore these two exceptional groups and everything that is volatile is odorous. Further postulates, such as that the odorant molecule possesses either some particular Raman shift or has cell-puncturing properties, are unnecessary, according to Moncrieff, especially when there is no experimental evidence to support them. He describes an instrument for measuring odor: "The odor stimulus is very simple indeed, and all that is necessary to detect the presence of an odorant material is a suitable film connected to some device which will indicate the heat gains and losses that the film sustains as a result of adsorption on it and desorption from it of the odorant." The principle underlying the function of this instrument is that odorous materials are adsorbed onto thermistors coated with thin films, and that the energy changes due to adsorption and desorption are thereby converted into changes in electrical resistance which can be suitably measured. The instrument reproduces such phenomena as olfactory fatigue and discrimination.

Friedman, MacKay, and Rosano (8) assumed that stimulation of olfactory receptors results in the adsorption of odoriferous molecules on the surface of the neuroepithelium and adopted the Moncrieff technique. The process involved passing the vapor of an odorant, using moist air as a carrier, over two pairs of thermistors—one pair coated with cephalin and the other uncoated—and recording the change in temperature. It was found that the resultant odor "profiles," produced by the interaction of the odorants and the cephalin on the thermistors, were reversible. The duration of the adsorption and desorption cycles and the shape of the curves which were recorded, depend on the nature of the vapor as well as on the experimental conditions. The positive and negative temperature changes can be interpreted in terms of adsorption and desorption of the odorant molecules on the cephalin layer.

These two studies imply that the initiation of smelling must be physical rather than chemical, the main process being direct adsorption of the odorant molecule onto the neuroepithelium surface. This device is limited since a substance with a low volatility cannot be detected. The device measures the heat of adsorption and desorption and therefore depends in first approximation on the number of molecules absorbed. In the case of the nose, a trigger mechanism must operate since minute quantities of odorant are detectable.

HARTMAN'S MODEL. Hartman (9, 10) postulated that the olfactory receptor hairs essentially act as polarized microelectrodes. He writes: "The olfactory hairs, surrounded or projecting through a mucous layer, are under a bioelectric potential, but little current flows along or across the nerve membrane in the absence of odorous molecules . . . Adsorption of odorous molecules at this double layer probably results in either disruption or enforcement of the double layer . . . The microelectrode does not perform as a true capacitor but more like a leaky condenser . . ." The electronic analog developed by Wilkins and Hartman (34) involves a series of five microelectrodes polarized at seven different potentials. Response amplitude profiles with 35 electrode conditions were obtained. The device provides odor profiles. Unfortunately, these profiles cannot be interpreted on the basis of physiochemical principles, as is possible, for example, with infrared (intravibrational molecular forces) or ultraviolet (electron, excitation around the molecules) spectra.

DRAVNIEKS' MODEL. Dravnieks (*1*) measured the change that is produced in the electrical potential of surfaces of substances when they absorb organic vapors carrying the odors.   The change is observed on an oscilloscope and measured by a precision potentiometer, both of which are connected to the sensor unit of the "smelling device."   The sensor unit itself consists of four stationary gold electrodes and one rotating gold paddle which passes 2 mm. above the electrodes at 900 r.p.m.   The electrodes and paddle are covered with a hood.

The vapor to be "smelled" is then mixed with oxygen and injected into a continuous stream of nitrogen, which carries it into the chamber. There, whirled about by the gold paddle, it comes into contact with substances (such as NaCl) which previously have been coated on the electrodes.   The change in electrical potential occurs and is recorded.   The problem with this surface potential-measuring device is that too many factors varying at the same time—i.e., simultaneous adsorption on the electrode surfaces, ionization in the capacitance, etc.—make the interpretation extremely difficult.   Dravnieks' recent publication did not convince the authors that his results will be interpretable in the near future, as are, in general, surface potential measurements.

Recently, Dravnieks reviewed the rise of contact potentials in the detection of airborne vapors.   He also described a new apparatus (based on the Kelvin-Zisman technique) consisting of a vibrating capacitor chamber through which the gases and vapors flow.

BERTON'S MODEL. Berton (*3*) set up a droplet between two electrodes upon which a vapor is blown and the resulting change in current is recorded as a function of time. In later work he utilized a cell very similar to the classical standard hydrogen electrode where he used a platinum gauze instead of a plate.   He called this system the "osmopile." This technique is of interest because it allows a simultaneous study of adsorption and chemical interaction.   Unfortunately, Berton's publications did not supply enough information for practical operation of the cell, and he did not propose a mechanism.

Rosano and Scheps (*24*) repeated Berton's experiments.   The working conditions have been specified and a probable mechanism has been advanced.   This particular technique is attractive because the response of the electrochemical cell depends on the interaction between the specific electrolyte chosen to react with the incoming vapor.   The system is equivalent to a concentration cell with transference.   So far, the current produced bears no simple relationship to the odor.

Conclusions

It is premature to speak of objective approaches to odor measurements because the mechanism of olfaction has not been completely explained.

Neurophysiologists have provided us with hypotheses worth investigating for an eventual understanding of olfaction. Meanwhile, we are forced to proceed with the available analytical tools.

In the area of basic investigation the great need is for a unifying hypothesis that connects the bulk odorant to the sensation of odor. In view of the active interest in this field of research, we feel that we can expect a breakthrough in the not too distant future.

Since the subject is highly speculative, the authors have not attempted to write a bibliography. The object of this article is to be provocative, and therefore we have been deliberately controversial.

In the meanwhile physiological means can still be used and can be both quantitative and objective. However, statistical means generally have to be applied to analysis of these data. On the other hand, if the color blue had to be measured by using human vision rather than by determining the maximum wavelength, the inconvenience and imprecision would be great. When we talk about objective odor measurement, we are searching for some method which is analogous to determining color by use of a spectrophotometer.

Literature Cited

(1) Amoore, J. E., *Proc. Scientific Sec., Toilet Goods Assoc.*, No. **37**, 13–23 (October 1962).

(2) Angeli, A., Polverini, A., *Gazz. Chim. Ital.* **61**, 276–80 (1931).

(3) Berton, A., *Chim. Anal. (Paris)* **9**, 351–8 (1959); *Rev. Franc Corps Gras* **4**, 187–92 (1962).

(4) Bronshtein, A. A., *Tsitologiya* **2**, 194–200 (1960).

(5) Davies, J. T., *J. Theoreti. Biol.* **8**, 1–7 (1965).

(6) Davies, J. T., Taylor, F. H., 2nd International Congress of Surface Activity, pp. 329–40, Butterworth, London, 1958.

(7) Dravnieks, A., *Ann. N. Y. Acad. Sci.* **116**, 429–39 (1964); Proceedings of Conference on Surface Effects in Detection, June 29–July 1, 1964, Washington, D. C.

(8) Friedman, H., MacKay, D. A., Rosano, H. L., *Ann. N. Y. Acad. Sci.* **116**, 602–7, (1964).

(9) Hartman, J. D., *Proc. Am. Soc. Hort. Sci.* **64**, 335, (1954).

(10) Hartman, J. D., Tolle W. E., *Food Technol.* **11**, 130, (1957).

(11) Hodgkin, A. L., Huxley, A. F., Keynes, R. D., *J. Physiol.* (London) **104**, 178 (1945); **108**, 33 (1945); **128**, 28 (1955); **131**, 592 (1956); **138**, 253 (1957).

(12) Jackson, R. T., *J. Cellular Compt. Phys.*, **55**, 143–47 (1960).

(13) Langmuir, I., Blodgett, K., *J. Franklin Inst.* **218**, 143 (1943); *J. Am. Chem. Soc.* **57**, 1007 (1935).

(14) Moncrieff, R. W., *Am. J. Psychol.* **70**, No. 1, 1–20 (1957).

(15) Moncrieff, R. W., *J. Physiol.* **130**, 543–58 (1955).

(16) *Ibid.*, **133**, 301–16 (1956).

(17) Moncrieff, R. W., Proceedings of 2nd International Congress on Surface Activity (London), Vol. 2, pp. 321–8, 1957.

(18) Moncrieff, R. W., Proceedings of 3rd International Congress on Surface Activity, Brussels, 1964, preprint **B/II-18**.

(19) Nachmansohn, D., "Chemical and Molecular Basis of Nerve Activity," Academic Press, New York, 1959.
(20) Oparin, A. I., "Origin of Life on Earth," Oliver S. Boyd, Edinburgh, 1957.
(21) Robertson, J. D., *Biochem. Soc. Symp.* **16**, 3–43 (1959).
(22) Rosano, H. L., *Chem. Eng. News* **39**, No. 15, 52 (1961).
(23) Rosano, H. L., Duby, P., Schulman, J. H., *J. Phys. Chem* **65**, 40–4 (1962).
(24) Rosano, H. L., Scheps, S. Q., *Ann. N. Y. Acad. Sci.* **112**, 590–601 (1964).
(25) Rosano, H. L., Schiff, H., Schulman, J. H., *J. Phys. Chem.* **66**, 1928–32 (1962).
(26) Rosano, H. L., Schulman, J. H., Weisbuch, J. B., *Ann. N. Y. Acad. Sci.* **92**, 457–92 (1961).
(27) Schulman, J. H., Rosano, H. L., "Retardation of Evaporation by Monolayers, V. K. LaMer, ed., pp. 97–118, Academic Press, New York, 1962.
(28) Stoeckinius, W., Proceedings of European Regional Conference on Electron-Microscopy," Delft, 1960), Vol. II, pp. 716–20 (1960). (1960).
(30) Veer Kamp, J. H., Mulder I., Deenen Van, L. L. M. *Biochim. Biophys. Acta* **57**, 299–310 (1962).
(31) Wilkens, W. F., Hartman, J. D., *J. Food Sci.* **29**, No. 3, 372–8 (1964).

RECEIVED May 20, 1965

4

Sensory Evaluation of Food Flavor

AMIHUD KRAMER

University of Maryland, College Park, Md.

In the absence of adequate physical-chemical methods for measuring quality attributes of foods, it becomes necessary to resort to the human instrument. Such sensory procedures may be classified as descriptive, preference, or difference tests. Descriptive testing is accomplished by one or more trained individuals who provide descriptive evaluation of quality, usually with the aid of reference samples. Preference tests used for consumer acceptance utilize large numbers of tasters. Difference tests employ trained panelists. If a test fails to demonstrate a statistically significant difference, it is assumed that the samples are the same. This last procedure approaches most closely the use of the human taster as a laboratory instrument.

Sensory evaluation of foods has been practiced ever since food was first produced. Various attributes of quality were measured and decisions made on the basis of sensory—human—evaluation. Although isolated instances of the development of instrumental methods for measuring esthetic qualities of food, and statistical procedures for interpreting results, have appeared from time to time during the past century or even earlier, only recently have such procedures become available in sufficient numbers so that an attempt could be made to organize them as a distinct discipline (9).

Since these food attributes are to be measured through the human senses, it is logical to classify this discipline in broad categories in accordance with the human senses of sight, kinesthetics (feel or the muscle sense), and taste and smell. In certain special instances, sound may be considered a fourth category—for example, crackle of breakfast cereals, crispness of some vegetables, or sizzle of carbonated beverages (4). Thus, attributes of appearance are evaluated by the eye; kinesthetics by the muscle sense in the hand, but primarily in the mouth; and flavor by the taste buds in the mouth and the odor-sensitive patch in the nose.

During the last several decades, there has been very substantial success in the development of instrumental or chemical methods for measuring appearance properties such as color, gloss, size, shape, and visual defects. Kinesthetic attributes, which may be defined in such descriptive terms as hardness, grittiness, and fibrousness, may also be measured satisfactorily by objective means. The principles of these measurements are thoroughly understood and all that needs to be done to evaluate the appearance or kinesthetic quality of specific food commodities is to relate scalar values obtained by instrumental methods with human evaluation in order to interpret such scalar values in terms of preferences, or differences, as they may be sensed by a human consumer. To this day, however, flavor factors are particularly difficult, if not impossible, to measure by any but the subjective human instrument.

Thus, in a food quality measuring system where objective methods should be relied upon, the use of a sensory taste testing panel is in a sense an admission of failure except where an objective method is being tested for conformance to human evaluation. Until there is a thorough physical-chemical understanding of flavor perception, it will be difficult to construct an instrument capable of measuring flavors, qualitatively and quantitatively, in a manner similar to the evaluation of flavor by the human senses (3).

Thus far there has been only one serious attempt to develop an instrument that will simulate human response to odor (6). This electro-chemical approach is still in the testing stage with testing of isolated compounds. With the rapid development of radically new research techniques, such as gas chromatography accompanied by spectroscopy and nuclear magnetic resonance, there is the hope that a means for measuring flavor quality directly may be discovered in the not too distant future (3). For the present, the four-dimension taste attributes of sweet, sour, salt, and bitter may be measured by determining quantitatively the chemical components contributing to these specific properties. In the odor area of flavor, much of the work with gas chromatography is in a similar direction —that is, identifying the volatile components that may be associated with the specific odor of the food product (3, 11). The study of the interrelationship of all of these volatile and nonvolatile substances to the perception, and more specifically to the preference, for particular flavors by the human consumer has only begun.

Statistical Procedures

Because of the vast number of individual substances that are isolated on the gas chromatogram that may or may not have some relationship to flavor perception, it is necessary to use rather elaborate statistical procedures to determine which specific components in which specific combinations have significant effects on flavor perception. This can be accomplished by using a statistical procedure called "stepwise multiple regression." In this procedure, the human taste panel is the criterion by which the usefulness of any particular component is measured, as contributing to the flavor sensation. Thus, the taste panel score is considered as the "dependent" variable, which is correlated with every one of the "independent" variables. These are the individual components, volatile or not, as found by chemical procedures including gas chromatography that may contribute to the flavor sensation.

Data for each component are correlated with the taste panel data separately and all of the components are correlated with each other, to form a correlation coefficient matrix. The highest correlation coefficient between panel results and one of the independent variables is selected and all of the other correlations are recalculated on a partial correlation basis. The next highest correlation is then selected and if the multiple correlation is significantly better than the previous single high correlation, both are retained for use in a regression equation, and the remaining correlations are recalculated, omitting the two selected. This process is repeated until all of the components which contribute to a significant increase in the multiple correlation coefficient with the taste panel data have been selected. In this way, the components having a significant effect on flavor perception are selected while the other components are omitted from the final regression analysis. Synergistic effects are revealed as significant interactions and antagonistic effects as negative correlations. The success of this procedure depends on the presence of an adequate set of samples in which all variables are represented at all levels of quality.

Such studies were conducted with fresh and processed green beans, where 32 components were separated by gas chromatography and correlated with taste panel scores for flavor preference. In this situation, the taste panelists were instructed to score for intensity and quality of bean flavor. Of the 32 components, six were found to contribute towards a significant correlation with the taste panels. The multiple correlation coefficient, using these six components, was 0.76. Since the coefficient of determination is the square of the coefficient of correlation, this would indicate that these six substances explain just a little more than half (0.76^2 = 0.58 or 58%) of the variability in the panel scores. Although this indicates a highly significant relationship between these six components and flavor evaluations of the taste panel, it still does not explain almost half of the variations in the panel scores for flavor. When measures of fiber content (indicating toughness or stringiness of the beans), size, and color, were also included in the analyses, the multiple correlation coefficient rose to 0.94, indicating that almost 90% (0.94^2 = 0.88) of the variations in panel evaluations for flavor were explained by these six gas chromatographic peaks, plus measurements of appearance and texture of the product.

This then is a demonstration that at least the ordinary consumer (if not the highly trained master taster) is influenced in his flavor perception, not only by the four primary taste stimuli, and an unknown number of odor stimuli, but also by stimuli affecting the sight and muscle senses. Stated in another way, this is merely repeating what has often been suspected—that the response to flavor quality is not entirely a function of taste and odor alone. Another possible explanation for the relatively low multiple correlation coefficient between panel scores and gas chromatographic data alone is that some relatively high boiling compounds, which were not measured by the gas chromatographic procedure used, are also contributing to flavor (*11*).

Taste Panels

The use of a taste panel, as described above, is merely to provide scalar equivalence to objective methods. The usual application of the taste panel is for the many situations where a complete objective-instrumental procedure for evaluating quality is not available (*7*). Since all types of taste panels may be grossly influenced by human psychological factors, results should be interpreted statistically. Thus, the taste panel conducted on a statistical basis can be said to be a psychophysical test based on psychometrics. As with any statistical procedure, the conditions must favor and one must assume a completely independent response for each individual who does the testing, and each sample must be presented under similar conditions. These sensory panels may be classified as descriptive, preference, or different panels. Descriptive testing is accomplished by one or more trained individuals who arrive at a descriptive evaluation of the product quality, usually with the aid of specific odor, taste, or texture samples used as reference points. Such descriptive panels are useful particularly for product development, where specific odor or taste notes are to be enhanced, or attenuated. There is no room for statistical treatment, and the procedure may be described as being more of a highly skilled art than a science (*2*).

Preference tests are used ordinarily merely to evaluate consumer acceptance. Relatively large numbers of individuals are used and each panelist is required to select the sample he prefers or to rank the samples in the order of his preference. Difference tests employ panelists who are selected for their aptitude or trained to detect differences. If a test fails to demonstrate a significant difference, it is assumed that the samples are the same. This difference-type panel approaches the use of the human taster as a laboratory instrument (*7*).

A member for such a difference-type panel is selected on the basis of two criteria: the individual's ability to distinguish among different samples, and his ability to duplicate results on the same sample. A third criterion may be of value only when an absolute scorer is required, such as when quality grades are provided (9).

The environment in which the panelist works is important in a number of respects. If he is to evaluate for flavor only, it is desirable to mask color differences. The panelist should also be relatively isolated so that he cannot be influenced by other panelists. The samples that are submitted to him should be as homogeneous as possible from the standpoint of the quality attributes other than the one which he is required to evaluate. Thus, if flavor is being evaluated, color, size, and texture should be as uniform as possible for all samples.

Order of presentation of the samples can be important. Ordinarily if the product is generally liked, the sample presented first will be scored too high; if a product is disliked, it will be scored too low. To avoid such errors in order of presentation, samples can be presented entirely at random, with sufficient replication, or they may be presented in a latin-square design in which each sample is presented in every position (5, 8).

Much has been said regarding the number of samples that can be tasted at one sitting. Some authorities insist that a true value cannot be obtained unless one sample and one alone is tasted at a particular time. Others insist that fatigue, or adaptation, sets in very rapidly after three, four, or five samples have been tasted at one sitting. In general, the opinion of some workers (8) is that particularly where samples are not very strongly flavored, or spicy, and do not have a carry-over effect, a time lapse of 1, possibly 2 minutes from one tasting to another is sufficient. The more samples are tasted within one session the more precise are the results likely to be, and more acuity may be achieved in differentiating small differences. This is because flavor memory is good over short periods of time but tends to fade rapidly from one day to the next. Ough *et al.* (10) present another attitude.

Responses are ordinarily recorded on some scalar basis. This can take the form of the usual scoring system on the basis of 1 to 10 or 1 to 100, with the top value indicating the highest intensity in the case of a difference test or the highest desirability in the case of a preference test. A scale balanced about 0 is frequently useful, particularly where two attributes are considered, one being positive and the other negative. Thus, for example, if the panel is required to score for sweetness-tartness, the center of the scale may be neither sweet nor tart and indicated as 0. Positive values indicate degrees of sweetness while negative values indicate degrees of tartness. In the case of preference tests a similar hedonic scale can be used with increasing positive values indicating degrees of liking from "like slightly" to "like extremely," while increasing negative values would indicate degrees of disliking, from "dislike slightly" to "dislike extremely." Another method of recording responses is to rank the samples in order of preferences or intensity. Such a ranking procedure has the advantage of handling responses which are not necessarily evenly spaced in a nonparametric manner. It should, however, be limited to ranking up to seven, possibly nine samples. Beyond this number, the ranking procedure becomes cumbersome (7). Recently Schutz (12) has suggested a Food Action (FACT) rating scale whereby the panelist indicates how frequently he would wish to purchase the product.

Finally, results obtained by these procedures, if they are obtained independently and psychological bias is either eliminated or balanced, can be then analyzed statistically, ordinarily by the analysis of variance. By this statistical procedure, differences due to method, time of presentation, and quality characteristics measurable by other means than panel scores, can be isolated and removed separately, and a decision can then be made on the basis of statistical probability regarding the difference in the particular attribute of quality which is being measured. Results of such an analysis would not only indicate a general difference in intensity or preference as indicated by all the panelists as a whole but also demonstrate any significant interactions among panelists and samples. Thus, it is possible that a number of individuals may prefer, or may be particularly sensitive, to a certain flavor while others may prefer another flavor attribute. Such results can be uncovered by the use of panels whose data are analyzed by these methods.

Literature Cited

(1) Beidler, L. M., "Facts and Theory on the Mechanism of Taste and Odor Perception," Quartermaster Food and Container Institute, Symposium, Chemistry of Natural Food Flavors, Chicago, Ill., 1957.
(2) Caul, J. F., *Advan. Food Res.* **7**, 1–40 (1957).
(3) Dimick, K. P., Corse, J., *Food Technol.* **10**, 360–364 (1956).
(4) Drake, B. K., *J. Food Sci.* **30**, 556–9 (1965).
(5) Eindhoven, Jan, *Ibid.*, **29**, 520 (1964).
(6) Hartman, J. D., *Food Technol.* **11**, 130 (1957).
(7) Institute of Food Technologists, *Food Technol.* **18** (8) 1135–1141 (1964).
(8) Kramer, A., *J. Agr. Food Chem.* **9**, 224 (1961).
(9) Kramer, A. "Fundamentals of Quality Control for the Food Industry," Avi Publication Co., Westport, Conn., 1962.
(10) Ough, C. S., *J. Food Sci.* **29**, 506–9 (1964).
(11) Pyne, A. W., *Ibid.*, **30**, 192–200 (1965).
(12) Schutz, H. G., *Ibid.*, **30**, 365–74 (1965).

RECEIVED May 4, 1965. Miscellaneous Publication 542. Contribution 3661, Maryland Agricultural Experiment Station (Department of Horticulture).

5

Progress and Limitations in the Identification of Flavor Components

WILLIAM S. RYDER

Technical Center, General Foods Corp., Tarrytown, N. Y.

Gas chromatography has made possible rapid strides in identifying components of many food flavors. High boiling compounds, however, often are of major importance to flavor and require special gas chromatographic conditions and more classical procedures to isolate and identify them. Headspace chromatograms often correlate with taste panel scores for good and off-flavors, as shown with tomato and potato products. Capillary columns with flame ionization detectors and vapor enrichment techniques give even more definitive patterns. Capillary columns used with a fast scan mass spectrometer provide high resolution and identifiable mass spectra of individual compounds. Odor evaluation of emerging compounds plus chemical class separations of complex mixtures provides useful tentative identifications before using the capillary column mass spectrometer unit. Infrared and NMR are reserved for identifying individual isolated compounds.

Flavor is one of the most important factors governing the selection of the foods we eat. Thus the creation and utilization of flavors of the highest quality are matters of major concern in the manufacture and sale of food products.

Inherent Difficulties in Flavor Analysis

As far as nature is concerned, the substances which contribute to flavor and aroma constitute a very minor part of the total product as consumed. Thus, many of the compounds which interest flavor chemists occur in concentrations measured in parts per million or even less. Three other factors complicate the task of the flavor chemist. First, the substances which contribute to flavor and aroma comprise many different classes of organic compounds. Secondly, there is usually a great variety of chemical compounds within a given class which arise naturally by biochemical processes or by subsequent treatment and processing by man. The third factor is the wide range in boiling point, extending from that of the fixed gases to about 300°C. The spectrum of flavor is never simple.

The advent of gas chromatography has given the research chemist a powerful tool for unlocking Nature's secrets on flavor composition. Tremendous progress has been made through the combined efforts of people with widely diversified interests and experience. However, much work remains to be done and much has yet to be learned about food flavors. Gas chromatography has served to focus particular attention on compounds of relatively low boiling point (50° to 150°C.). There may be a danger in this if one becomes shortsighted and neglects to consider compounds outside this range. Compounding experience has shown, in most cases, that the relatively low boiling compounds modify flavors in important and demonstrable ways but nonetheless fail to duplicate the total flavor. Low boiling alcohols, aldehydes, ketones, and sulfur compounds are ubiquitous constituents of food volatiles although the ratios of their occurrence may vary widely, depending on the ratios of precursor substances present and other physical and chemical factors in the environment of the food (*4, 5, 9, 19, 22, 26, 29, 31 34, 38*). Occasionally with the aid of sophisticated instruments, the presence of unique volatile components is brought to light. The identification by Teranishi *et al.* (*35*) of four acetals among the volatiles of strawberries is a good example.

Growing recognition that an essential "core" or "heart" of flavor is due to higher boiling compounds has broadened the range of investigation of many flavor researchers. Important flavor values are being described among high boiling point compounds in maple sirup (*36*), orange juice (*30, 33, 38*), orange and other citrus oils (*10, 11, 12, 13*), pears (*16, 17, 18*), peaches (*15*), and Cheddar cheese (*7*), to mention a few detailed investigations currently in progress. Of particular interest is the compound nootkatone, a bicyclic sesquiterpene ketone recently identified by MacLeod (*23*) in grapefruit juice and peel oil, which reputedly possesses a powerful and persistent grapefruit-like odor even at very low concentrations. The phthalide compounds identified by Gold (*8*) in celery are another example of important flavor characteristics contributed by high boiling compounds. These compounds are difficult to analyze by conventional gas chromatography, but the range of applicability of the technique is being constantly expanded to meet this challenge. Kung and Romagnoli (*20*) have shown that a column packed with coated Nichrome helices will provide rapid elution and well defined peaks for compounds such as maltol, vanillin, and some substituted coumarins. Sugars are now determined as trimethylsilyl derivatives (*28*) or methyl ethers of their glycosides (*1*).

Amino acids have graduated from paper chromatography to analysis by gas chromatography by formation of volatile amines during controlled pyrolysis (37) or by formation of N-trifluoroacetylamino methyl esters (6). There is concurrently a reawakened and increasing interest in the use of thin-layer chromatography and in paper and column chromatography.

Sample Preparation

Sample preparation is a very critical aspect of flavor research. Analysis of artifacts arising from oxidation, metal catalysis, enzyme action, heat, or chemical interaction is costly and limits the value of the information obtained. At General Foods, we prefer to work with quantities of raw material which can be handled conveniently, as quickly and under as mild conditions as possible. Organoleptic evaluations are used to guard against untoward flavor changes resulting from variations in raw material or processing conditions. As a matter of course, frequent progress checks are made by recombining isolates and fractions to reconstitute the starting material. While this procedure is not always successful, it is useful and worthwhile since it is capable of calling immediate attention when something has gone wrong and thus avoids serious complications later on. Ultimately isolates or fractions from separate batch operations are combined prior to further fractionation and analysis.

Generally speaking, our sampling procedures take into account the manner in which the food is prepared for eating in order to establish the degree to which contact by water and heat might be detrimental. Obviously the flavor of fresh strawberries will be sampled more gently than vegetables and meat which are cooked before eating.

A great many procedures are employed to obtain flavor fractions for evaluation and analysis. Conventional vacuum and steam distillation seem to be used less frequently today than in the past. Figure 1 is a diagram of a falling-film flash evaporator which has been found very useful when dealing with fluid materials such as juice, serum, or diluted purees. By programming the temperature of the hot zone, fractions, which are somewhat less complex in composition, can be obtained for evaluation and analysis.

Where contact with heat is felt to be undesirable, continuous countercurrent liquid-liquid extraction may be used with low-boiling solvents and a packed column to provide intimate contact of the phases. While this procedure tends to isolate a varying amount of nonvolatile material and sacrifices some of the very low boiling compounds during concentration, we have been more successful in isolating a total flavor fraction by this procedure than by any other we have employed.

FALLING FILM FLASH EVAPORATOR

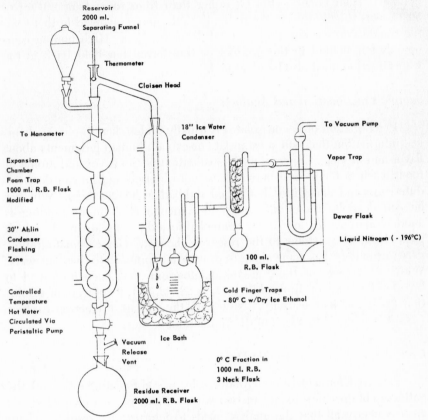

Figure 1.   Diagram of falling film flash evaporator

High-vacuum, low-temperature distillation—a technique perfected by Merritt and coworkers (*24*) at the Quartermaster Laboratories, Natick, Mass. is excellent for isolating a rather broad spectrum of volatiles. This procedure essentially involves vapor transferring volatiles at about 1-micron pressure from the sample warmed to room temperature into a receiver maintained at —196°C. Subsequently, temperature gradients are imposed which permit the removal of carbon dioxide and water. We have used this technique to advantage in characterizing volatiles associated with differences in flavor character which might be described as "freshness" and "staleness."

To exploit this technique to the fullest extent demands reasonably sophisticated facilities for fractionation and identification. The greatest amount of useful data is obtained when a Bendix Time-of-Flight or similar mass spectrometer is employed as the detector for the gas chormatographic column system. Also, the column temperature should be programmed from about —100°C. rather than from room temperature or 50°C. as is usually done. Secondly, the substances involved in this volatile fraction do not constitute a total flavor fraction. High boiling compounds left behind in the product or transferred but held back in the water fraction must also be identified.

Sample Fractionation and Analysis

Fractionation of flavor isolates is usually undertaken to obtain chemical information that will substantiate or explain human judgments about flavor and aroma. Concerning the evaluation of the flavor and aroma of foods, each taster is an expert at least unto himself and he can describe differences and similarities, both good and bad, as he sees them. Whether he can describe these differences to someone else's understanding is another matter. In any case, organoleptic judgments are made which pose chemical questions to the research chemist. Gas chromatography, very fortunately, has come along to provide an approach to these answers. With the passage of time, gas chromatography has been improved to broaden its range of applicability (1, 6, 28, 32, 37), its powers of resolution (20), and its sensitivity. Now with the advent of electron capture (27) it is achieving powers of discrimination.

Uses of Gas Chromatographic Data

Pattern Characteristics. Analyses by gas chromatography and the patterns obtained are useful in two ways. First, pattern characteristics are frequently all that the analyst needs to interpret his results. There are many examples involving comparative evaluation of foods by sensory panels and also in product and process quality control where decisions to be made are greatly aided by inspection of gas chromatograph pattern characteristics. Secondly, because of the ability of gas chromatography to resolve complex mixtures of organic substances, one is able to locate in the chromatogram the peak or peaks that are associated with a particular characteristic, favorable or otherwise, which may be of singular importance at that moment. In many respects and with good reason, purity of chemical composition is equated with prime quality. In the fields of flavorings and perfumes and cosmetics, however, where essential oils are extensively used, prices paid for apparently similar materials may vary over wide limits because of subtle but important differences which are now known to be associated with minor chemical components. This might be thought of as "pseudo Lysenko," inasmuch as manufacturers and consumers have acquired firm and definite preferences for certain characteristics attributable to unique combinations of "desirable impurities." Gas chromatography has been able to point this out rather dramatically and is being employed as an important part of quality control.

HEADSPACE ANALYSIS. Organoleptic profiles of a food product consist of a list of all detectable flavor and aroma characteristics expressed as a descriptive word or phrase with an appropriate intensity rating. Frequently, it is difficult to tell from a series of these profiles what really sets a particular sample apart from other apparently similar samples.

Concentrated solvent extracts of the volatiles from a food product usually provide complex gas chromatograms containing many component peaks representing a wide range of boiling points. Interpretation of differences among such complicated chromatograms is no easier than among organoleptic profiles.

Headspace aroma patterns obtained by gas chromatography can provide a graphic picture of the composition of the vapor which a taste panel encounters while evaluating a series of samples. While tasters respond to far more components than are shown in the headspace aroma pattern, nevertheless differences among these patterns may agree very closely with taste panel evaluations. Headspace aroma patterns may be used in a number of situations to reflect both good and bad flavors. Headspace patterns reflect the qualitative composition of orange juice aroma and aroma volatiles recovered during concentration. Wolford *et al.* (38) report that the potentialities of semiquantitative determination are good and that quantitative differences noted between patterns might be sufficient to differentiate between varieties of oranges. In the case of oxidative deterioration of stored dehydrated potato granules good agreement was obtained between taste panel scores for flavor and gas chromatograms which reflected the increasing concentration of N-hexanal, the chief off-flavor component (3).

In Figure 2 the headspace chromatograms confirm the fact that sample A had a different flavor and aroma than the other two samples. Comparison of the patterns locates some of the components which account for the difference. Depending upon the type of flavor preferred, headspace analysis combined with taste panel evaluation can quickly and reliably select lots of raw material for intensive investigation of flavor composition.

A taste panel evaluated four samples of instant potato and found that one sample had a serious flavor defect. Of the three remaining samples, two received borderline acceptance for flavor. The headspace chromatograms that were run concurrently (Figure 3) reveal differences which appear to corroborate the panel's decision to reject sample D and give only conditional acceptance to samples B and C. A check of the process traced the problem to insufficient contact time in a sulfite bath. The procedure was quickly corrected and subsequent samples had acceptable flavor. It would be naive to assume without detailed investigation that the chromatograms reflected the entire chemical basis for this

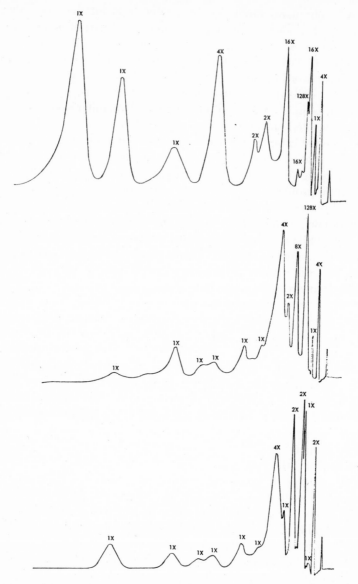

Figure 2. Comparative headspace chromatograms of three tomato samples

Perkin-Elmer Model 154 C gas chromatograph
Flame ionization detector
2-meter $^1/_4$-inch column
23% Carbowax 1500 on Chromosorb W, 60–100 mesh
Temperature. 50°C.
Flow rate. 50 ml. helium per minute
Sample 2.5 cc. vapor over 10 cc. steam distillate

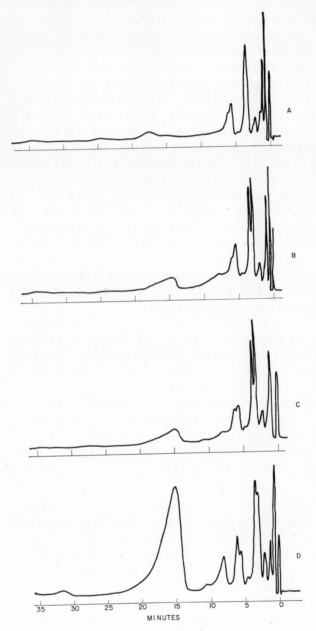

*Figure 3.   Comparative headspace chromatograms of four instant
potato samples*

Conditions.   Same as for Figure 2
Sample.   2.5 cc. vapor over 5 grams of dry product reconstituted with
15 cc. of boiling distilled water

off-flavor. However, the chromatograms called attention to the fact that something was wrong even before the taste panel results were completed and the combined results signaled immediate corrective action. This is another example of how gas chromatography can make a significant contribution to product or process quality control.

Certainly the interpretation of headspace aroma patterns as a complete objective aroma measurement must be approached with caution. A general limitation of headspace analysis is that it is applicable only to low boiling compounds. This is true to some extent. A sample of the vapor taken over a hot aqueous suspension of a food product contains a large amount of water vapor, and molecules of the lowest boiling compounds having very high vapor pressures. Under these conditions, the headspace chromatograms will be rather limited and tend to give an oversimplified picture of aroma composition, particularly if the chromatographic system is not tuned to give high sensitivity and if the detector is responsive to water. With capillary columns and a flame ionization detector headspace chromatograms now reveal peaks for compounds, up to say, butyric acid, which covers a rather wide range of boiling points and many compounds with potent odors.

The sensitivity of the olfactory nerves exceeds that of even the best flame ionization detectors, so that to get the most out of this technique one must try to achieve the highest level of detector sensitivity possible and elminate the detractive influence of noise and drift from the chromatographic system (34). Enrichment techniques are also of benefit in measuring important higher-boiling components which may be present in trace amounts (26, 34). A further refinement in the interpretation of headspace chromatograms has been suggested by Burr (4), Western Regional Laboratory, U.S. Department of Agriculture. An index of odor contribution is achieved by dividing the apparent concentration of each component peak by its odor threshold. This presupposes that you know what each peak is and have established all the threshold values. This is probably worth doing because ultimately you will never be misled in interpreting patterns containing hugh peaks due to methanol and ethanol and small peaks due to methyl mercaptan and diacetyl. Kepner et al. (19) have reported on some studies aimed at obtaining quantitative data by means of headspace techniques. Although each researcher will have to work out the details for his own particular system, attention to factors such as temperature of equilibration, use of internal standards, and influence of major and minor components including additives on headspace composition will improve chances of success. Bernhard and coworkers (2, 14, 29) at Davis, Calif., have done some very interesting work on species classification in the *Genus Allium* by comparing headspace chromatograms of the volatile sulfur compounds evolved.

In some cases other instrumental measurements may correlate with taste panel scores for flavor. Heinz *et al.* (9) found that esters of 2,4-decadienoic acid, which are important flavor and aroma components of Bartlett pears, show a characteristic ultraviolet absorption at 263 to 267 mμ. Panel ratings of different samples of pear essence correlated well with intensity of absorption measured at this wavelength.

Individual Components. The phenomenon of odor perception has been thought of as a process somewhat like that which occurs in the column of a gas chromatograph, the nerve impulses transmitted to the brain being analogous to the electrometer signals producing peaks on the strip chart recorder. This analogy may have some merit for purposes of illustration. However, anyone who has spent time sniffing the exit gas from a chromatographic column realizes that: first, he is presented with an intriguing array of odors, not all of which are sharply defined but which tend to blend and change and blend again from one peak to the next; and second, that each odor associated with a peak must be considered individually, forgetting those which have gone before and being ignorant of those which are to follow. The nose provides such an integrated response to all of the odor-producing substances present over such a short time span that it does not appear to detect any separation which may have occurred. The gas chromatograph is too slow and in some cases not sufficiently sensitive to duplicate the performance of the nose. This "human *vs.* mechanical" nose analogy is a two-edged sword, and we must be quick to recognize that the gas chromatograph succeeds where the nose fails in separating the components of complex mixtures so that we may "see" them as well as smell them.

An additional limitation to this procedure bears mentioning. The gas chromatograph electrometer system operates with an electrical background signal which can be adjusted by turning knobs. The odor background in the exit gas stream, however, cannot be "bucked out" and thus odor descriptions of emerging peaks may be masked or altered to some extent. However, the chromatographic process, by way of retention time data, odor descriptions, and subtractive analyses—i.e., difference chromatography—has been used effectively to obtain tentative identification of many compounds important to flavor. This sort of information accumulated in an orderly fashion with or without other supporting analytical procedures is being used by food scientists in creating appealing imitation flavors and in the quality control of raw materials and food products during processing and through storage.

LIQUID SAMPLE ANALYSIS. Analysis by gas chromatography of concentrated flavor extracts provides a reasonably clear picture of flavor composition with respect to complexity, relative magnitude, and distribution (low, intermediate, and high-boiling point). Flavor concentrates, however, are usually very complex mixtures with respect to chemical classes and boiling point range. For this reason it is probably impossible to establish analytical conditions which are optimum for all components present. Thus the limitations of any single analysis are due to overlapping of peaks and absorption losses of polar high-boiling components.

Analysis of flavor samples on columns of different separation characteristics uncover many cases of peak overlapping but probably not all and it sometimes creates additional overlaps. With the aid of some plumbing changes and a dual pen recorder we are now able to run simultaneous analyses on two different columns. Programmed temperature operation of parallel capillary columns may afford the ultimate in component resolution of complex mixtures. We have tried bubbling the vent gas through a series of functional group reagents but have not been completely satisfied with the results.

We are currently working with capillary columns and low liquidload packed columns in order to assure ourselves that everything that went in comes out again. Even though such columns are more difficult to operate because they are more readily overloaded, there are three benefits to be derived. Since the background noise is greatly reduced, smaller samples produce good results—i.e., our sensitivity of detection is actually increased. Proper use of capillary and low-load columns usually affords improved resolution of individual components. Highboiling compounds are resolved at temperatures significantly lower than is possible with conventional packed columns, thereby reducing the risk of chemical aberration or losses due to adsorption.

Programmed temperature operation has been helpful in fractionating complex mixtures. But we have to be careful in the selection of column substrate and particularly in conditioning the column before use. There are no real short cuts to conditioning. Published accounts refer to several hours and several days for different stages of the coating and conditioning operations. We have found that haste only leads to future trouble, so we normally take about a week to condition a new column. At one time we were satisfied to program the column temperature from about 50°C. but now recognize the necessity to start at room temperature or below for best results. Merritt and his coworkers (25) at the Natick Quartermaster Laboratory have reported on the benefits of programming from cryogenic temperatures (about —130°C.).

Three patterns show progressively better resolution without bunching or spreading of individual peaks achieved by slow program over wide temperature range (Figure 4).

These results are most impressive. The procedures employed appear capable of achieving complete resolution and identifying complex mixtures of low boiling compounds, which is truly significant accomplishment. What also is intriguing is that you can, without interruption, continue to program up into the higher boiling point regions wherein, I believe, lie answers to many of our important flavor problems.

Figure 5 contains a chromatogram of a concentrated flavor sample analyzed on a thermal conductivity unit. Included with the pattern are word descriptions of the different odor notes that were detected as the sample components emerged from the column. It is difficult to recognize the starting flavor when a whole "dinner table" full of odors parade forth from the column during the analysis. Since the odor background cannot be bucked out, the odor of each peak is probably influenced by those that have preceded it. In spite of this limitation, odor and retention time data provide tentative identification of many flavor components.

The chromatogram shown in Figure 6 illustrates one effective method of simplifying identification of important flavor components in a

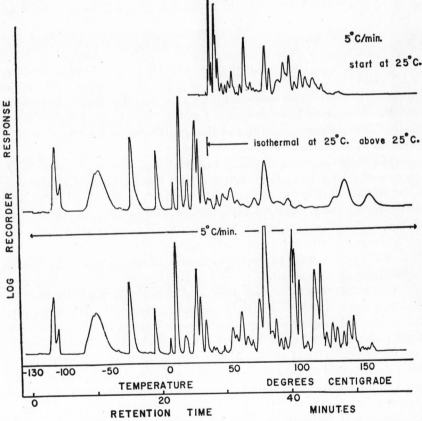

Figure 4. Effect of temperature programming from cryogenic mixtures
(25)

Barber-Colman gas chromatograph
5% SE 30 on Chromosorb W 80–100 mesh

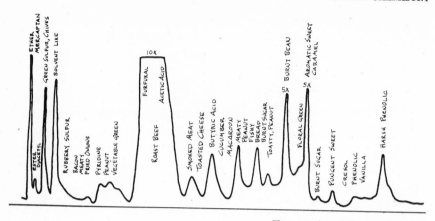

Figure 5. Odor evaluation

Burrell-Kromotog K-2 gas chromatograph
Thermal conductivity detector
2-meter $^1/_4$-inch glass column

complex mixture. The total pattern was divided into six rather arbitrary subfractions by cold trapping groups of peaks as they emerged from the column. Evaluation by taste and odor indicated that flavor components of interest occurred in subfractions 4 and 5. Efforts were thus directed toward accumulating quantities of these subfractions for intensive isolation and identification work.

The chromatograms shown in Figures 7 and 8 were prepared by recording the total ionization energy of the Bendix Time-of-Flight mass spectrometer during the analysis through a $^1/_4$-inch packed column of concentrated steam volatiles from tomato and potato. Operating conditions required using a high split ratio at the column exist so that peaks of 2X intensity or less did not give definitive spectra. Cases where low concentrations as well as overlapping and spreading of peaks hinders identification are apparent.

One interesting thing that developed during this work involved the identification of methional in the same peak as furfural. The mass spectral pattern taken at or shortly after the peak maximum showed only furfural to be present. Odor evaluation had previously indicated that the "oniony-meaty" odor of methional occurred as the peak started to emerge from the column but soon changed to that of furfural. Subsequently mass spectral patterns taken before and after the peak maximum confirmed the presence of methional. In Figure 9 the fragmentation patterns of methional and furfural are shown. In the original spectrum furfural overwhelmed the methional. In this case the human nose, acting as a very sensitive and discriminating detector, was able to call attention to the occurrence of this important flavor component.

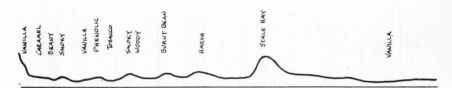

with gas chromatography

15% DEGS on Anakrom ABS 80–90 mesh
Temperature program. 65° to 180°C. at 5°C. per minute
Sample. 17 μ liters of concentrated ether extract

IDENTIFICATION OF COMPONENTS BY GAS CHROMATOGRAPHY. Analyses by gas chromatography of a concentrated flavor extract under two or three sets of conditions, including column substrate, provide a reasonably clear picture of flavor composition with respect to complexity, relative magnitude, and distribution (low, intermediate, and high boiling point). Odor evaluations of the exist gas stream usually provide some definitive characterization of the emerging peaks. In most cases one can be reasonably sure of the identity of several compounds on the basis of odor and retention time. Next, the original flavor concentrate is fractionated by chemical means. Using the shake-out technique, basic compounds are removed with 5% HCl, acids with 5% Na_2CO_3 and weak acids, such as phenolics, with 5% NaOH. By careful manipulation, including repetitive extractions and backwashing with fresh solvent, we guard against losses and attempt to make these separations as clean as possible.

Odor evaluation of the recovered fractions establishes the relative importance and the qualitative contribution of the acid, phenolic, basic, and neutral components to the total flavor. Analyses by gas chromatography, combined with odor evaluations of the subfractions and of concentrated flavor extracts before and after selective removal of the various classes of components, provide additional information leading to the identification of individual components.

This procedure might be described as "difference chromatography with a vengeance" since we analyze the flavor concentrates before and after each chemical separation step and also at the recovered subfraction. This cautious procedure has been found worthwhile since the chemical separations are not entirely specific nor are they quantitative for every

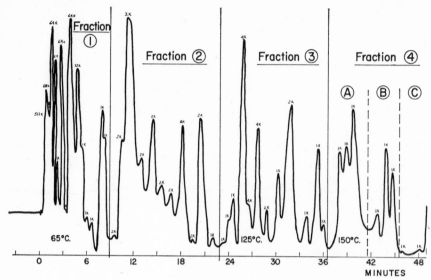

Figure 6.   Chromatogram of concentrated

F & M Model 500 gas chromatograph
Thermal conductivity detector
2-meter $^1/_4$-inch column
20% Carbowax 20M on Chromosorb W 60–100 mesh

component of a given class which may be present.   It is at this point that
mass spectrometry and infrared spectroscopy are more effective.   Retention time data and odor characterizations take on added significance
once the chemical class is reasonably well established.   In many instances
this information, when pooled, will result in additional tentative identifications.   This degree of confidence is lacking when dealing with complex
mixtures representing a variety of chemical classes.   With the aid of this
file of information, the interpretation of mass and infrared spectra is
greatly facilitated.   Analyses by these instrumental methods are also
benefited since the chemical separations decrease interference due to
overlapping and greatly increase the effective concentration of each component relative to its concentration in the total flavor extract.   Thus, by
the chemical separation procedure satisfactory special patterns are often
obtained which could not have been obtained on the original sample, and
the interpretation of these spectra is aided by the tentative identifications
which have been deduced previously.

It often happens that the acidic, phenolic, and basic fractions contain
compounds which modify the total flavor.   Essential flavor components
frequently occur in the neutral fraction, which consists primarily of
alcohols, esters, and carbonyls.   Difference gas chromatograms reflecting
the removal of carbonyl compounds by treating with sodium bisulfite or

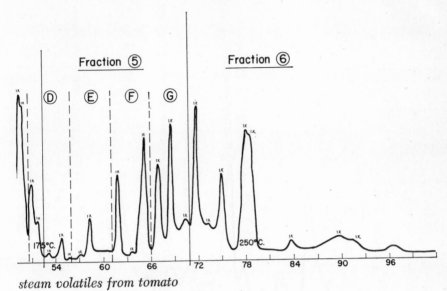

steam volatiles from tomato

Programmed temperature. 65°–250°C. at 2.9°C. per minute
Flow rate. 60 ml. helium per minute
Sample. 20 μl. of concentrated ether extract of steam volatiles

2,4-dinitrophenyl hydrazine (2,4-DNPH) reagent are very useful. Carbonyl hydrazone derivatives may be analyzed by paper chromatography or a combination of column and paper chromatography. We have used the 2,4-DNPH method in some of our work but have found it to be less sensitive and not as reproducible as gas chromatography. Also, some substances form more than one derivative with the reagent. This has also been the experience of other workers (21). Regeneration of free carbonyls from their 2,4-DNPH derivatives or sodium bisulfite adducts leaves much to be desired. Quantitative studies with model mixtures indicate that the recovery ranges from about 10 to 50% of theory. With carbonyls present in very low concentration these regeneration values are too low to permit identification. A recent paper by Soukup, Scarpellino, and Danielczik at the General Foods Technical Center presents a significant step forward in identifying carbonyls by gas chromatography. Imaginative use of flame ionization detection and high temperature analytical conditions permits direct identification of carbonyl 2,4-dinitrophenyl hydrazones (32).

Gas chromatography of the carbonyl-free neutral fraction provides a pattern of the ester and alcohol components. These two classes are resolved by reduction with lithium aluminum hydride which breaks the ester-ether linkage and permits characterization of the ester alcohols by

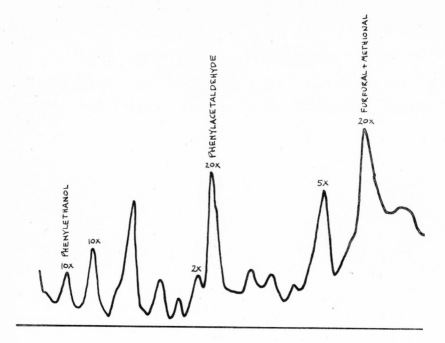

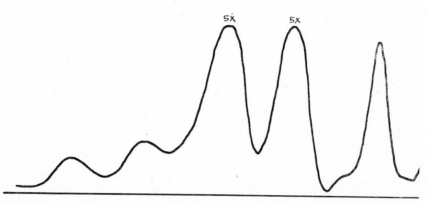

Figure 7.   Mass spectrometry

Total ionization pattern from packed columns for tomato volatiles
Beckman GC-2 gas chromatograph joined to Bendix Time-of-Flight mass
spectrometer

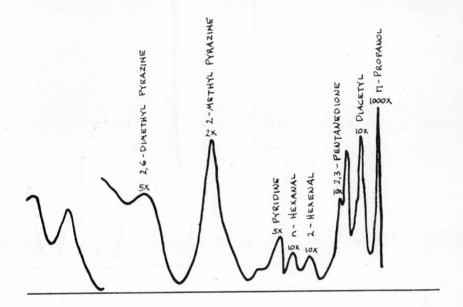

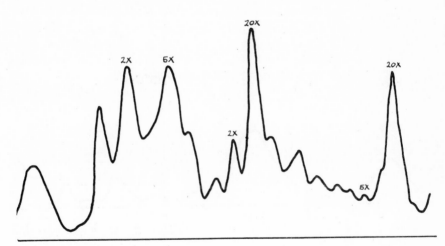

with gas chromatography

Split 1/1000; 12-foot ¹/₄-inch column; 15% DEGS on Anakrom ABS 80–90 mesh; Programmed temperature, 68° to 175°C. nonlinear; Sample, 150 μl. of concentrated ether extract of steam volatiles

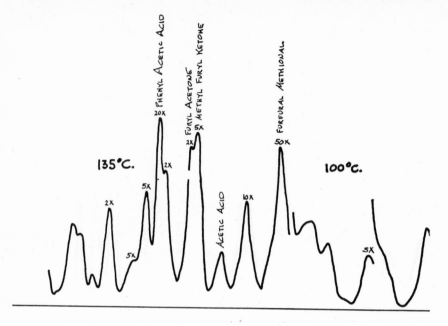

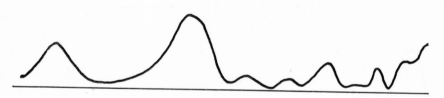

Figure 8. *Mass spectrometry*

Total ionization pattern from packed columns for

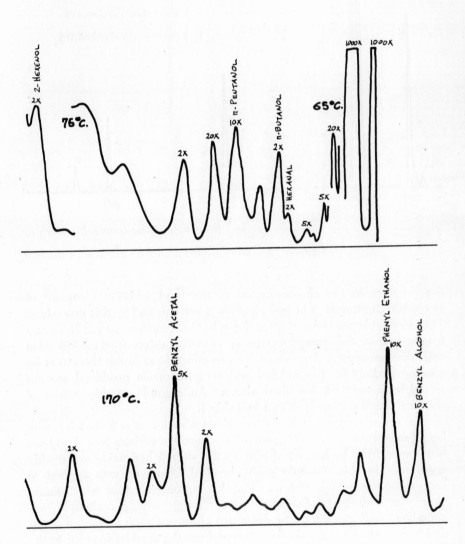

with gas chromatography

potato volatiles; conditions same as for Figure 7

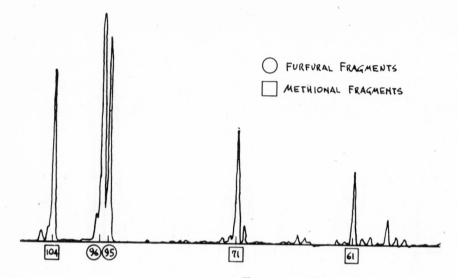

FURFURAL FRAGMENTS
METHIONAL FRAGMENTS

Figure 9. Mass spectral pattern of Sample. 2 μ liters of model mixture introduced through

the presence in the chromatogram of new and additional amount of alcohols. Unsaturation in free alcohols is not affected by this procedure. The ester acids are isolated after the reduction reaction with sodium carbonate and are determined separately as methyl esters after esterification with diazomethane. An alternative procedure is to break the esters by alkaline hydrolysis. The alcohol and acid fragments produced are analyzed separately as described above. An example of this system of chemical fractionation is shown in Table I.

In Table I, changes in pattern characteristics as reflected by peak height measurements resulting from the removal of carbonyls with sodium bisulfite and the hydrolysis of esters with sodium hydroxide are readily apparent. In this example each chemical treatment was applied to aliquots of the model mixture. For this reason reduction with lithium aluminum hydride produces extensive changes among carbonyl compounds as well as esters. In difference chromatography changes of individual components would be followed from the original fraction to the isolated subfraction and the residual fraction since the separations achieved are not entirely specific or quantitative.

Lactones constitute some analytical problems. Under some conditions they are reasonably well resolved by gas chromatography; however, their thermal stability on various column substrates needs clarification. In the presence of lithium aluminum hydride, lactones are reduced to diols and may be determined as such along with free and ester alcohols.

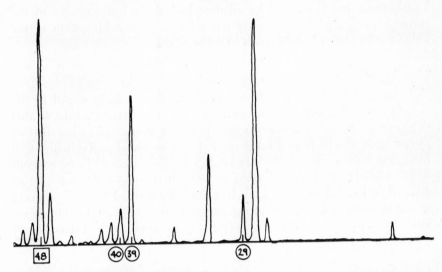

mixture of methional and furfural

batch inlet system of Bendix Time-of-Flight mass spectrometer

Table I. Chemical Treatment of Volatile Flavor Components

Recorder Response (Ampere $\times$ 10^{-4})

Compound	Original Fraction	Carbonyls Removed, w/NaHSO₃	NaOH Hydrolysis	LiAlH₄ Reduction
2-Pentanone	625	4	578	—
1-Propanol	—	—	—	207
2-Pentanol	66	87	46	800
1-Penten-4-ol	433	425	400	604
Ethyl valerate	468	425	—	3
Methyl hexanoate	484	416	2	4
1-Pentanol	17	—	8	476
cis-2-Hexenal	21	12	5	—
trans-2-Hexenal	316	12	5	4
Methyl pyruvate	183	6	—	—
1-Hexenol	—	—	12	333
cis-2-Hexenol	—	—	—	6
2-Methyl-2-hepten-6-one	194	16	146	—
trans-2-Hexenol	—	—	—	77
1-Octen-3-ol	204	187	204	122
2-Methyl-2-hepten-6-ol	90	90	85	357
Methional	408	49	5	—
Methyl benzoate	119	114	—	—
Methionol	—	—	—	150
Benzyl alcohol	—	—	—	122

The lactone ring is opened by alkaline hydrolysis, but recovery of the corresponding acid is apparently not reliable since acidification of the sodium salts causes lactonization to occur again.

Conclusions

The analytical scheme described above is extremely useful in the orderly determination of flavor composition. The flavor chemist is able to separate a complex flavor concentrate into a number of rather distinct pieces, each of which may be evaluated and analyzed individually, free from, but bearing a definite relationship to, the original flavor concentrate. Isolation and identification of individual components may be as detailed or limited as needed. When carefully applied to food products or raw materials subjected to processing and storage, it can provide chemical information on the origin and fate of both good and bad flavor characteristics.

Literature Cited

(1) Bayer, E., Widder, Rudi, *Anal. Chem.* **36**, 1452 (1964).
(2) Bernhard, R. A. Saghir, A. R., Jacobsen, J. V., Mann, L. K., *Arch. Biochem. Biophys.* **107**, 137–40 (1964).
(3) Boggs, M. M., Buttery, R. G., Venstrom, D. W., Belote, M. L., *J. Food Sci.* **29**, 487 (1964).
(4) Burr, H. K., *Food Technol.* **18** (12), 60–2 (1964).
(5) Casey, J. C., Self, R., *Chem. Ind (London)* **1964**, 33.
(6) Cruickshank, P. A., Sheehan, J. C., *Anal. Chem.* **36**, 1191 (1964).
(7) Day, E. A., Libbey, L. M., *J. Food Sci.* **29**, 583 (1964).
(8) Gold, H. J., Wilson, C. W., *Ibid.*, **28**, 484–8 (1963).
(9) Heniz, D. E., Panborn, R. M., *J. Food Sci.* **29**, 756 (1964).
(10) Hunter, G. L. K., Brogen, W. B., Jr., *Anal. Chem.* **36**, 1122 (1964).
(11) Hunter, G. L. K., *J. Food Sci.* **30**, 1 (1965).
(12) Hunter, G. L. K., Moshonas, M. G., *Anal. Chem.* **36**, 378 (1965).
(13) Ikeda, R. M., Rolle, L. A., Vannier, S. H., Stanley, W. L., *J. Agr. Food Chem.* **10**, 98 (1962).
(14) Jacobsen, J. V., Bernhard, R. A., Mann, L. K., Saghir, A. R., *Arch. Biochem. Biophys.* **104**, 473–7 (1964).
(15) Jennings, W. G., *J. Food Sci.* **29** (6), 796 (1964).
(16) Jennings, W. G., Creveling, R. K., Heinz, D. E., *Ibid.*, **29** (6), 730 (1964).
(17) Jennings, W. G., Greveling, R. K., *Ibid.*, **28** (1), 91 (1963).
(18) Jennings, W. G. Severants, M. R., *Ibid.*, **29** (2), 158 (1964).
(19) Kepner, R. E., Maarse, H., Strating, Jacobies, *Anal. Chem.* **36**, 77 (1964).
(20) Kung, J. T., Romagnoli, R. J., *Ibid.*, **36**, 1161 (1964).
(21) Lindsay, R. C., Day, E. A., Sandine, W. E., *J. Food Sci.* **27** (2), 210 (1962).
(22) McCarthy, A. I., Palmer, J. K., Shaw, C. P., Anderson, E. E., *Ibid.*, **28** (4) 379 (1963).
(23) MacLeod, W. D., Jr., Buigues, N. M., *Ibid.*, **29** (5), 565–8 (1964).
(24) Merritt, Charles Jr., Bresnick, S. R., Bazinet, M. L., Walsh, J. T., Angelini, Pio, *J. Agr. Food Chem.* **7**, 784–7 (1959).
(25) Merritt, Charles, Jr., T., Forss, D. A., Angelino, Pio, Swift, S. M., *Anal. Chem.* **36**, 1502–8 (1964).

(26) Nawar, W. W., Fagerson, I. S., *Food Technol.* **16** (11), 107 (1962).
(27) Oaks, D. M., Hartman, H., Dimick, K. P., "Analysis of Sulfur Compounds With Electron Capture, Hydrogen Flame Dual Channel Gas Chromatography," Wickens Instrument & Research, Inc., Walnut Creek, Calif.
(28) Richey, J. M., Richey, H. G., Jr., Schraer, R., *Anal. Biochem.* **9**, 272 (1964).
(29) Saghir, A. R., Mann, L. K., Bernhard, R. A., Jacobsen, J. V., *Am. Soc. Hort. Sci. Proc.* **84**, 386 (1964).
(30) Schultz, T. H., Teranishi, R., McFadden, W. H., Kilpatrick, P. W., Corse, J., *J. Food Sci.* **29** (6), 790 (1964).
(31) Self, R., Casey, J. C., Swain, T., *Chem. Ind.* (London) **1963**, 863.
(32) Soukup, R. J., Scarpellino, R. J., Danielczik, E., *Anal. Chem.* **36**, 2255 (1964).
(33) Teranishi, Roy, *et al.*, *J. Food Sci.* **28** (5), 541 (1963).
(34) Teranishi, Roy, Buttery, R. G., Lundin, R. E., McFadden, W. H., Mon, T. R., *Am. Soc. Brewing Chem. Proc.* (1963). *Am. Soc. Brewing Chem. Proc.* 52–57 (1963).
T. R., *Am. Soc. Brewing Chem. Proc.* 52–57 (1963).
(35) Teranishi, R., Corse, J. W., McFadden, W. H., Black, D. R., Morgan, A. I., Jr., *J. Food Sci.* **28**, 478 (1963).
(36) Underwood, J. C., Fillipic, V. J., *Ibid.*, **29** 6, 814 (1964).
(37) Winter, L. N., Albro, P. W., *J. Gas Chromatog.* **2** (1), 1 (1964).
(38) Wolford, R. W., Attaway, J. A., Alberding, G. E., Atkins, C. D., *J. Food Sci.* **28**, 320 (1963).

RECEIVED June 1, 1965

6

Role of Milk Lipids in Flavors of Dairy Products

EDGAR A. DAY

Department of Food Science and Technology, Oregon State University, Corvallis, Ore.

Chemical and biochemical reactions occurring during manufacture, storage, and utilization of dairy products convert lipid components into flavorful compounds. Methyl ketones cause flavor defects in beverage milk, whereas relatively large quantities are necessary for Blue cheese. Small amounts of free fatty acids, from hydrolysis of glycerides of milk lipids, appear desirable in beverage milk, and progressively larger amounts are essential in Cheddar and Blue cheese. δ-Lactones arise from milk lipids via nonoxidative mechanisms and are both beneficial and detrimental in certain dairy flavors. Esters containing monohydroxy alcohols and fatty acids are important in the fruity flavor defect of Cheddar cheese and possibly in normal cheese. A number of aldehyde classes appear in autoxidized dairy products. Most aldehydes cause flavor defects.

Of the various milk constituents, the lipids have the greatest effect on the flavor of dairy products. They serve as solvent and precursor of both desirable and undesirable flavor. Chemical and biochemical reactions occurring during the manufacture, storage, and utilization of dairy products convert lipid components into a multitude of organic compounds, some of which are very flavorful. The most important known reactions are hydrolysis, autoxidation, β-oxidation, decarboxylation, dehydration, reduction, and esterification. The flavorful classes of compounds produced are fatty acids, ketones, lactones, aldehydes, alcohols, hydrocarbons, and esters.

Most of the lipid exists in milk as small globules averaging 4 to 5 microns in size, dispersed as a stable emulsion in the aqueous phase of milk.

[1] Address for the ACS Award in Milk Chemistry sponsored by the Borden Foundation, Inc.

Stability of the emulsion is determined by the composition and properties of the materials adsorbed at the interphase. The latter is referred to as the fat globule membrane, and its properties and composition have been discussed in a recent review (*13*). The globule membrane plays a key role in the susceptibility of milk and its products to certain types of flavor deterioration. In some cases, the manner in which the membrane components are oriented in relation to each other will determine whether milk is susceptible or resistant to oxidative and hydrolytic rancidity and light-activated flavors.

The physical state and distribution of the lipids differ considerably among dairy products. In each product, the distribution of the lipids affects the flavor through the ability of the lipids to undergo chemical and biochemical reactions and to act as a partitioning medium for flavor components. In addition, the lipids have a pronounced effect upon the rheological properties of dairy products, which in turn are intimately connected with flavor.

The fatty acid composition of milk lipids is complex and unique among food lipids. At present, well over 60 fatty acids have been reported (*40*). The presence of 10 mole % of butyric acid and liberal quantities of the 6:0, 8:0, and 10:0 acids is unique and important in the flavor development of many cheese varieties and possibly in the normal flavor of milk. The presence of branched-chain acids, unsaturated acids with up to five double bonds and with various isomeric configurations, hydroxy acids, and keto acids must all be considered in studies of normal flavors and flavor defects of dairy products. As a general rule, trace constituents of the lipids are involved as important flavor precursors. For example, 4-*cis*-heptenal, a creamlike flavor component of butter, occurs at a concentration of 1.5 parts per billion (p.p.b.) (*6*). This compound apparently results from the oxidation of 11-*cis*-, 15-*cis*-, and 10-*cis*, 15-*cis*-octadecadienoic acids; the total amount of all *cis-cis*-octadecadienoic acids in milk fat is 0.02% (*23*).

Unfortunately, very few flavors in dairy products have been completely defined. This paper relates recent advances in flavor chemistry research to the role milk lipids assume in flavor. This area of research has been active for the past half century, and many scientists have made noteworthy contributions.

Free Fatty Acids

The fatty acids exist in dairy products both esterified and unesterified. The unesterified fraction is termed "free fatty acids" (FFA), even though in most dairy products a large portion of the fraction cannot be considered free. The ratio of acids to salts can be estimated by the well known Henderson-Hasselbalch equation, where the pKa of the acids ranges from

4.76 to 4.90. Counteracting the acid-salt equilibrium, however, are the partition coefficients of the acids between the aqueous and lipid phases of the system and the manner in which the two phases exist in a dairy product. A further complication with respect to ascertaining the flavor-contributing ability of the FFA is differences in their flavor potency, depending upon whether they exist in the lipid or aqueous phase of a dairy product (68).

Because of these difficulties, the importance of FFA in dairy flavors is not known with certainty. They are generally recognized, however, as key contributors to normal flavors and to the rancid flavor defect. Therefore, considerable work has been devoted to developing methods for FFA determination (12, 26). Earlier methods were designed to estimate the degree of lipolysis in milk fat by titrating a fat sample, dissolved in a suitable solvent, with standard base (41). Increasing amounts of titratable acidity indicated higher mole concentrations of FFA, but individual acids could not be evaluated by these methods.

Methods of partition and adsorption chromatography have been successfully used to isolate and separate individual short-chain fatty acids (47, 59, 88). Resolution of these acids is adequate, but separating the complete series of FFA found in dairy products has been difficult. With the advent of gas-liquid chromatography (GLC), the members of a homologous series can be easily separated. A problem in dairy products is to employ procedures that will recover FFA in the presence of large amounts of unsaponified fat. The method of Hornstein et al. (43) as modified by Bills et al. (9) enables isolation of the acids from a lipid–organic solvent solution by absorption of the FFA on a strong anion base exchange resin; the resin is washed free of fat, and the adsorbed acids are simultaneously released and esterified by methanol-HCl. The methyl esters of the FFA are recovered by extraction with ethyl chloride. By carefully removing the solvent, reasonable recovery of the FFA can be achieved. Internal standards permit quantitative analysis. The procedure (9) has been applied to fresh and rancid cream, butter, Cheddar cheese (8), Blue cheese (1), and fluid milk (51).

Data depicting the quantity and per cent distribution of FFA in several dairy products are given in Table I. The fatty acid distribution in milk triglycerides, based on per cent by weight, is given for comparative purposes. The per cent of butyric acid in the FFA mixture is high in both fresh and rancid milk, compared to its concentration in the glycerides of milk fat. The milk exhibiting the rancid flavor was an aliquot of the fresh milk in which lipolysis was induced. Since the per cent butyric was essentially the same in both the fresh and rancid aliquots, selective hydrolysis by the milk lipases is not apparent. Other workers, however, have shown that milk lipase is preferential for the alpha position of tri-

Table I. Free Fatty Acid Composition of Some Dairy Products[a]

Fatty Acid	Fresh[b] Milk	Moderate[b] Rancid Milk	Butter[c]	Cheddar Cheese[d]		Blue Cheese[e]			Milk fat[f]	
				Range	Av.	Sample A	Sample C	Sample D	g	h
4:0	7.23	6.03	1.32	4.7–9.5	6.36	2.60	3.77	1.43	2.8	3.5
6:0	3.40	3.42	0.65	1.1–3.2	2.10	1.81	2.20	1.90	2.3	1.4
8:0	1.37	2.07	0.83	1.8–3.0	2.23	1.61	1.85	2.87	1.1	1.7
10:0	5.16	3.98	1.41	2.7–3.4	3.09	2.90	3.04	6.00	3.0	2.7
12:0	4.89	3.98	4.22	3.8–5.8	4.51	3.45	3.68	4.10	2.9	4.5
14:0	10.02	9.58	11.02	11.0–13.4	12.09	12.71	13.98	9.73	8.9	14.7
16:0	23.61	26.09	22.69	23.5–34.5	28.29	27.08	30.44	21.92	23.8	30.0
18:0	9.98	13.65	12.04	6.9–11.3	9.53	110.0	9.35	8.54	13.2	10.4
18:1	29.78	27.05	38.40	21.2–32.1	25.83	29.40	27.28	31.76	29.6	18.7
18:2	4.55	4.14	4.66	2.5–5.4	3.80	2.74	2.42	4.99	2.1	
18:3	—	—	2.69	1.4–2.9	2.17	2.78	1.98	6.74	0.5	—
Total FFA, mg./kg.	415	1,027.5	2,733		1,793	48,791	66,714	23,546		

[a] Expressed as per cent by weight of total FFA.
[b] Kintner and Day (51).
[c] Bills et al. (9).
[d] Bills and Day (8).
[e] Anderson and Day (1).
[f] Fatty acids of milk triglycerides expressed as per cent by weight.
[g] Herb et al. (40).
[h] Jack (44).

glycerides (14, 39), and since approximately 75% of butyric reportedly is in the alpha position, selective hydrolysis should be expected.

The significance of the FFA in the normal flavor of milk is not known. Kintner and Day (51) found that from 71 to 75% of the FFA partition into the glyceride fraction of milk, from 21 to 25% was associated with the fat globule membrane, and only trace quantities were found in the milk serum. At the pH of milk, the small quantity of acids in the serum phase might be expected to exist in a salt-acid ratio of approximately 60 to 1 (based on the Henderson-Hasselbalch equation). Hence, in normal flavored milk, even though the total quantity of FFA is large, the amount in the serum is small. It would appear that the fat globule membrane serves as a barrier which affects the equilibrium of the free acids and salts between the serum and lipid phase. In the event of lipolysis, which must occur at the interphase, the fatty acids might distribute predominantly to the aqueous phase, where they eventually reach the flavor threshold. This hypothesis is supported by the effect observed on rancid odor when the pH of two samples of milk are adjusted to the pKa of the FFA; one sample is normal and an aliquot has induced lipolysis. The pH adjustment will immediately intensify the rancid odor in the lipolyzed sample, whereas no rancid odor will be noticeable in the normal milk. The flavor threshold data published by Patton (68) also support this hypothesis. Kintner and Day (51) found that the short-chain acids (4:0 and 6:0) partitioned more to the aqueous phase where their flavor threshold is higher, but their flavor also is diminished by salt formation whereas the longer chain acids >8:0 partition predominantly to the lipid phase where the flavor threshold is higher. This would allow for the relatively large concentration of unesterified fatty acids in normal milk without a noticeable rancid flavor.

The average concentrations of FFA in 12 Cheddar cheese samples exhibiting a range of flavors are presented in Table I. The percentage FFA composition agrees closely with the fatty acids of milk triglycerides except for butyric acid. Free butyric acid was always present in the cheese samples in about twice the amount of its reported percentage by weight in the triglycerides (8). Comparable results were obtained for fluid milk (51). Hence, the earlier suggestion by Bills and Day (8) that the higher concentrations of butyric acid in Cheddar cheese might be due to selective hydrolysis or microbial synthesis requires reevaluation. The greatest error in GLC analysis of FFA occurs for the 4:0 methyl ester (9). Additional studies will be necessary to ascertain whether the high values in fluid milk are real or artifacts. The butyric acid in the Cheddar and Blue cheeses was measured by column chromatography and titration of the eluted acid. The values for butyric in the cheese samples are valid, whereas those for fluid milk still may be questioned.

The relative significance of the FFA in Cheddar cheese flavor remains to be elucidated. The fact that Cheddar cheese made with skimmilk is practically devoid of Cheddar character suggests that lipid degradation products are essential. Patton (67) has concluded that the 2:0, 4:0, 6:0, and 8:0 acids constitute the "backbone" of Cheddar cheese aroma. He suggested that acetic acid was of special importance in the unique aroma of the cheese. Bills and Day (8) analyzed 14 Cheddar cheese samples that exhibited typical flavors and various flavor defects. With the exception of the cheeses with rancid flavor defects, the differences observed in the concentration of FFA from cheese to cheese were not as striking as might be expected, considering the differences in flavor, age, and manufacturing conditions. There was no marked difference in the range of FFA concentration between cheeses made from raw and pasteurized milk. Acetic acid showed the greatest variability in concentration and was usually the most abundant. Hence it was concluded that in view of the variation in individual FFA concentrations and the lack of a direct relationship of FFA with the flavor of good Cheddar cheeses, the balance between FFA and other flavor constituents is more important to Cheddar flavor than the concentration of FFA alone.

In Blue cheese, lipolysis is a necessary step in the development of flavor. It is purposely induced in most domestic Blue cheese manufacturing processes. In addition, the mold *Penicillium roqueforti* elaborates lipases that carry out further hydrolysis of milk fat. A comparison of the total FFA isolated from Blue cheese varieties and the quantities found in Cheddar cheese demonstrates the point (Table I). The Blue cheeses contain from 13 to 37 times as much FFA. Samples A and C of Table I were domestic varieties, whereas sample D was imported Roquefort. Roquefort is made from sheep milk, and this was noted in the difference in its flavor from that of the domestic Blue cheese. Part of the flavor difference apparently is due to the lower concentration of 4:0 FFA in Roquefort and the relatively larger concentrations of the 8:0 and 10:0 FFA. These differences are shown in Table I.

Origin of Methyl Ketones in β-Keto Glycerides

Methyl ketones, containing odd-numbered carbon atoms from C_3 to C_{15}, have been observed in a number of dairy products. While these compounds have been reported in autoxidized dairy products, and mechanisms have been proposed to show their formation through hydroperoxide dismutation (7), most evidence supports a nonoxidative reaction leading to ketones. Wong *et al.* (90) first observed the ketones in evaporated milk and postulated their formation from the β-keto acids in milk fat. Patton and Tharp (71) found the complete series of odd-numbered methyl ketones from C_3 to C_{15} in the distillate of steam-stripped fresh fat. Day and Lillard (19) attributed their presence in oxidized milk fat to the heat treatments employed for isolation of other carbonyls, and Lawrence (53) demonstrated that they were produced during steam distillation of butter oil.

Recently, Ven *et al.* (85) obtained evidence that the methyl ketone precursors exist in milk fat as β-keto esters, by reaction of milk fat with Girard-T reagent, followed by isolation and identification of a homologous series of pyrazalones that corresponded to the appropriate β-keto acids. These data have been substantiated by Parks *et al.* (62), who have isolated and identified the methyl ketone precursors as β-keto esters. Methyl ketones were liberated from the purified β-keto ester fraction by heating in the presence of water or by saponification.

Langler and Day (52) studied the influence of temperature during heat treatment, time of heat treatment, and the effect of air and water on the quantity of methyl ketones produced in milk fat. The maximum yield of ketones was obtained by heating a degassed sample for 3 hours at 140°C.; heating an additional 15 hours had no further effect. Milk fat, prepared by degassing at 2 to 5 microns of Hg for 1 hour at 40°C. still contained sufficient water for maximum ketone production. It was necessary to remove the final traces of water with a drying agent such as calcium hydride. When this was done, methyl ketone formation was inhibited.

Hence, water is essential for significant methyl ketone formation in milk fat.

From the foregoing evidence, the mechanism of ketone formation is well established and is as follows:

This reaction is of major concern to manufacturers of butter oil and concentrated milk products. The heat treatments employed during manufacture of the products are sufficient to cause ketone formation. Prolonged storage of these products also fosters ketone formation; ketones have been implicated in the stale flavor of dry whole milk (65) and butter oil (92).

Langler and Day (52) have demonstrated a synergistic interaction of the ketones whereby a perceptible flavor is evident when the concentration of all components in the mixtures are below their average flavor threshold (AFT). Comparison of the values in columns 3 and 4 of Table II shows that the potential ketone concentration in milk fat is sufficient to give rise to detectable flavors in a beverage milk.

**Table II. Average Flavor Threshold of Methyl Ketones in 4%
Homogenized Milk and Their Concentrations in Heated Milk Fat[a]**

		Concentration, P.P.M.	
n-Alk-2-one	*AFT, p.p.m.[b]*	*At AFT of mixture*	*Obtainble in 4% milk prepared from heat milk fat*
C_4	79.50 ± 6.03	0.13	0.52
C_5	8.38 ± 0.75	0.20	0.80
C_7	0.70 ± 0.04	0.38	1.52
C_9	3.48 ± 0.26	0.18	0.72
C_{11}	15.50 ± 0.75	0.20	0.80
C_{13}	18.43 ± 0.99	0.46	1.84
Total	129	1.55	6.20

[a] From Langler and Day (52).
[b] Standard deviation determined from four replications.

Methyl Ketones in Cheese Flavor

Methyl ketones have been identified, and in some cases quantitated, in a number of cheese varieties (*5, 17, 18, 38, 61, 66, 72, 75, 76*), and in most instances they appear to be derived from milk lipids. As early as 1924 (*79*) the typical flavor of Blue cheese was attributed to the ketones, but it has taken considerable time since then to identify the compounds and establish their origin. Hammer and Bryant (*37*) on the assumption that 2-heptanone was an important flavor component of cheese demonstrated that *Penicillium roqueforti* converted *n*-octanoic acid to 2-heptanone. Patton (*66*) confirmed the presence of methyl ketones by isolating and identifying the C_5, C_7, and C_9 compounds as 2,4-dinitrophenylhydrazones (DNP-hydrazones). He suggested that the methyl ketones were formed by oxidizing the fatty acids to the corresponding keto acids, which were then decarboxylated. In 1955, Girolami and Knight (*35*) demonstrated that the ketone formed by fatty acid oxidation contains one less carbon atom than the fatty acid from which it was produced. Oxidation of fatty acids longer than 10:0 did not yield a ketone. More recently, Gehrig and Knight (*33, 34*) presented evidence that the site of ketone formation is primarily the spore rather than the young hyphal cell of *P. roqueforti*.

The original list of ketones found by Patton (*66*) in Blue cheese has been extended to the complete series of odd-numbered compounds from C_3 to C_{15}. 2-Heptanone occurs in highest concentration, but the quantities of the others vary considerably (*75*). Ketones with carbon chain lengths of C_{11} and longer occur in very low concentration in relation to those with shorter chain lengths. This might be expected in view of the reported inability of the mold to act upon acids with carbon chains longer than 10:0. Of interest is the predominance of 2- heptanone in the cheese, yet the precursor, *n*-octanoic acid, occurs at the lowest concentration in milk fat of all acids with less than 10 carbons. Apparently the mold spore is most permeable to octanoic acid.

In addition to the ketones mentioned above, methyl ketones with an even number of carbons in the chain have been reported. Morgan and Andersen (*61*) reported butanone, Bavisotto *et al.* (*5*) found 2-octanone, and Day and Anderson (*17*) identified the C_6, C_8, and C_{10} compounds. These probably result from degradation of the corresponding 7:0, 9:0, and 11:0 acids which occur as minor constituents of the milk glycerides.

The complete series of methyl ketones with odd-numbered carbon atoms from C_3 to C_{15} has been observed in Cheddar cheese (*18, 38, 72*). The origin of most of these compounds would appear to be the lipids although there is no direct evidence to verify this point. Patton *et al.* (*72*) and Day *et al.* (*18*) isolated the ketones from cheese slurry distillates obtained by distilling at reduced pressure. Harvey and Walker (*38*) isolated the ketones by steam distillation at atmospheric pressure. Walker (86) prepared mixtures of fatty acids and ketones which were added to cheese curd. He reported that after 3 weeks of curing, the flavor was comparable to a normal 3 month old Cheddar. He concluded, therefore, that the ketones play a major role in Cheddar cheese flavor.

Lawrence (53) has questioned the findings of Harvey and Walker (38) and Walker (86) as well as other workers by demonstrating that the ketones could be produced from the β-keto esters of milk fat by the isolation techniques employed. When he isolated the ketones by distilling a Cheddar cheese slurry at 40° C. and reduced pressure, he concluded that not all of the ketones were artifacts although he did not report how much was due to artifacts. In view of the danger of heat-induced methyl ketone formation and the relative instability of β-keto acids, quantitative determination of the ketones is extremely difficult. It is not possible, therefore, to assess the significance of these compounds in Cheddar flavor until the problem is resolved. Day and Libbey (20) used very mild isolation techniques for obtaining the aroma fraction of Cheddar and still found relatively large amounts of methyl ketones in the volatiles. In addition, they identified a number of the secondary alcohols that correspond to the ketone analogs. The alcohols apparently result from reduction of the ketones by dehydrogenase enzymes elaborated by bacteria in the cheese. Hence, some ketone precursor must occur as normal constituents of the cheese ripening process. Isolation techniques employing 40° C. or less should not create serious artifacts. This is the approximate body temperature of the cow, and the cheese material receives higher heat treatments during the manufacturing operation.

Secondary Alcohols in Blue Cheese

Jackson and Hussong (45) observed 2-pentanol, 2-heptanol, and 2-nonanol in the neutral noncarbonyl volatiles from Blue cheese and presented evidence that they resulted from reduction of the corresponding ketones. Mycelia of *Penicillium roqueforti* caused reduction of 2-heptanone to the alcohol and also oxidized the alcohol to the ketone. The equilibrium favored the ketone. In studies with Blue cheese, the secondary alcohols did not appear until considerable amounts of ketones were produced.

Recently, Day and Anderson (17) identified 2-propanol, 2-pentanol, 2-heptanol, 2-octanol, and 2-nonanol in the aroma fraction of Blue cheese. Ketones corresponding to all of the alcohols also were found. In addition, the 2-methyl- and 3-methylbutanols that would result from reducing the aldehyde analogs were identified.

In an attempt to determine the effect of the various microorganisms found in Blue cheese on ketone-alcohol interconversion, Anderson and

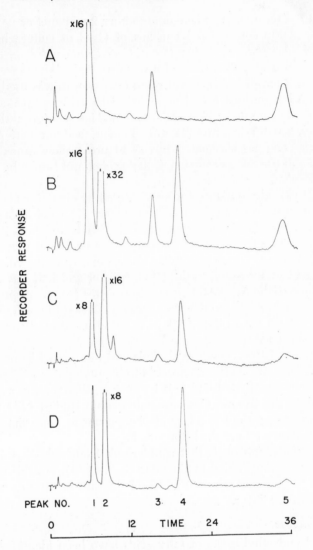

Figure 1.   Gas chromatograms of 2 ml. of head-space from Penicillium roqueforti spore suspensions

Column.   *12-foot × ¹/₈-inch o.d., containing 15% Carbowax 1500 on 80–100-mesh Celite 545 (acid-alkali washed)*
Column temp.   *70° C.*   Carrier flow.   *20 ml./min.*

Chromatograms   *Peaks*
    A. *Culture medium + spores*
    B. *Culture medium + spores + hexanoic acid*   1. *Ethanol*
    C. *Culture medium + spores + 2-pentanone*   2. *2-Pentanol*
    D. *Culture medium + spores + 2-pentanol*   4. *2-Pentanol*

Day (2) used pure cultures containing either 2-pentanol or 2-pentanone and followed the conversion by means of GLC of culture headspace. *Penicillium roqueforti, Bacterium linens, Geotricum candidum, Torulopsis sphaerica,* and a *Mycoderma* species were studied. After incubation of the cultures, 2 ml. of headspace at room temperature was used for GLC analyses. All organisms tested were found to oxidize 2-pentanol to 2-pentanone. A spore suspension of *P. roqueforti* interconverted the alcohol and ketone, as did the mycelia grown on a medium that prevented sporulation. The gas chromatograms of Figure 1 show formation of 2-pentanone and the interconversion of the alcohol and ketone by the mold spose suspension.

The GLC peaks in Figure 1 were identified by obtaining mass spectra of the components in the GLC column effluent. This particular application demonstrates the sensitivity achieved by the technique. Five milliliters of headspace from each of the cultures indicated in Figure 1 were injected into the gas chromatograph. The effluent from the GLC column was split; half was directed to the GLC detector and half was passed to the EC-1 inlet of the Atla CH-4 mass spectrometer (MS). Approximately 5% of the effluent passed to the MS inlet was allowed to reach the ionization source. This means that 2.5% of the 5-ml. headspace was required to give usuable mass spectra.

The odors of the secondary alcohols and the methyl ketone analogs are very similar, but the ketone appears to be more potent. The alcohols have not been quantitated and it is impossible, therefore, to assess their importance in the flavor. Gas chromatographic studies (17) indicates that in Blue cheese the secondary alcohols occur at approximately one-tenth the concentration of the ketone analogs.

The secondary alcohols that could result from reduction of methyl ketones also were identified in Cheddar cheese (20). In this case, they occur in very low concentration and probably are of little or no significance in Cheddar flavor.

Esters in Cheese

Methyl and ethyl esters of fatty acids have been identified in both Cheddar (20) and Blue cheese (17). Esters of the fatty acids and secondary alcohols also have been identified in Blue cheese (17). The esters apparently are formed nonenzymatically according to normal esterification equilibria. Free fatty acids are relatively abundant in both Blue and Cheddar cheese, and esterification apparently occurs in the presence of alcohols.

The significance of the esters in normal cheese flavor has not been elucidated for either Cheddar or Blue cheese. Relatively large concentrations occur in the neutral fraction of Cheddar and Blue cheese volatiles (17, 20), and it is likely that they contribute.

Recently, Bills *et al.* (*10*) have found that excessive amounts of the ethyl esters are responsible for the fruity flavor defect of Cheddar cheese. Cheddar cheese having a definite fruity odor and flavor was centrifuged and the isolated fat had the same typical fruity odor as the intact cheese. The fat was submitted to a molecular distillation technique (*54*) and the volatile compounds thus obtained were separated by GLC. Sensory evaluation of the separated components at the end of the GLC column coupled with identification by fast scan mass spectrometry implicated ethyl butyrate and ethyl hexanoate as the compounds primarily responsible for the fruity defect.

Experimental fruity and normal cheeses were obtained which had been manufactured from the same lot of milk under identical conditions except for the use of different starter cultures. GLC analyses of the volatiles entrained from the fat of a normal and a fruity cheese made from the same milk are shown in Figure 2. The concentrations of ethanol, ethyl butyrate, and ethyl hexanoate are much larger in the fruity flavored cheese. In the cheeses studied, levels of ethyl butyrate and ethyl hexa-

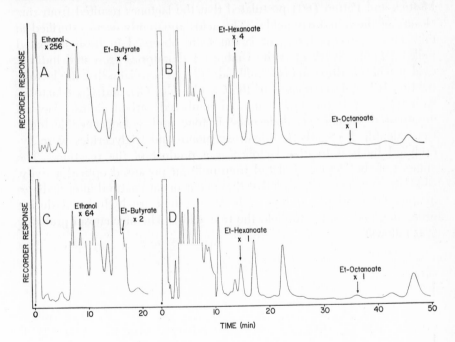

Figure 2. Gas chromatograms of volatiles from fruity and normal flavored Cheddar cheeses

Column. *12-foot × ¹/₈-inch o.d. containing 20% 1,2,3-tris-(2-cyanoethoxy) propane, on 80–100-mesh Celite 545 (acid-alkali washed)*
Column temp. *Chromatograms A, C, 50° C. B, D, 80° C.*
Chromatograms. *A, B, fruity Cheddar. C, D, normal Cheddar*

noate were up to six times greater in fruity cheeses than in normal cheeses and the ethanol concentration was up to 16 times greater in the fruity samples (*10*). This suggests that excessive ethanol production may be responsible for the accentuated esterification of free fatty acids, thus resulting in higher levels of ethyl esters. The basteria used in the starter cultures that resulted in fruity flavored cheese were strains of *Streptococcus lactis* and *Streptococcus diacetilactis* which were found by Vedamuthu *et al.* (*84*) to give the defect. These bacteria produce relatively large quantities of acetaldehyde (*57*) some of which is converted to ethanol (*46*).

Lactones

Another unique property of milk fat is its ability to form δ-lactones under certain conditions. Keeney and Patton (*48*) first isolated δ-decalactone from heated milk fat and demonstrated its presence in evaporated milk, dried cream, and dried whole milk. Tharp and Patton (*81*) subsequently found δ-dodecalactone in the steam distillates of milk fat. Mattick and Patton (*60*) postulated that the lactones resulted from ring closure of the 5-hydroxy acids. The acids apparently occur esterified in milk fat, since only traces of lactones are observed in fresh unheated milk fat (*11*). Workers at the Unilever Laboratories presented indirect evidence of 5-hydroxy acids in milk fat (*11*). They claim that the lactone fraction is largely composed of the C_8, C_{10}, C_{12}, C_{14}, and C_{16} δ-lactones with traces of lactones with uneven-numbered carbon atoms. Several unsaturated lactones (δ-dodecene-9-lactone and γ-dodecene-6-lactone) were identified. Synthetic 5-hydroxy mono- and triglycerides were hydrolyzed by heat to give lactones as a product of the reaction. The anilides of the lactones isolated from milk fat possessed optical activity. This latter evidence suggests that the precursors are natural intermediates in milk fat synthesis and the 5-hydroxy esters are hydrolyzed during processing and storage to yield the free acids. The mechanism probably is as follows:

$$
\begin{array}{l}
\text{CH}_2\text{O}-\overset{\overset{\displaystyle O}{\|}}{\text{C}}-\text{R} \\[6pt]
\text{CHO}-\overset{\overset{\displaystyle O}{\|}}{\text{C}}-\text{R} \\[6pt]
\text{CH}_2\text{O}-\overset{\overset{\displaystyle O}{\|}}{\text{C}}-\text{CH}_2-\text{CH}_2-\overset{\overset{\displaystyle OH}{|}}{\text{CH}}-\text{CH}-\text{R}
\end{array}
\xrightarrow[\Delta]{\text{H}_2\text{O}}
\text{diglyceride} + \text{HOOC}-\text{CH}_2-\text{CH}_2-\text{CH}_2-\overset{\overset{\displaystyle OH}{|}}{\text{CH}}-\text{R}
$$

The lactones are significant in flavor defects of most concentrated milks and in the staling of butter oil. Heat treatment of hydrous milk fat apparently hydrolyzes the hydroxy esters, and lactone formation readily follows. Trace amounts of lactones have been reported in fresh unheated milk fat (*11*). Whether the lactones contribute to the flavor of fresh milk and butter is still uncertain. The lactone flavor is important when butter is used in cooking and baking, where it is subjected to heat. This property of butter has made it unique for such purposes.

Aldehydes via Lipid Autoxidation

Many of the aldehydes encountered in dairy products result from lipid autoxidation. This reaction creates serious problems in the dairy industry and leads to costly manufacturing and handling procedures for a number of dairy products. In some instances, it has been a serious deterrent to developing new products.

The subject of lipid autoxidation has been treated extensively in a number of reviews and in a recent symposium (*74*). Important to this discussion is the generally accepted free radical mechanism whereby the various isomeric hydroperoxides of the unsaturated fatty acids decompose to alkoxy radicals, which in turn decompose by several routes to give a variety of compounds and free radicals. Aldehyde formation is depicted as follows:

$$R\text{—}CH(OOH)\text{—}R \rightarrow R\text{—}\underset{\underset{\textstyle O\cdot}{|}}{C}H\text{—}R + HO\cdot$$

$$R\text{—}\underset{\underset{\textstyle O\cdot}{|}}{C}H\text{—}R \rightarrow R\cdot + R\text{—}CHO$$

where R = alkyl and carboxyl ends of the fatty acid carbon chain; both chains may be saturated or unsaturated.

The aldehydes formed by this reaction scheme may be saturated, unsaturated conjugated, and unsaturated unconjugated. The unsaturated aldehydes also can exist as the cis and trans isomers, which have a marked influence on the flavor properties of the molecules (*42*).

The qualitative and quantitative composition of aldehyde mixtures encountered in autoxidized milk lipids is influenced by many factors; some are known and some are unknown. Attempts to explain anomalies by studies on model systems has provided valuable information on basic mechanisms, but the picture frequently becomes blurred by the complexity of systems such as milk and its products. Whether the lipids in a dairy product will autoxidize, which lipid fraction will be the site of initial oxidative attack, and what the products will be are influenced by variables such as the physical state of the lipid in the product, the presence of pro- and antioxidants, the fatty acid composition of the milk lipids, etc. In fluid milk, the unsaturated fatty acids of the phospholipids are the primary sites of oxidative attack (69). The susceptibility of the phospholipids to oxidative degradation seems to be related to the pro-oxidant activity of ascorbic acid through its ability to reduce the cupric ion and the specific association of the two in relation to the lipid (77).

In butter, which represents an aqueous concentration of phospholipid dispersed in fat, both fat and phospholipid are susceptible, the latter being most readily oxidized (69). In dried dairy products and in anhydrous milk fat, the triglycerides may serve as a major reactant in oxidation. Hence it is difficult to apply the same corrective measures to overcome the problem in all products and it becomes impossible to expect the same qualitative and quantitative aldehyde picture from each system.

In Table III, the types of aldehyde isolated and identified in various dairy products are tabulated. Some differences in the qualitative composition of the aldehyde classes are evident. Aside from the aforementioned variables that can influence the aldehydes formed, variations in the

Table III. Aldehydes Identified as Lipid Autoxidation Products of Dairy Products

Product	n-Alkanal	n-Alk-2-enal	n-Alk-2,4-dienal	Miscellaneous
Phospholipids of butter (82)	C_2 to C_{14}	C_5 to C_{11}	C_8, C_9	
Butter oil (71)	C_1 to C_{10}	C_4 to C_{11}	C_7	
Butter oil (25)	C_2 to C_9	C_5 to C_{10}	C_7, C_{10}	
Fishy butter oil (28, 78)	C_3, C_5 to C_{10}	C_3, C_5, C_6, C_8, C_9	C_7	Nona-trans-2, cis-6-dienal; oct-1-en-3-one
Tallowy, painty butter oil (29)	C_5 to C_{10}	C_5 to C_{10}	C_7	
Butter oil (32)	C_1 to C_3, C_5 to C_{10}	C_4 to C_{11}	C_7, C_9, C_{10}, C_{11}	
Skimmilk (30, 31)	C_2, C_6	C_4 to C_{11}	C_6 to C_{11}	
Nonfat dry milk (4)	C_1, C_2, C_6 to C_{10}, C_{12}, C_{14}			
Dry whole milk (65)	C_1 to C_3, C_5 to C_{10}, C_{12}	C_5 to C_{11}		
Fluid whole milk (64)	C_5 to C_{10}	C_6 to C_{11}	C_8 to C_{12}	
Butter oil (6) (cream flavored)				4-cis-Heptenal

technique of the investigators probably account for some of the discrepancies. Comparisons of the aldehydes found in dairy products (Table III) with those theoretically possible from the major unsaturated acids of milk lipid (Table IV) reveal, first, that a number of the aldehydes theoretically possible are not found and, second, a substantial number of aldehydes have been isolated which are not theoretically predictable.

Table IV. Hydroperoxides and Aldehydes (with Single Oxygen Function) Theoretically Possible in Autoxidation of Some Unsaturated Fatty Acids

Fatty Acid	Isomeric Hydroperoxide	Aldehyde Formed
Oleic	8	C_{11}-2-enal
	9	C_{10}-2-enal
	10	C_9-al
	11	C_8-al
Linoleic	9	C_{10}-2,4-dienal
	11	C_8-2-enal
	13	C_6-al
Linolenic	9	C_{10}-2,4,7-trienal
	11	C_8-2,5-dienal
	12	C_7-2,4-dienal
	13	C_6-3-enal
	14	C_5-2-enal
	16	C_3-al
Arachidonic	5	C_{16}-2,4,7,10-tetraenal
	7	C_{14}-2,5,8-trienal
	8	C_{13}-2,4,7-trienal
	9	C_{10}-3,6-dienal
	10	C_{11}-2,5-dienal
	11	C_{10}-2,4-dienal
	12	C_9-3-enal
	13	C_8-2-enal
	15	C_6-al

The absence of unconjugated diene, triene, and tetraene aldehydes from the isolates from dairy products may be attributed to the instability of these compounds both to oxidation and to conjugation either prior to or during isolation and derivative formation. As an example, 3-*cis*-hexenal is the theoretical degradation product of the 13-hydroperoxy radical of linolenic acid, but 2-*trans*-hexenal is the compound reported (Table III). The following aldehydes have been isolated from dairy products but are not theoretically possible from the hydroperoxides listed in Table V: C_1, C_2, C_4, C_5, C_7, C_{10} n-alkanals; C_4, C_6, C_7, C_9 alk-2-enals; C_6, C_8, C_9, C_{11} alk-2,4-dienals. Some of these aldehydes could arise from the "trace" unsaturated fatty acids in milk lipids (40). For example, heptanal could result from decomposition of the 10-hydroperoxy radical of 9-hexadecenoic acid, but the large concentration of heptanal observed in aldehyde isolates from milk lipids (29, 56) rules out the acid as the sole source. The discrepancy can be rationalized by observing that aldehydes formed as initial hydroperoxide decomposition products can undergo oxidation (55).

The mechanism of the initial reaction between aldehyde and oxygen is unknown. Baeyer and Villiger (3), however, in working with benzaldehyde found that perbenzoic acid was an intermediate in the reaction. Haber and Willstätter (36) postulated the following mechanism for benzaldehyde autoxidation:

$$C_6H_5-\overset{\overset{\displaystyle O}{\|}}{C}-H \xrightarrow{\quad -H\cdot \quad} C_6H_5-\overset{\overset{\displaystyle O}{\|}}{C}\cdot + H\cdot$$

$$C_6H_5-\overset{\overset{\displaystyle O}{\|}}{C}\cdot \xrightarrow{\quad C_6H_5\overset{\overset{\displaystyle O}{\|}}{C}-H \quad} C_6H_5-\overset{\overset{\displaystyle O}{\|}}{C}-OOH + C_6H_5-\overset{\overset{\displaystyle O}{\|}}{C}\cdot$$

$$C_6H_5-\overset{\overset{\displaystyle O}{\|}}{C}-OOH + C_6H_5-\overset{\overset{\displaystyle O}{\|}}{C}-H \rightarrow C_6H_5-\overset{\overset{\displaystyle O}{\|}}{C}-\underset{\underset{\displaystyle OH}{|}}{OO}-CHC_6H_5$$

$$\downarrow$$

$$2C_6H_5COOH$$

Cooper and Melville (15) conducted kinetic studies on the autoxidation of *n*-decanal and concluded that it had the same mechanism as postulated for benzaldehyde.

Lillard and Day (55) found that *n*-nonanal oxidized almost quantitatively to the acid when 0.5 mole of oxygen had reacted. The reaction was very slow, however, when compared with the unsaturated aldehydes. Non-2-enal and hepta-2,4-dienal oxidized much faster than nonanal, methyl linoleate, and methyl linolenate; a number of aldehydes and dicarbonyls with shorter carbon chains were formed as oxidation products. Non-2-enoic acid was a major product from non-2-enal, but nine aldehydes were isolated after oxidation (55). A postulated mechanism for formation of the aldehyde oxidation products from non-2-enal involves oxygen attack at the double bond as follows:

$$R-CH_2-CH=CH-CHO$$

$$\downarrow + O_2$$

$$R-CH_2-\underset{\cdot}{C}H-CH-CHO$$

$$\underset{\displaystyle O}{|}$$

$$\underset{\displaystyle O\cdot}{|}$$

$$\downarrow + 2\ RCH_2-CH=CH-CHO$$

$$\overset{4\qquad 3\quad 2}{R-CH_2-CH_2-\underset{\underset{\displaystyle OOH}{|}}{C}-CHO} + 2R-CH-CH=CH-CHO$$

where R equals $CH_3-CH_2-CH_2-CH_2-CH_2-$.

According to this mechanism, isomeric hydroperoxides can be formed on carbons 2, 3, and 4 of non-2-enal. Decomposition of the hydroperoxy radicals would yield: carbon 2 = octanal or glyoxal; carbon 3 = heptanal or malonaldehyde; carbon 4 = hexanal or but-2-en-1,4-dial. Products of the 2 and 3 isomeric hydroperoxides were isolated, but those for the 4 isomer were not observed. The same mechanism is applicable to the oxidation of alk-2,4-dienals. In the oxidation of hepta-2,4-dienal (55) polymerization was a major reaction of the diradicals initially formed but as in the case of non-2-enal, a number of aldehydes were formed. According to the mechanism, hydroperoxy radicals could occur on carbons 2, 3, 4, 5, and 6 of hepta-2,4-dienal. Decomposition of the radicals would yield: carbon 2 = hex-3-enal or glyoxal; carbon 3 = pent-2-enal or malonaldehyde; carbon 4 = butanal or but-2-en-1,4-dial; carbon 5 = propanal or pent-2-en-1,5-dial; carbon 6 = ethanal or hex-2,4-diene-1,6-dial. Aldehydes that could result from each of the isomeric hydroperoxides were identified (55). Similar reaction schemes for other unsaturated aldehydes could result in a variety of aldehydes in addition to those derived from decomposition of fatty acid hydroperoxides.

The relative susceptibilities of the three major classes of aldehydes, encountered in dairy products, to oxidative attack and the observed production of saturated aldehydes from unsaturated aldehydes explain the predominance of the alkanals in oxidized milk lipids (29, 56). The alkanals accumulate because of their relative stability and at the expense of the unsaturated compounds.

Previous investigators (70, 80) have reported that oxidized alk-2-enals and alk-2,4-dienals react with 2-thiobarbituric acid to form the malonaldehyde pigment. Lillard and Day (55) found that the dienal yields approximately ten times as much malonaldehyde as the enal. The dienals, in particular, could serve as important malonaldehyde precursors and probably are the major source of malonaldehyde in the case of diene esters that give a significant TBA reaction only at late stages of oxidation (16).

The aldehydes are of special importance in lipid autoxidation because of the objectionable flavors imparted to dairy products. The flavors of the compounds are detectable at concentration levels of parts per million and parts per billion (21). Flavors imparted by these compounds have been described as oxidized, fishy, metallic, painty, tallowy, green, etc. (27, 29, 78). The metallic fraction has been attributed to oct-1-en-3-one (78) rather than to an aldehyde, but the other flavors have been associated with specific aldehyde combinations. In our laboratories, milk fat, regardless of the stage of oxidation, exhibited a typical oxidized flavor when evaluated by reconstituting into skimmilk at concentrations near the threshold of oxidized flavor (56, 92). When the concentrations of aldehydes present in the milk where the flavor was just detectable were calculated, all of the aldehydes were at the parts per billion concentration. On the basis of flavor threshold values for aldehydes, it was concluded that most of the aldehydes existed at subthreshold levels and that the flavor was due to an additive interaction of the aldehydes (56)—that is, each compound occurred at a subthreshold concentration, but the combined concentration of several compounds equaled or exceeded the flavor threshold. These observations were confirmed in subsequent work on aldehydes (21) and methyl ketones (52). These findings conflict with reports (25) that single compounds are responsible for flavor defects resulting from lipid autoxidation. Some compounds undoubtedly are more important than others, but our experiences have led us to conclude that oxidized flavor is the result of a combination of compounds.

Since aldehydes are major contributors to the oxidized flavor of dairy products, methods for measuring the compounds are desired in detecting the defect prior to sensory detection. Many methods have been developed to satisfy this need, with varying degrees of success. For routine analysis of fluid milk, the 2-thiobarbituric acid method has proved very useful (24). In this test, as with methods for peroxide determination, the products measured are not the compounds responsible for the flavor defect but they indicate the extent of the autoxidation reaction. Tests applicable to the lipid fraction of milk and which measure the aldehydes have shown significant correlations with oxidized flavor intensity (56). A recent procedure reported by Keith and Day (49) for measuring the classes of free aldehydes of lipids is well suited to routine analysis. The method was applied to butter oil and gave highly significant correlations with oxidized flavor development (92). Results in our laboratory indicate that while a still better test is needed for measuring oxidative rancidity, considerable improvement in the correlation of existing tests is possible by applying a more precise sensory evaluation technique and by recognizing the reciprocal relationship of chemical data to quantitative sensory evaluation data (56, 91, 92).

Aldehydes from Light-Induced Oxidation of Milk Lipids

Two distinct flavors may develop in milk exposed to light. One is associated with protein degradation and the other is the typical oxidized flavor. The oxidized flavor is comparable to that resulting from autoxidation, except that light serves as an energy source to initiate the reaction. Wishner and Keeney (89) found some differences in the aldehyde pattern of milk subjected to light-induced oxidation when compared to spontaneously oxidized milk (64). The flavor was attributed to the possible preferential oxidation of monoene fatty acids in the photosensitized systems.

Lipid Bound Aldehydes

Aldehydes with chain lengths ranging from 9 to 20 carbon atoms have been found as normal components of milk triglycerides and phospholipids. Van Duin (83) first observed these compounds in the phospholipids from butter. He reported aldehydes with chain lengths of 14 to 18 carbons. Evidence was obtained for saturated, unsaturated, and possibly branched-chain aldehydes. Schogt *et al.* (73) found the same types of aldehydes in the glyceride fraction of milk lipids. Relatively large quantities of the aldehydes were observed: fresh milk fat contained from 0.1 to 8.0 mg. of free aldehyde per kg., whereas 50 mg. of bound aldehyde (calculated on the basis of tetradecanal) were reported per kilogram of fat. This represents a relatively large pool of potential flavor compounds in milk and its products. Parks *et al.* (63) extended the findings of Van Duin (83) and Schogt *et al.* (73) by isolating the bound aldehydes from the plasmalogens and triglycerides and comparing the qualitative composition of the compounds from the two sources. Aldehydes with straight chains from C_9 to C_{18}, branched chains from C_{11} to C_{18}, the C_{12}, C_{18} and C_{20} enals, and traces of dienals were found. The most apparent differences in the aldehydes from the two sources was the shorter chain members in the glyceride fraction.

The aldehydes are bound to the glyceride in an enol-ether linkage; the linkage is labile to acid, and it has been suggested that enzymes and metal complexes may cause cleavage of the bond (83). Parks *et al.* (64) attributed the C_{11} to C_{16} aldehydes found in milk that had undergone spontaneous oxidation to either milk lipid synthesis or hydrolysis of lipid-bound aldehydes during pasteurization of the milk. The maximum aldehyde chain length to be expected from liquid oxidation is 11 carbons. Hence, aldehydes isolated with longer carbon chains probably can be attributed to hydrolysis of plasmalogen-type lipids.

Gamma-Irradiation–Induced Aldehydes from Milk Lipids

In general, irradiation of milk fat under atmospheric pressure results in hydroperoxide production, carotenoid destruction, and flavor deterioration. Reduction of oxygen pressure tends to limit hydroperoxide production, but the fat rapidly oxidizes upon exposure to air. Observations in our laboratories have indicated that milk fat irradiated under reduced pressure exhibits a flavor atypical of that encountered through autoxidation (22). The flavor of the irradiated fat appears to have three components: hydrolytic rancidity, oxidative rancidity, and candlelike. The candlelike flavor apparently is comparable to the chalky fraction described by Wertheim *et al.* (87) and attributed to hydroperoxides. Aldehydes with chain lengths of C_1 to C_{16} were observed as well as a number of methyl ketones (22). In view of the presence of methyl ketones, long-chain aldehydes, and a hydrolytic rancidity flavor defect, it was postulated that gamma–irradiation effects hydrolysis of the ester linkage to give rise to these compounds and that the long-chain aldehydes were a possible cause of the candlelike defect.

Subsequent work by Khatri *et al.* (50) has shown that gamma–irradiation causes FFA production in milk fat, but the reaction appears to be a free radical type rather than ester hydrolysis. This is supported by the types of products identified in irradiated milk fat and model systems. Octanoic acid was produced by irradiation of anhydrous methyl octanoate. In irradiated milk fat, CO, CO_2, FFA, hydrocarbons, methyl ketones, and aldehydes were identified. All of these compounds can result from the free radical mechanism suggested by Lück *et al.* (58). Essentials of the proposed reactions are:

$$
\text{I} \quad R-\overset{\overset{\displaystyle O}{\|}}{C}-O-\overset{\overset{\displaystyle \cdot CH_2}{|}}{CH} + R-\overset{\overset{\displaystyle O}{\|}}{C}-O\cdot \ \rightarrow\ R\cdot\ +\ CO_2
$$

$$
\text{II} \quad R-\overset{\overset{\displaystyle O}{\|}}{C}-O-\overset{\overset{\displaystyle \cdot O-CH_2}{\diagdown}}{CH} + R-\overset{\overset{\displaystyle O}{\|}}{C}\cdot \ \rightarrow\ CO\ +\ R\cdot
$$

$$
\text{III} \quad R-\overset{\overset{\displaystyle O}{\|}}{C}-O-\overset{|}{C}\cdot\ +\ H\cdot
$$

$$
\underset{\gamma\text{-rays}}{\overset{\displaystyle R-\overset{\overset{\displaystyle O}{\|}}{C}-O-CH_2 }{\underset{\displaystyle R-\overset{\overset{\displaystyle O}{\|}}{C}-O-CH \ \ }{R-\overset{\overset{\displaystyle O}{\|}}{C}-O-CH_2}}}
$$

Reaction I could yield an acid through combination of the carboxy radical with a proton or it could yield the alkyl radical and CO_2. The alkyl radical would combine with hydrogen to give hydrocarbons or with other radicals. Reaction II could result in aldehyde formation via the alkoxy radical plus hydrogen, or the alkoxy radical could decompose to give the alkyl radical and CO. Reaction III would provide one of a

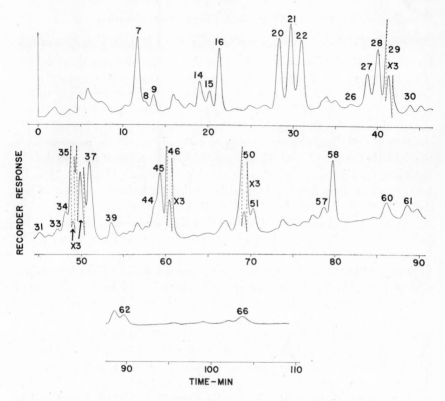

Figure 3.   Gas chromatogram of neutral volatiles from milk fat gamma-irradiated at 4.5 mrad

Column.   12-foot × 1/8-inch o.d., containing 20% Apiezon M on 100–120-mesh
Celite 545 (acid-base washed)
Column temp.   75° C. 6 min., then programmed at 2°/min. to 225° C.

number of possible sources for protons.   Methyl ketones could arise via decarboxylation of the β-keto acids of milk fat which are released from the glycerides by the above reaction scheme.

In an attempt to characterize the candlelike flavor of irradiated milk fat, Khatri *et al.* (50) separated the volatiles by GLC and the various peaks shown in Figure 3 were evaluated for odor properties.   Chromatographic peaks 26 and 33 gave a strong candlelike odor and peaks 30, 32, and 34 exhibited a mild odor similar to candlelike.   A portion of the volatiles, treated to remove carbonyls, was submitted to GLC and only peak 33 of Figure 3 was absent.   Other carbonyl peaks were numbers 7, 27, 35, 44, and 50.   Saturated and unsaturated hydrocarbons with 5 to 15 carbon atoms in the chain also were identified by GLC-MS analysis.   The hydrocarbons could result from chain fission of the lipid in addition to the mechanism proposed by Lück *et al.* (58).

Stabilization of Butter Oil against Flavor Deterioration

The most common flavor defects that develop during storage of butter oil are described as stale and oxidized. For many years these defects have been associated with lipid autoxidation. However, attempts to use antioxidants to prevent flavor deterioration have been relatively unsuccessful. The failure of antioxidants to prevent flavor deterioration is now explainable by the findings that methyl ketones (*71*) and δ-lactones (*81*) develop in milk lipids by conversion of naturally occurring precursors via nonoxidative mechanisms. These compounds can account for initial stale-type defects that were previously attributed to autoxidation. Milk fat has been notorious for developing flavor defects before evidence of oxidation is obtainable by chemical detection methods.

Patton and Tharp (*71*) observed that the precursor of the methyl ketones and δ-lactones could be converted and removed from butter oil by steam stripping at a high temperature and low pressure. Butter oil carefully refined in this manner provides a more suitable medium for evaluation of antioxidants. By stripping the butter oil prior to the addition of antioxidants, one can eliminate the lactone-ketone flavor problem and can then be concerned with oxidative changes without interference from nonoxidative artifacts. Wyatt and Day (*92*) utilized butter oil, prepared in this manner, to evaluate a number of antioxidants. Nondeodorized butter oil was used for comparative purposes. Antioxidants selected for the study were charred nonfat milk solids (NFMS), 2,4,5-trihydroxybutrophenone (THBP), nordihydroguaiaretic acid (NDGA), lauryl gallate (LG), propyl gallate (PG), quercetin (Q), and Tenox 2 (20% butylated hydroxyanisol, 6% PG, and 4% citric acid in propylene glycol). The oil samples were evaluated for flavor changes by flavor panels and oxidative changes were followed by tests for peroxides, carbonyls, etc.

The effect of antioxidants on the flavor stability of deodorized and nondeodorized butter oil during storage at 30°C. is shown in Figure 4. The ordinate axis is represented by 1/AFT, which is the reciprocal of the average flavor thresholds for the oil samples when evaluated after reconstituting in milk. Curve *A* (ND) is the average values for all antioxidants studied in nondeodorized butter oil. Curve *A* (D) presents the average values for all antioxidants in deodorized oil. The control curve represents deodorized oil without antioxidants. A comparison of the curve for the control oil with the curves for deodorized and antioxidant containing oils demonstrates that the antioxidants were effective in protecting the oil against flavor deterioration. The antioxidants were less effective, however, in preventing flavor deterioration in the nondeodorized samples [curve *A* (ND) in Figure 4]. This indicates that flavor deterioration in nondeodorized samples protected by antioxidants largely is due to nonoxidative mechanisms. The flavor defects for nondeodorized samples

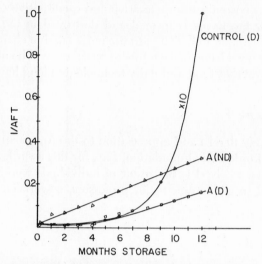

*Figure 4. Effect of antioxidants (A) on
flavor stability of deodorized (D) and nondeodorized (ND) butter oil stored at 30°C.
for 12 months*

were most frequently described as lactone or stale. These defects were
not observed by the panel in the deodorized samples.

Some of the antioxidants studied were more effective than others in
protecting the butter oil. In the deodorized butter oil, the rank of effectiveness on flavor stability was: NFMS, Q, Tenox 2, PG, THBP, LG,
and NDGA. While not shown in the figure, quercetin and charred nonfat milk solids extended the storage life of deodorized butter oil to one
year without any significant flavor change. Hence, butter oil can be protected against oxidative deterioration, but to keep the product palatable,
nonoxidative changes also must be controlled.

Conclusions

The lipids play a key role in the flavors of dairy products by imparting
certain flavor properties rarely encountered in other natural foods. In
many instances, the information still is fragmentary. Hopefully, the picture will become more complete. Rapid advances in instrumentation and
analytical technique over the past two decades augur an optimistic future
for the flavor chemists.

In dairy products, as in other foods, the biggest task is to be able to
"sort the wheat from the chaff" when confronted with a flavor isolate
containing from 100 to 200 components. The nose and a working knowledge of the food material still are valuable assests to progress in this area.

We must know not only the qualitative and quantitative composition of
flavor but how the flavor is formed and destroyed in the food. These
areas of research offer a challenge to the most capable chemists and food
scientists. Once we have achieved these goals, we will be able to provide
the flavor control that food and dairy technologists long have sought.

Acknowledgment

I express my thanks and appreciation to the American Chemical Society and the Borden Co. Foundation, Inc., for this award. The recognition that I have received is the result of individuals working as a team.
I am indebted to my former major professors, coworkers, and graduate
students.

Literature Cited

(1) Anderson, D., Day, E. A., *J. Dairy Sci.* **48**, 248 (1965).
(2) Anderson, D. F., Day, E. A., *J. Agr. Food Chem.* **14**, 241 (1966).
(3) Baeyer, A., Villiger, V., *Ber.* **33**, 1569 (1900).
(4) Bassette, R., Keeney, M., *J. Dairy Sci.* **43**, 1744 (1960).
(5) Bavisotto, V. S., Rock, L. A., Lesniewski, R. S., *Ibid.*, **43**, 849 (1962).
(6) Begemann, P. H., Koster, J. C., *Nature* **202**, 552 (1964).
(7) Bell, E. R., Raley, J. H., Rust, F. F., Seubold, F. H., Vaughn, W. E.,
    Discuss. Faraday Soc. **10**, 242 (1960).
(8) Bills, D. D., Day, E. A., *J. Dairy Sci.* **47**, 733 (1964).
(9) Bills, D. D., Khatri, L. L., Day, E. A., *Ibid.*, **46**, 1342 (1963).
(10) Bills, D. D., Morgan, M. E., Libbey, L. M., Day, E. A., *Ibid.*, **48**,
    in press (1965).
(11) Boldingh, J., Taylor, R. J., *Nature* **194**, 909 (1962).
(12) Breazeale, D. F., Bird, E. W., *J. Dairy Sci.* **21**, 335 (1938).
(13) Brunner, J. R., *Ibid.*, **45**, 943 (1962).
(14) Clement, G., Clement, J., Bezard, J., Costanzo, G., Parris, R., *Arch. Sci.
    Physiol.* **16**, 237 (1962).
(15) Cooper, H. R., Melville, H. W., *J. Chem. Soc.* **1951**, (1984).
(16) Dahle, L. K., Hill, E. G., Holman, R. T., *Arch Biochem. Biophys.* **98**,
    253 (1962).
(17) Day, E. A., Anderson, D. F., *J. Agr. Food Chem.* **13**, 2 (1965).
(18) Day, E. A., Bassette, R., Keeney, M., *J. Dairy Sci.* **43**, 463 (1960).
(19) Day, E. A., Libbey, L. M., *J. Food Sci.* **29**, 583 (1964).
(20) Day, E. A., Lillard, D. A., *Ibid.*, **43**, 585 (1960).
(21) Day, E. A., Lillard, D. A., Montgomery, M. W., *J. Dairy Sci.* **46**, 291
    (1963).
(22) Day, E. A., Papaionnou, S. E., *Ibid.*, **46**, 1201 (1963).
(23) de Jong, K., van der Wol, H., *Nature* **202**, 553 (1964).
(24) Dunkley, W. L., Jennings, W. G., *J. Dairy Sci.* **34**, 1064 (1951).
(25) El-Negoumy, A. M., Miles, D. M., Hammond, E. G., *Ibid.*, **44**, 1047
    (1961).
(26) Frankel, E. N., Tarassuk, N. P., *Ibid.*, **38**, 751 (1953).
(27) Forss, D. A., *Ibid.*, **47**, 245 (1964).
(28) Forss D. A., Dunstone, E. A., Stark, W., *J. Dairy Res.* **27**, 211 (1960).
(29) *Ibid.*, p. 381.
(30) Forss, D. A., Pont, E. G., Stark, W., *Ibid.*, **22**, 91 (1955).
(31) *Ibid.*, p. 345.

(32) Gaddis, A. M., Ellis, R., Currie, G. T., *J. Am. Oil Chemists' Soc.* **38**, 371 (1961).
(33) Gehrig, R. F., Knight, S. G., *Appl. Microbiol.* **11**, 166 (1963).
(34) Gehrig, R. F., Knight, S. G., *Nature* **182**, 1937 (1958).
(35) Girolami, R. L., Knight, S. G., *Ibid.*, **3**, 264 (1955).
(36) Haber, F., Willstätter, R., *Ber.* **64**, 2844 (1931).
(37) Hammer, B. W., Bryant, H. W., *Iowa State College J. Sci.* **11**, 281 (1937).
(38) Harvey, R. J., Walker, J. R. L., *J. Dairy Res.* **27**, 335 (1960).
(39) Harwalker, V. R., Calbert, H. E., *J. Dairy Sci.* **44**, 1169 (1961).
(40) Herb, S. F., Magidman, P., Luddy, F. E., Riemenschneider, R. W., *J. Am. Oil Chemists' Soc.* **39**, 142 (1962).
(41) Hillig, F., *J. Assoc. Offic. Agr. Chemists* **35**, 748 (1952).
(42) Hoffman, G., *J. Am. Oil Chemists' Soc.* **38**, 1 (1961).
(43) Hornstein, I., Alford, J. A., Elliott, L. E., Crowe, P. F., *Anal. Chem.* **32**, 540 (1960).
(44) Jack, E. L., *J. Agr. Food Chem.* **8**, 377 (1960).
(45) Jackson, H. W., Hussong, R. V., *J. Dairy Sci.* **41**, 920 (1958).
(46) Keenan, T. W., Lindsay, R. C., Day, E. A., unpublished data.
(47) Keeney, M. *J. Assoc. Offic. Agr. Chemists* **39**, 212 (1956).
(48) Keeney, P. G., Patton, S., *J. Dairy Sci.* **39**, 1104 (1956).
(49) Keith, R. W., Day, E. A., *J. Am. Oil Chemists' Soc.* **40**, 121 (1963).
(50) Khatri, L. L., Libbey, L. M., Day, E. A., to be published.
(51) Kintner, J. A., Day, E. A., *J. Dairy Sci.* **48**, 1575 (1965).
(52) Langler, J. E., Day, E. A., *Ibid.*, **47**, 1291 (1964).
(53) Lawrence, R. C., *J. Dairy Res.* **30**, 161 (1963).
(54) Libbey, L. M., Bills, D. D., Day, E. A., *J. Food Sci.* **28**, 329 (1963).
(55) Lillard, D. A., Day, E. A., *J. Am. Oil Chemists' Soc.* **41**, 549 (1964).
(56) Lillard, D. A., Day, E. A., *J. Dairy Sci.* **44**, 623 (1961).
(57) Lindsay, R. C., Day, E. A., Sandine, W. E., *Ibid.*, **48**, 863 (1965).
(58) Lück, H., Deffner, C. U., Kohn, R., *Fette Seifen Anstrichmittel* **66**, 249 (1964).
(59) McCarthy, R. D., Duthie, A. H., *J. Lipid Res.* **3**, 117 (1960).
(60) Mattick, L. R., Patton, S., Keeney, P. G., *J. Dairy Sci.* **42**, 791 (1959).
(61) Morgan, M. E., Andersen, E. O., *Ibid.*, **39**, 253 (1956).
(62) Parks, O. W., Keeney, M., Katz, I. Schwartz, D. P., *J. Lipid Res.* **5**, 232 (1964).
(63) Parks, O. W., Keeney, M., Schwartz, D. P., *J. Dairy Sci.* **44**, 1940 (1961).
(64) *Ibid.*, **46**, 295 (1963).
(65) Parks, O. W., Patton, S., *Ibid.*, **44**, 1 (1961).
(66) Patton, S., *Ibid.*, **33**, 680 (1950).
(67) *Ibid.*, **46**, 856 (1963).
(68) Patton, S., *J. Food Sci.* **29**, 679 (1964).
(69) Patton, S., "Symposium on Foods: Lipids and Their Oxidation," p. 190, Avi Publishing Co., Westport, Conn., 1962.
(70) Patton, S., Kurtz, G. W., *J. Dairy Sci.* **38**, 901 (1955).
(71) Patton, S., Tharp, B. W., *Ibid.*, **42**, 49 (1959).
(72) Patton, S., Wong, N. P., Forss, D. A., *Ibid.*, **41**, 857 (1958).
(73) Schogt, J. C. M., Begemann, P. H., Koster, J., *J. Lipid Res.* **1**, 446, (1960).
(74) Schultz, H. W., Day, E. A., Sinnhuber, R. O., ed., "Symposium on Foods: Lipids and Their Oxidation," p. 79, Avi Publishing Co., Westport, Conn., 1962.
(75) Schwartz, D. P., Parks, O. W., *J. Dairy Sci.* **46**, 989 (1963).
(76) *Ibid.*, p. 1136.
(77) Smith, G. J., Dunkley, W. L., *Ibid.*, **45**, 170 (1962).
(78) Stark, W., Forss, D. A., *J. Dairy Res.* **29**, 173 (1962).

(79) Starkle, M., *Biochem. Z.* **151,** 371 (1924).
(80) Taufel, K., Zimmermann, R., *Fette Seifen Anstrichmittel* **61** , 226 (1961).
(81) Tharp, B. W., Patton, S., *J. Dairy Sci.* **43,** 475 (1960).
(82) Van Duin, H., *Netherlands Milk Dairy J.* **12,** 81 (1958).
(83) *Ibid.*, p. 90.
(84) Vedamuthu, E. R., Sandine, W. E., Elliker, P. R., *J. Dairy Sci.* **47,** 679
     (1964).
(85) Ven, V. van der, Begemann, P. Haverkamp, Schogt, J. C. M., *J. Lipid
     Res.* **4,** 91 (1963).
(86) Walker, J. R. L., *J. Dairy Res.* **28,** 1 (1961).
(87) Wertheim, J. H., Roychoudhary, R. N., Hoff, J., Goldblith, S. A., Proctor,
     B. E., *J. Agr. Food Chem.* **5,** 944 (1957).
(88) Wiseman, H. G., Irvin, H. M., *Ibid.,* **5,** 213 (1957).
(89) Wishner, L. A., Keeney, M., *J. Dairy Sci.* **46,** 785 (1963).
(90) Wong, N. P., Patton, S., Forss, D. A., *Ibid.,* **41,** 1699 (1958).
(91) Wyatt, C. J., Day, E. A., *J. Am. Oil Chemists' Soc.* **42,** 734 (1965).
(92) Wyatt, C. J., Day, E. A., *J. Dairy Sci.* **48,** in press (1965).

RECEIVED May 4, 1965. Borden Award Address. Technical Paper 1967,
Oregon Agricultural Experiment Station.

7

Advances in Fruit Flavor Chemistry

ROY TERANISHI

Western Regional Research Laboratory, Western Utilization Research and Development Division, U. S. Department of Agriculture, Albany, Calif.

Advances in separation, physical measurement equipment, and manipulation techniques have overcome some of the difficulties encountered in fruit flavor research. Capacity of high resolution gas chromatography columns has been increased. Gas chromatography and mass spectrometry have been combined to give information with submicrogram quantities. Sample sizes required for proton magnetic resonance studies have been reduced to submilligram quantities. A flavor component of Bartlett pears has been identified. Most of the volatile constituents of mandarin peel oil and lime oil have been identified. The constituent mainly responsible for grapefruit aroma has been identified as nootkatone. The chief bitter principle of grapefruit, naringin, has been changed to an intensely sweet compound, a chalcone.

The quantities that one deals with in aroma chemistry research vary greatly: in one phase of the research, tens of tons of fruit are extracted and concentrated for the volatile constituents; in another, as little as tenths of nanograms are separated and detected in the vapor from a single fruit. This is indeed a staggering ratio, comparable to the ratio of the earth's diameter to that of an atom!

Because the concentration of the compounds responsible for the desirable aroma of fruits is small, even though we start with large amounts of raw material, only very small amounts of pure material are isolated. Thus, assignment of chemical structure is difficult, and the degree of certainty of the assignment decreases with decreasing amount of material isolated and purified. However, advances in gas chromatographic separations and in physical measurement equipment and techniques are now being applied in the field of fruit flavor chemistry, and the impact of obtaining more information with much less material than previously necessary is just now being felt.

One of the major advances in identification is from coupling the gas chromatograph with the fast-scan mass spectrometer (GC-MS), (9, 10, 26, 28). With this arrangement, we are able to obtain the molecular weight and, to some extent, the chemical structure with the micrograms to nanograms separated by the elegant small-bore open tubular columns. Continuous monitoring of column effluent eliminates manipulation losses, contamination, and decomposition often encountered when submilligram quantities are first collected, then manually transferred for analytical treatment.

An example of what can be done with the GC-MS combination was the analysis of strawberry oil (29, 35). A highly odoriferous oil (50 grams) was isolated from 10 tons of condensate obtained from a strawberry jam processing unit. Analysis with a programmed temperature, small-bore, open tubular column gas chromatograph showed this material to be a very complicated mixture (Figure 1). An enormous amount

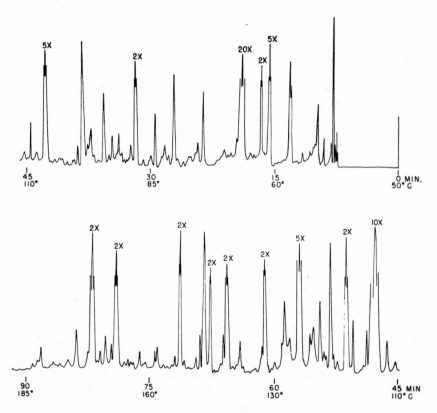

Figure 1. Gas chromatogram of strawberry oil

Programmed temperature, 200-foot, 0.01-inch i.d., open tubular column coated with Tween-20

of data is obtained with a GC-MS analysis of such a mixture. Over 160 compounds were detected and identified (29). GC retention times were verified by enriching the strawberry oil with purified authentic compounds, either purchased or synthesized, and the enriched sample was analyzed with the same temperature program as in the original analysis. Thus, small variations in experimental conditions could not lead to erroneous conclusions because the enriched compound could be related to known, internal standards in the mixture.

However, in spite of the wealth of information obtained by such analyses, GC-MS data are not sufficient for a high degree of certainty of identification for some closely related compounds. Figure 2 shows GC analyses indicating the number of oxygenated terpenes and sesquiterpenes found in three sequential fractions obtained from silica chromatography of orange oil. For such compounds, it is necessary to obtain infrared (IR) and proton magnetic resonance (PMR) spectral data for detailed structure assignment. Fortunately, recent advances in PMR techniques (1, 23, 27) have lowered the sample size requirements to fractions of milligrams, to a range comparable to the simple size requirements for infrared analyses. The resolution and capacity of high efficiency packed and large-bore open tubular gas chromatography columns (36) permit separation and collection of milligrams of closely related compounds, and therefore, permit PMR and infrared analyses of such compounds.

In our GC-MS investigations of an orange oil fraction (36) we noticed that material emerging closely together, yet as separate peaks, had very similar MS fragmentation patterns. These compounds were isolated, and infrared and PMR analyses (Figures 3 and 4), showed that they were isopulegol and neo-isopulegol, which differ only in that the hydroxyl group is either equatorial or axial. Although the isopulegol epimers are not greatly different in aroma, Demole (8) has shown the importance of such differences in aroma properties by showing that one epimer can have a very interesting aroma of sandalwood; the other, no aroma.

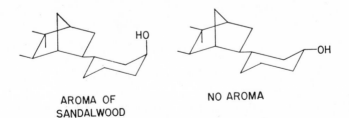

AROMA OF
SANDALWOOD

NO AROMA

Obviously, the goal of fruit flavor research is not merely to find and identify compounds but to find organoleptically important compounds.

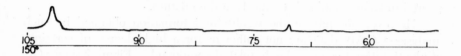

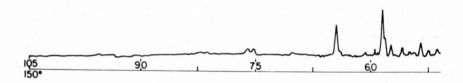

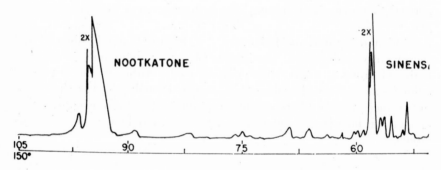

Figure 2. Gas chromatogram

Programmed temperature, 75-foot, 0.01-inch

To find such compounds is difficult not only because of the concentration and amounts involved but also because organoleptic purity is much more difficult to attain than spectroscopic purity, which is difficult enough to attain at times. Also, no single compound is completely responsible for any single fruit aroma. In spite of such difficulties, some organoleptically important compounds, such as amyl esters (bananas), citral

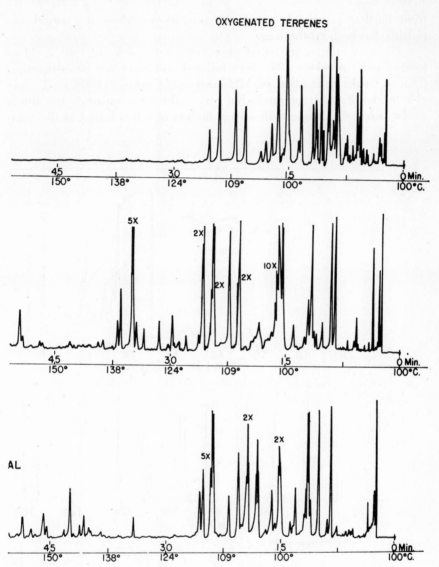

OXYGENATED TERPENES

of orange oil fractions

i.d., open tubular column coated with DC 550 silicone oil

(lemons), "raspberry ketone" (raspberries), lactones (peaches), etc., have been found.

Jennings (*18–21*) has studied the volatiles from Bartlett pears and evaluated their roles in determining flavors. Ethyl *trans*-2-*cis*-4-deca-dienoate was identified as a flavor component of Bartlett pears. The acid moiety was synthesized and found to be identical with that isolated from Bartlett pears. A series of esters whose odors are remarkably pearlike has been synthesized.

Different aromas are noted among different species of apples. MacGregor and coworkers (*30*) have isolated and identified 30 compounds from the volatile fraction of McIntosh apple juice. Hirose (*32*) was able to identify 21 compounds, but was unable to reconstitute the aroma of the "Kogyoku" apple with a combination of esters found in the vola-

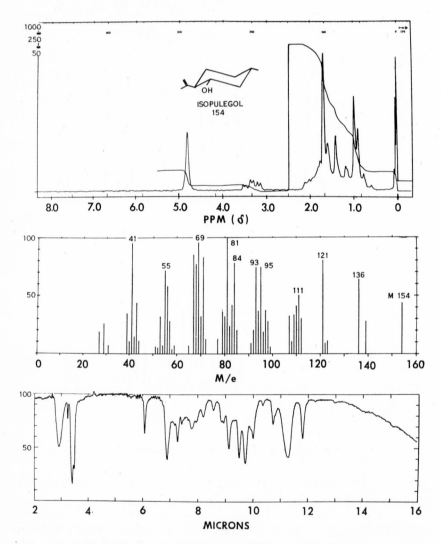

Figure 3. Infrared mass spectrometric, and proton magnetic resonance of isopulegol

tiles. Pollard (*22*) has been able to make an artificial mixture with 14 compounds which, when added to diluted stripped apple concentrate, gave a product not entirely harmonious, but not too dissimilar to a fresh apple juice. Guadagni (*11*) has been able to show not only the proportion of the constituents varying with varieties but also those which seem to be the important ones for a given variety. It seems that

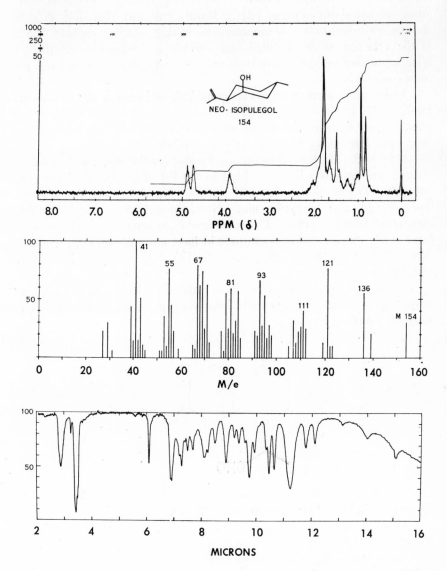

Figure 4. Infrared mass spectrometric, and proton magnetic resonance of neo-isopulegol

the organoleptically important compounds responsible for the aroma of various apples will soon be known.

The most comprehensive studies on citrus oils have been accomplished by Kováts (24, 25). He has identified 48 substances which constitute 99.2% of the volatile part of the essential oil of mandarin orange peel and has applied for a patent on the mixture of N-methyl methyl anthranilate and thymol, in correct proportions, having the characteristic aroma of mandarin oranges (24). Kováts has also identified 44 substances, including two new monoterpene oxides, which constitute 97.6% of the volatiles of the distilled lime oil (25). In both cases, the remainder of the unidentified substances are distributed over at least 100 trace components.

There are numerous papers on grapefruit and orange oil constituents (2–7, 13–17, 33, 34, 36, 38, 39, 40). Most of the substances isolated and identified are known aliphatic or terpenoid compounds. Recently, however, some interesting additions have been made.

MacLeod (31) has reported a sesquiterpene ketone, nootkatone, as a significant compound to be added to the list of grapefruit flavor constituents. Traces of this material are also found in bergamot, lemon, lime, orange, and tangerine oils. Nootkatone is a reasonably stable compound, largely unaffected by prolonged exposure to ambient temperatures in air, or elevated temperatures in inert atmosphere, refluxing conditions for 30 minutes in 10% ethanolic KOH, or overnight heating at 100° in glacial acetic acid.

Stevens and coworkers (34) have isolated and characterized a new sesquiterpene aldehyde, sinensal, from cold pressed orange oil. The assigned structure is:

This compound, unlike nootkatone, is unstable to acid, base, or to exposure to light and air at room temperatures.

Although most of the activity is in aroma chemistry research, an important contribution has been made in taste chemistry. Horowitz (12) has shown that if the flavanone naringin, chief bitter principle of grapefruit, is converted to its chalcone, the taste changes from intensely bitter to intensely sweet. Because the chalcone reverts easily to the flavanone, it is possible to alter the taste from bitter to sweet to bitter by simple chemical manipulations (Here R is neohisperidose).

NARINGIN
BITTER

dil. KOH
warm H_2O
(NaOAc)

NARINGIN CHALCONE
SWEET

Horowitz has also shown that reduction of the sweet chalcones to their dihydrochalcones by catalytic hydrogenation enhances the sweetness and yields stable compounds. Such changes point to the interesting possibility of modifying, on a commercial scale, the excessive bitterness of certain citrus juices.

Literature Cited

(1) Allen, L. C., Johnson L. F., *J. Am. Chem. Soc.* **85**, 2668 (1963).
(2) Attaway, J. A., Wolford, R. W., 5th International Gas Chromatography Symposium, Brighton, England, 1964, in press.
(3) Attaway, J. A., Wolford, R. W., Alberding, G. E., Edwards, G., *Anal. Chem.* **34**, 671 (1962).
(4) *Ibid.*, **35**, 234 (1963).
(5) Attaway, J. A., Wolford, R. W., Alberding, G. E., Edwards, G., *J. Agr. Food Chem.* **12**, 118 (1964).
(6) Attaway, J. A., Wolford, R. W., Edwards, G., *Ibid.*, **37**, 74 (1965).
(7) Attaway, J. A., Wolford, R. W., Edwards, G., *J. Agr. Food Chem.* **10**, 102 (1962).
(8) Demole, E., *Helv. Chim. Acta* **47**, 1766 (1964).
(9) Ebert, A. A. Jr., *Anal. Chem.* **33**, 1865 (1961).
(10) Gohlke, R. S., *Ibid.*, **31**, 535 (1959).
(11) Guadagni, D. G., U. S. Department of Agriculture, Albany, Calif., private communication.
(12) Horowitz, R. M., in "Biochemistry of Phenolic Compounds," J. R. Harborne, ed., p. 545, Academic Press, London and New York, 1964.
(13) Hunter, G. L. K., Brodgen, W. B., Jr., *Anal. Chem.* **36**, 1122 (1964).
(14) Hunter, G. L. K., Brodgen, W. B., Jr., *J. Org. Chem.* **29**, 982 (1964).
(15) *Ibid.*, p. 2100.
(16) Hunter, G. L. K., Moshonas, M. G., *Anal. Chem.* **37**, 378 (1965).
(17) Hunter, G. L. K., Parks, G. L., *J. Food Sci.* **29**, 25 (1964).
(18) Jennings, W. G., *Ibid.*, **26**, 564 (1961).
(19) Jennings, W. G., Creveling, R. K., *Ibid.*, **28**, 91 (1963).
(20) Jennings, W. G., Creveling, R. K., Heinz, D. E., *Ibid.*, **29**, 730 (1964).
(21) Jennings, W. G., Sevenants, M. R., *Ibid.*, **29**, 158 (1964).
(22) Kieser, M., Pollard, A., in "Volatile Fruit Flavours," International Federation of Fruit Juice Producers Symposium, Juris-Verlag, Zurich, p. 249, 1962.
(23) Klein, M. P., Baton, G. W., *Rev. Sci. Instr.* **34**, 754 (1963).
(24) Kováts, E. sz., *Helv. Chim. Acta* **46**, 2705 (1963).

(25) Kugler, E., Kováts, E. sz., *Ibid.*, **46**, 1480 (1963).
(26) Lindeman, L. P., Annis, J. L., *Anal. Chem.* **32**, 1742 (1960).
(27) Lundin, R. E., Elsken, R. H., Flath, R. A., Henderson, N., Mon, T. R., Teranishi, R., *Ibid.*, **38**, 291 (1966).
(28) McFadden, W. H., Teranishi, R., Black, D. R., Day, J. C., *J. Food Sci.* **28**, 316 (1963).
(29) McFadden, W. H., Teranishi, R., Corse, J., Black, D. R., Mon, T. R., *J. Chromatog.* **18**, 10 (1965).
(30) MacGregor, D. R., Sugisawa, H., Matthews, J. S., *J. Food Sci.* **29**, 448 (1964).
(31) MacLeod, W. D., Jr., Buigues, N. M., *Ibid.*, **29**, 565 (1964).
(32) Nishimura, K., Hirose, Y., *Agr. Biol. Chem.* (*Japan*) **28**, 1, (1964).
(33) Schultz, T. H., Teranishi, R., McFadden, W. H., Kilpatrick, P. W., Corse, J., *J. Food Sci.* **29**, 790 (1964).
(34) Stevens, K. L., Lundin, R. E., Teranishi, R., *J. Org. Chem.*, **30**, 1690 (1965).
(35) Teranishi, R., Corse, J. W., McFadden, W. H., Black, D. R., Morgan, A. I., Jr., *J. Food Sci.* **28**, 478 (1963).
(36) Teranishi, R., Lundin, R. E., McFadden, W. H., Mon, T. R., Schultz, T. H., Stevens, K. L., Wasserman, J., Abstracts of papers, 150th meeting, ACS, Atlantic City, N. J., Sept. 12–17, 1965, p. 33A.
(37) Teranishi, R., Mon, T. R., *Anal. Chem.* **36**, 1490 (1964).
(38) Teranishi, R., Schultz, T. H., McFadden, W. H., Lundin, R. E., Black, D. R., *J. Food Sci.* **28**, 541 (1963).
(39) Wolford, R. W., Alberding, G. E., Attaway, J. A., *J. Agr. Food Chem.* **10**, 297 (1962).
(40) Wolford, R. W., Attaway, J. A., Alberding, G. E., Atkins, C. D., *J. Food Sci.* **28**, 320 (1963).

RECEIVED April 27, 1965. Reference to a company or product name does not imply approval or recommendation of the product by the U. S. Department of Agriculture to the exclusion of others that may be suitable.

Separation and Characterization of Flavor Components from Vegetables

RICHARD A. BERNHARD

Department of Food Science and Technology, University of California, Davis, Calif.

Aliphatic disulfides appear to be the principal compounds responsible for the aroma and flavor of onions. Gold has demonstrated that alkylidene phthalides and dihydrophthalides are intimately concerned with the flavor of celery. While little is known about the flavor compounds of lettuce, certain off-flavors of carrots are due to the violet-like aromas of the ionones. Aliphatic acids produce the cheeselike flavor of sauerkraut, while the odor of rutabaga is caused by mercaptans and isothiocyanates. Forss found that cucumber flavor arises from a series of aliphatic aldehydes, as does the flavor of potatoes, tomatoes, and beans. Cooked vegetable flavors arise from a variety of simple substance produced during heating. Methods of isolation, separation, and characterization of vegetable flavor are critically discussed.

Comparatively few studies have been made on the flavor of vegetables *vs.* fruits and essential oils. It is interesting to speculate on why this is so.

Examination of agricultural statistics shows that total production in the United States of 18 of the most common fruits is in the neighborhood of 18 million tons a year, and that of all common vegetables is about 19 million tons. Thus on the basis of sheer bulk, one could expect the two groups to be of about equal importance. From an economic standpoint, the total value of all fruits in the United States for 1960 was approximately $1.2 billion and that of all vegetables about $1.15 billion (*24*): not much to choose from here either. It appears that the two groups are of equal importance in both volume and value.

Why then is research on vegetable flavor chemistry lagging so far behind that of fruit flavor chemistry? It is this reviewer's opinion that this lag results from the difficulty of working with vegetable flavor. The flavors and odors of many vegetables are difficult to describe and worse to differentiate from each other. Potatoes and peas have little characteristic aroma and flavor, but such close relatives as oranges and lemons have quite different and easily recognizable flavor and aroma differences. One may raise the objection, what about onions, cabbage, turnips, and even rutabaga? Do not these have distinctive aromas and flavors? Indeed they do, and as a consequence, the preponderance of investigations conducted in vegetable flavor chemistry has been directed toward some of these plants. Apparently the strong, characteristic aromas and flavors of these vegetables have influenced many experimenters' choice of study area. This cannot be the sole reason for selection of a research program since economic factors and many issues influence this decision too. Some of these are brought out in the following discussion.

With the increasing sophistication in analytical techniques and instrumentation has come a greater knowledge of food flavor composition. There has been a flood of research papers on the volatile compounds in foods, and most of these studies are reported in the name of "flavor" chemistry. There seems little doubt that many important constituents contributing to the aroma of foods have been isolated and identified, but what has not been done, to any appreciable extent, is to establish which of these components is responsible for what sensory properties. Stewart (34) has stated that many of the compounds isolated probably have little or no sensory effect. He suggests greater emphasis on what he refers to as the significance of these compounds of flavor. Reliable tools are available for this purpose, and others should be developed. Flavor profile, odor recognition, dilution index, and difference tests can all prove useful for studying this problem. Appropriate tests with isolated fractions and compounds will help answer such questions as: Does the compound have sensory properties? If so, what is their nature? What combination of components results in the sensory properties typical of the original product from which they were derived? Only after such studies have been made, will we know the significance of the compounds isolated.

Isolation and Concentration Procedures

Vegetables by their very nature are difficult to examine chemically. Flavor substances frequently occur in concentrations of a few parts per million, surrounded by large amounts of other organic materials and huge quantities of water. This poses a real problem.

The vegetable is usually comminuted, chopped, or otherwise reduced to a pulpy or powdery mass and then subjected to an isolation procedure. Five major methods are commonly employed to obtain flavor fractions from plant materials. Traditionally steam distillation has been used for years to isolate volatile organic substances from plants. This is still the preferred method of many researchers although it has many obvious disadvantages. The plant material is subjected to considerable heat and hydrolytic activity of a high order for long periods of time. Distillation under reduced pressure is another common procedure for isolating flavor fractions. A variant of this technique is the use of short-path distillation, frequently called molecular distillation. Using this procedure, decomposition of high-boiling, high molecular weight compounds is often materially retarded.

Another way to isolate organic material is by liquid-solid or liquid-liquid extraction. Generally the product is exposed to prolonged heating and the less volatile components are subjected to pot heats that can materially alter many labile organic constituents. All this is further complicated by the introduction of large volumes of solvent and the problems of its subsequent removal or concentration.

Three newer methods use gas chromatographic techniques. One method places the sample in a closed system and allows an inert gas to sweep across it and carry away entrained volatiles (*21*). These gases are condensed in a series of cold-finger traps and the gas is recirculated over the food material. The cycle is usually repeated a number of times until sufficient volatile material is collected in traps for subsequent analysis. There are other variations of this gas sweeping procedure, in which single passes are made in open systems (*33*). Sampling of head-space vapors with subsequent introduction of the sample into the chromatograph has been the choice of a number of workers in recent months (*1, 2, 3, 5, 6, 22, 26, 30, 31*). This has the great advantage of offering a rapid, convenient technique for analysis. Using flame ionization detectors, Buttery and Teranishi (*6*) have studied direct injection of aqueous vapors from a number of foods. Fortunately, flame ionization detectors show little or no response to moderate amounts of water vapor, and thus this procedure can be applied most successfully.

There is an obvious advantage to the latter three systems over the former four procedures when working with volatile flavor substances. The conditions for removal of the flavor segment are mild, usually room temperature, and contact period is brief. This minimizes sample handling with any attendant possibility of artifact production. Its major disadvantages are that only the most volatile components are usually determined, since only substances with appreciable vapor pressures would be expected to be in the vapor phase. Additionally, compounds present in minute concentration may remain dissolved or entrapped in the main mass of material. Thus it is not always possible to obtain a representative sample of the substances desired for study using gas sweeping or head-space techniques. Here the concentration of volatiles will vary also with sample temperature, and the relative concentrations collected will not necessarily be those of the same materials normally present in the vegetable. One frequently reasons that the samples garnered by these two methods are fairly representative of the odor components of the products examined, but this has yet to be experimentally verified to any extent. Of course, there is the fervent hope that better isolation techniques will come in the coming years. Certainly there is a pressing need for them.

Separation and Characterization

Once the flavor fraction has been isolated from the vegetable, attention must be directed to separation and identification of the individual components responsible for its make-up.

To date the preferred means of separating these constituents has been by gas-liquid chromatography (GLC). Other procedures run a poor second to the versatility, speed, and resolution of GLC. Separation by additional chromatographic techniques has been used to some extent too—e.g., solid-liquid, liquid-liquid, thin-layer, paper partition, and ion exchange (13, 14, 18, 19). Some have resorted to fractional distillation, crystallization, and sublimation procedures (7, 11, 12, 13). All, of course, can be most useful, and one is often the procedure of choice in a given situation; but for universality, GLC is hard to surpass.

Despite its unquestioned advantages as a tool for separation, GLC does not offer the best means for identifying substances. True, retention volumes (and its imprecise variations—e.g., retention time) are most helpful in a rough qualitative sense, but one can never be certain as to identities based solely on retention data, no matter how many stationary liquid phases have been employed. This leaves the problem of characterization to other physical and chemical means.

Preparation of solid chemical derivatives—e.g., hydrazones of carbonyl compounds—is a useful and reliable means of identification. In flavor work one is often prohibited from using this time-honored method for lack of sufficient material. Frequently, one may trap effluent substances from a chromatograph in a suitable reagent and form these derivatives, but this method suffers from a number of disadvantages, most of which are associated with sample size. A crystalline derivative, whose melting point agrees with accepted literature values (and is not depressed by admixture with an authentic sample) will usually provide accepted identification. If this method gives no satisfactory agreement with any known derivatives, one must resort to combustion analyses, molecular weight determinations, and lastly, to degradation studies. It takes a skilled analyst to get by on much less than 20 mg. of a compound that has been described in the literature; a good deal more may be necessary for a compound that has not been described.

If less than 0.1 mg. is available, the investigator is forced to seek refuge in physical methods of identification that require only minute amounts of material for subsequent examination. In this instance spectral methods of analysis are most common. Infrared and ultraviolet spectra can be determined in solution using microcells. The solvent can be removed and a mass spectrum obtained. There is an increasing trend towards the use of mass spectrographs for identification. In the hands of a skilled analyst, this provides an elegant way in which to identify effluent fractions directly from a gas chromatograph. To date the major deterrent to the use of such instrumentation has been the high cost of the equipment. Infrared spectrometry has provided the major means of identifying flavor components during the current decade.

Allium, Onions

The largest number of investigations of vegetable flavor chemistry has been carried out with members of the genus *Allium*, onions. Their distinctive aromas have no doubt been largely responsible for this interest. Although investigation of *Allium* flavor has been going on since the late nineteenth century (32), much remains to be learned.

In 1961 Carson and Wong (7) conducted an extensive study of the volatile components of a particularly pungent variety of onion called sunspice. This onion was the result of breeding programs designed to produce an onion of unusual pungency suitable for dehydration. After drying, the onion has a flavor potency similar to that of common fresh onions. Thus they selected a strain that is a rich source of volatile materials.

Two separate batches of *ca.* 142 pounds of onions were chopped, mixed with 25 gallons of water, and distilled under vacuum. The distilling vapors were led through two parallel columns containing 400 grams of activated charcoal. Distillation was continued for 40 hours at a pot temperature of 25°. The carbon columns were dried under vacuum and extracted in a Soxhlet extractor with peroxide-free ether for 40 hours. This extraction was performed in the dark to minimize possible light-induced decomposition or isomerization. The combined ether extracts (3 liters) were dried, and the solvent was removed by distillation to yield 115 ml. of concentrate. Further concentration yielded 14 grams of a pale yellow oil, which was further distilled under vacuum to give 8.7 grams of an oil boiling between 40° and 60° at 1 mm. of Hg. This represents an oil concentration of about 75 p.p.m. based on fresh weight of onion.

Another procedure was tried in which the juice from 142 pounds of onions was steam distilled, and extracted with isopentane. The two methods of isolation yielded oils giving different chromatographic patterns, but the same disulfides and trisulfides were found in each case.

Analysis of the concentrates was made using GLC, and effluent fractions were identified by derivatization and infrared spectral analyses.

The compounds that Carson and Wong (7) isolated and identified are recorded in Table I. Their most important new findings were that allyl 1-propyl disulfide is not present in onions in significant amounts; methyl as well as 1-propyl derivatives occur; and substantial quantities of trisulfides corresponding to the disulfides are present. Indeed, this work is believed to represent the first unequivocal isolation of pure, well-defined aliphatic trisulfides from plant sources.

Table I. Volatile Components Found in Onions by Carson and Wong (7)

Ethanol	Hydrogen sulfide
1-Propanol	1-Propanethiol
2-Propanol	Methyl disulfide
Methanal	Methyl 1-propyl disulfide
Propanal	1-Propyl disulfide
1-Butanal	Methyl trisulfide
Acetone	Methyl 1-propyl trisulfide
Methyl ethyl ketone	1-Propyl trisulfide

Carson and Wong (7) presented no experimental evidence that any of the compounds isolated from onions has a role in the flavor or aroma of onions. In reality the association of these onion components with onion flavor is intuitive. This is not leveled as a criticism of Carson and Wong's work but really applies to many so-called flavor studies.

Members of the genus *Allium*—onions, garlic, leek, chives, etc. (16)—possess strong, characteristic flavors and aromas not found in other vegetables. Another remarkable attribute is that most members of the genus have no odor unless there is damage to the plant tissue. These characteristic volatiles are absent from intact tissue, and are produced enzymatically when injury occurs (35). Substrates for the production of these volatiles are known as alliins, and are derivatives of the amino acid cysteine. These derivatives give rise, through several reactions, to the sulfur-containing volatiles. S-Allyl cysteine sulfoxide of garlic, the first alliin to be identified (35), when treated with a preparation of garlic containing the enzyme alliinase (28), gives rise to allicin (diallyl thiosulfinate), pyruvic acid, and ammonia (26, 35):

$$2CH_2=CH-CH_2-\overset{\overset{O}{\uparrow}}{S}-CH_2-\underset{\underset{NH_2}{|}}{CH}-COOH + H_2O \xrightarrow{\text{Alliinase}}$$

Alliin

$$CH_2{=}CH{-}CH_2{-}\overset{\overset{O}{\uparrow}}{S}{-}S{-}CH_2{-}CH{=}CH_2 + 2NH_3 + 2CH_3{-}CO{-}COOH \quad (1)$$

Allicin   Pyruvic acid

Allicin, unlike the odorless alliin, is volatile and has a pleasant, garlic-like odor. It is unstable, however, and allyl disulfide is produced as one of the breakdown products:

$$2R{-}\overset{\overset{O}{\uparrow}}{S}{-}S{-}R' \rightarrow R{-}\underset{\underset{O}{\downarrow}}{\overset{\overset{O}{\uparrow}}{S}}{-}S{-}R' + R{-}S{-}S{-}R' + SO_2 + polymers \quad (2)$$

Thiosulfonate   Disulfide

Following the discovery of alliin and allicin in garlic, the methyl and 1-propyl homologs of these compounds were found in onion by Virtanen and Matikkala (*36*). Where two or more alliin homologs are found together, mixed or asymmetrical allicins may be produced—e.g., methyl-1-propyl allicin in garlic. Mixed allicins are, in turn, associated with the production of mixed disulfides.

The allicins and sulfide compounds are presumed to be the principal source of the flavor and aroma of *Allium* species. Thus the differences in odor among species may be accounted for, at least in part, by the sulfur compounds in their vapors.

With the above in mind, Bernhard and Mann decided to use this information and attempt to classify various alliums on the basis of their chemical constituents, especially the disulfides since these are so characteristic of the genus. Thus the original intent of this work was taxonomic in nature.

Employing the classical procedures of paper chromatography, Kuon and Bernhard (*18*) isolated and identified a number of the free amino acids of the common onion. This work confirmed the presence of S-substituted cysteines and alliins that were originally found by many others workers (*35, 36*). It appears that taxonomic differentiation based on free amino acid composition is not feasible at the varietal level (*18*), but may offer some promise for differentiation between species.

Jacobsen *et al.* (*15*) examined some asymmetric disulfides produced by *Allium* and confirmed the production of these compounds and their structures. Four species were examined in this initial undertaking—A. *sativum* L. (garlic), A. *chinense* G. Don (rakkyo), A. *ampeloprasum* L. (great-headed garlic), and A. *cepa* L. (onion) (*16*).

The technique of isolation used was to chop the tissue and distill under reduced pressure (3 cm. of Hg at 40°). This procedure allowed the distillation and collection of volatile materials with little accumulation of water. After 1 ½ hours of distillation, the distillate was collected, extracted with ethyl ether, and dried, and the solvent removed under vacuum. A yellowish-brown oil resulted. Using 300 to 400 gram samples of fresh tissues, these procedures gave yields of the order of 20 to 60 μl. per sample. No attempts were made to obtain maximum yields of oil.

The oils thus obtained were examined by GLC, and the various components separated and collected by the use of preparative scale GLC. Effluent fractions were examined by infrared spectrometry. Asymmetric disulfides were prepared synthetically by oxidizing the corresponding mercaptans with potassium ferricyanide in aqueous alkaline solution. These synthetic disulfides were then purified via preparative scale GLC and examined by infrared techniques. In addition to spectral comparisons, carbon, hydrogen, and sulfur were determined quantitatively on both the naturally occurring and synthetic disulfides. Additionally, retention volume measurements were made as further confirmation of identity.

In the *Allium* oils examined, three asymmetric disulfides were found and identified: allyl-1-propyl disulfide from great-headed garlic, methyl allyl disulfide from great-headed garlic and garlic, and methyl-1-propyl disulfide from great-headed garlic, rakkyo, and onions. This paper (15) marked the first rigorous identification and first presentation of infrared spectra of these mixed disulfides.

Following the confirmation of the presence of mixed disulfides in certain alliums, Saghir *et al.* (26) conducted a determination of aliphatic mono- and disulfides in *Allium* by GLC and their distribution in common food species. The Bernhard-Mann group felt that it was desirable to examine these onions in such a manner that a minimum amount of handling and chemical reactions was involved. An analytical scheme evolved that is so simple as to seem almost ridiculous but proved amazingly effective.

Vapor samples for gas chromatographic analyses were obtained from finely chopped fresh tissue. Bulbs or foliage leaves were used, depending upon the species. Ten grams of chopped tissue were placed in a 30-ml. screw-capped glass vial. Prior to introducing the sample, a small hole was drilled in the cap, and a circular silicone rubber septum placed inside the cap. Samples could be withdrawn from and added to the vial through the rubber septum without loss of vapor. The vial was held at 40° in an oven for 30 minutes before withdrawal of 1 ml. of vapor for analysis. Five minutes prior to sampling, 0.05 μl. of *p*-cymene was added to the vial to provide a reference peak.

There were rapid changes in the composition of the vapor over chopped alliums with time. Qualitative and quantitative experiments were made to ascertain the nature of these changes (Figure 1). From the time fresh tissue was chopped, four of the sulfides increased in concentration for about 30 minutes and then the concentrations leveled off. Two of the sulfides reached a maximum concentration level in about 30 minutes also, but then the concentrations dropped rapidly. Thus the time of sampling appears to be critical when fresh tissue is examined.

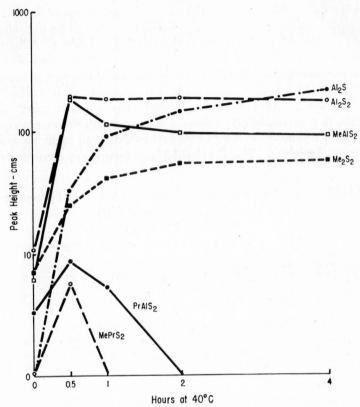

Courtesy Proceedings of American Society for Horticultural Science

Figure 1. Relation of period of incubation to change in peak height

Chopped tissue of California Late garlic incubated at 40°C. (26)

From these data (Figure 1) it is obvious that 30 minutes after chopping is the optimum time for examination of the volatiles in these systems. Sulfide peaks were identified by calculation of relative retention times using polar and nonpolar stationary liquid phases, by addition of known compounds prepared in the study described above, and by infrared examination of each sulfide peak effluent. Table II presents a summary of the sulfides found in this study (26) together with an approximate quantitative estimate of their concentrations. This study reports the finding of some sulfides not previously found in oils of various alliums.

Allyl radicals were found to be present in onions, contrary to previous reports (7).

Using the procedure of Schwimmer and Weston (29) to measure enzymatically produced pyruvate, the authors (26) could find no correlation between total sulfide peak area and pyruvate production.

Although sulfides are not the only odorous compounds that have been recovered from alliums, they contribute so much to the odor that evident relationships exist between the sulfides and odors. Although no rigorous taste panel work was done by these authors, they did draw certain conclusions from the data they accumulated concerning the aroma of alliums. Many allyl compounds are pungent, with radishlike or garliclike odors. Allyl disulfide definitely has a garlic odor. Propyl disulfide, in contrast, has the odor we associate with the common onion, and methyl disulfide the odor of cooked cabbage, an odor we associate with many brassicas. The Bernhard-Mann group was conscious of the

Table II. Peak Areas[a] of Sulfides in Allium Vapor as Percentage of Total Sulfides Measured (26)

Species	Me_2S_2	Al_2S	$MePrS_2$	Sulfides, % $MeAlS_2$	Pr_2S_2	$PrAlS_2$	Al_2S_2
Allium ampeloprasum L. great-headed garlic	4	<1	3	31	<1	5	55
A. ampeloprasum L., leek	0	2	54	2	38	3	<1
A. cepa L. Australian Brown 5 onion	2	0	4	<1	86	6	<1
Crystal Grano onion	0	0	2	<1	93	4	<1
Potato onion	4	0	9	1	80	5	<1
Top-set onion	4	0	25	2	60	9	<1
A. chinense G. Don (*A. bak-eri Regel*), Toyama rakkyo	87	<1	9	3	<1	<1	<1
A. fistulosum L., Japanese bunching onion	9	5	15	2	65	4	<1
A. sativum L. California Early garlic	1	3	<1	22	<1	<1	74
California Late garlic	3	3	<1	33	<1	<1	61
A. schoenoprasum L., chive	10	0	19	4	63	4	<1
A. tuberosum Rottler ex Sprengel, Chinese chive	83	<1	<1	16	<1	<1	<1

[a] Assuming peaks are triangular, area = height × width of base/2. Where peaks are attenuated, area is multiplied by attenuation factor.

odors of the alliums examined chromatographically, and in general this odor can be related to the nature of their sulfide content (Figure 2). The four graphs for onions (*A. cepa*) (Figure 2), for example, show a relatively high level of propyl compounds and small amounts of methyl and allyl compounds. Other edible alliums with odors or flavors very like *A. cepa* are the Japanese bunching onion, chive, and leek (Figure 2). These too, are predominantly producers of propyl disulfide (Figure 2).

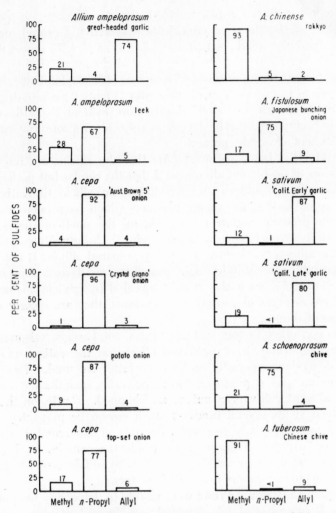

Courtesy Proceedings of American Society for Horticultural Science

Figure 2. Proportions, based on peak area from a Carbowax 20M column of methyl, n-propyl, and allyl radicals in vapors from chopped Allium tissues

Total of 3 radicals for each Allium equals 100 (26)

The two cultivars of garlic show a preponderance of allyl compounds. Great-headed garlic likewise has a high proportion of allyl compounds. It differs strikingly from garlic in its low production of pyruvate, presumably an indication of its mildness.

Rakkyo and Chinese chives have high proportions of methyl compounds, and a cabbagelike odor can be detected in both; Chinese chives also have a strong garlic odor.

Among the alliums grown for food, there is at least one species in which each of the three common radicals—methyl, 1-propyl, or allyl—is the predominant sulfide constituent. Saghir *et al.* (25) report that one can make a fair estimate of the propyl and allyl content of many species of *Allium* from their odors alone. These two radicals dominate the odor, so that even in species such as *A. tuberosum* (Figure 2) where the methyl radical predominates, the allyl odor is more evident than the methyl. The methyl component can be detected easily only if it forms an extremely large portion of all sulfides present.

The idea has been advanced (26) that the allicins are responsible for the odors of freshly cut alliums, and that the similar but perhaps less-pleasant-smelling disulfides and trisulfides are allicin derivatives. It seems reasonable that the sulfide products which have been recovered are not the products mainly responsible for the smell of fresh alliums but are derivatives having a similar odor. Unfortunately, just how rapidly the allicins break down in freshly prepared alliums is not known at present; thus the sulfides may contribute to flavors, especially in cooked alliums. Even if the sulfides revealed by gas chromatographic analyses are artifacts of analytical procedures, they are clearly related to the odor of alliums.

However, other factors such as sugars, total solids, crispness, and the lachrymator may have profound effects on the eating quality of alliums, depending especially on how the latter are used. The lachrymator, for example, is produced in overpowering quantities when large amounts of most cultivars of onions are chopped. Garlic, on the other hand, which yields several times as much enzymatic pyruvate as does the onion, produces only moderate amounts of lachrymator and may appear less "strong." Thus pyruvate production can be used only to estimate one aspect of onion flavor. Likewise sulfide content gives information on only another of many flavor factors.

Although Carson and Wong were unable to detect any monosulfides in onions, Bernhard *et al.* (4) detected two chromatographic peaks that did not fit any of the known disulfides examined; one had a characteristic sulfurlike odor. It was subsequently identified as allyl monosulfide. This marked the first confirmation of a monosulfide from *Allium*, although there is evidence of allyl monosulfide in horseradish and a species of *Diplotaxis* (4). The second unknown peak was identified as allyl alcohol. Up to this time allyl alcohol had not been reported as present in a plant material. Identities were confirmed by infrared spectral comparisons with authentic known materials, and rather careful, repeated trials using some six stationary liquid phases to give retention volume data. Evidently these researchers found it hard to accept the presence of allyl alcohol in a plant material and checked and rechecked many times.

In a study primarily designed to demonstrate the versatility of dual-channel gas chromatography for the detection and identification of sulfides in general, Oaks *et al.* (*23*) examined the volatile sulfides in garlic. Dual-channel gas chromatography refers to a technique using a single column with two different detectors. In this study (*23*) a hydrogen flame and an electron-capture detector were used. The flame detector is quite sensitive and responds nearly equally to all organic compounds. The electron-capture detector is sensitive only to certain organic compounds such as conjugated carbonyls, nitro, halogenated, and sulfur-containing compounds. Sensitivity varies markedly between types of compounds. Recording the responses from the two different detectors using a dual-pen recorder, a differential examination is obtained that will reflect the various characteristic properties of each type of detector.

Examining the headspace of macerated garlic cloves, Oaks *et al.* (*23*) found a series of sulfur compounds similar to those reported by Carson and Wong (*7*) and Saghir, *et al.* (*26*) with four interesting additions: methyl mercaptan, methyl monosulfide, methyl allyl trisulfide, and allyl trisulfide. Unfortunately these investigators made no rigorous identification of any of the compounds detected, basing their tentative identification on relative retention times and the ratio of electron-capture response to flame response, the ϕ value. (ϕ Values increase as the amount of sulfur in a compound increases.) Analyses were also made using hexane extracts of garlic and some variation in sulfur-containing compounds was noted. Another point that cast some doubt as to the validity of these results is that head space vapors were examined after a 2-hour period. As noted above (*26*), this can cause a remarkable change in the compositional picture of the volatile sulfides from alliums.

Using milder conditions for isolating onion components than did Carson and Wong (*7*), Spåre and Virtanen (*33*) isolated volatile carbonyls and alcohols from Finnish onions. These workers sucked air through a homogenized onion mass and led the vapors through a dilute solution of 2,4-dinitrophenylhydrazine. The resulting phenylhydrazones were separated on a cellulose powder chromatographic column. In this manner Spåre and Virtanen (*33*) isolated 1-propanal, methanal, and an interesting variation, 2-methyl-2-pentenal, and also reported the presence of methanol, ethanol, and an unknown substance. Once again no experimental evidence is presented of any determination as to which, if any, of these compounds has a role in onion flavor or aroma.

Onion pungency or strength is difficult to measure, or even to define. There seems little doubt that pungency is intimately tied in with onion flavor and aroma, but just how? To assist breeders and processors, many objective methods of measuring pungency have been proposed.

Recently Schwimmer and Weston (*29*) have demonstrated a correlation between enzymatically produced pyruvic acid in onions and degree of pungency. They report that weak onions produce some 2 to 4 μmoles of pyruvic acid per gram of fresh tissue; those of intermediate strength produce 8 to 10 μmoles per gram; and strong onions produce 15 to 20 μmoles per gram. Unfortunately, the labels weak, intermediate, and strong were assigned with the only tools at hand, rankings of pungency found in seed catalogs and old U. S. Department of Agriculture publications. This does not reflect on Schwimmer and Weston, but on the unsophisticated state of precise knowledge in this area.

Pyruvic acid production presumably comes about via the reaction scheme presented in Equation 2. This method offers only an empirical approach to the solution of this age-old question. The procedure is rapid (95% of total pyruvate production occurring in about 6 minutes), and pyruvate formation can be followed colorimetrically using the phenylhydrazone derivative. As noted above, results of this procedure do not correlate well with accepted pungency rankings for all alliums.

It seems probable that a major contribution to onion pungency is derived from the lachrymatory principle found in the species. There has been an almost constant search for more information as to its nature for many years. Kohman (17) suggested that it is really thiopropanal, $CH_3—CH_2—CH=S$, but this is subject to some question on the grounds that such thioaldehydes are extremely unstable, especially in the presence of water, a condition certainly present in the onion. This would result in the following type of reaction sequence:

$$R—\underset{\underset{H}{|}}{C}{=}S + H_2O \rightleftharpoons \left[R—\underset{\underset{SH}{|}}{\overset{\overset{OH}{|}}{C}}—H \right] \rightleftharpoons R—\underset{\underset{H}{|}}{C}{=}O + H_2S \tag{3}$$

The energetics of this reaction show that the equilibrium lies far to the right, there being a 70-kcal. difference in energy between the carbon-sulfur and the carbon-oxygen double bond.

Using low temperature entrainment procedures, Wilkins (39) isolated a compound from onions which he considered to be the lachrymator. This was assigned the following structure:

$$CH_3—CH_2—CH=S=O$$

being thiopropanal-S-oxide. If one examines the possible resonance forms of this proposed structure, it becomes evident that it is highly susceptible to virtually any nucleophilic attack. Thus its stability is low, and it could not be expected to be present to any extent in tissue of high water content. It should, of course, react with similar molecules to form polymers or condensation products. There is the distinct possibility that there is some mechanism in the plant that protects these unstable compounds, or allows them to be formed only at specific times. These are questions that await further clarification.

In a series of publications, Virtanen and coworkers (*20, 37*) suggested that the lachrymator in onions is derived by enzymatic splitting of a precursor, S-(1-propenyl) cysteine sulfoxide. They believe that one of the principal products of the reaction, propenesulfenic acid, is in reality the lachrymatory principle of alliums.

Recently Saghir and Mann (*25*) have demonstrated that there is no lachrymator in American wild alliums. These onions do have considerable aroma and flavor. Thus one must conclude that the lachrymator, whatever its nature, is not completely essential to onion flavor.

Celery

A fine example of the proper blending of classical and modern techniques to elucidate the complex structures of the flavor compounds of celery is exemplified by the work of Gold and Wilson (*12, 13*). It is also an example of the lengths to which chemists will go to achieve a better knowledge of food flavor.

Their studies indicated that the concentration of recoverable volatiles in celery juice was of the order of only 1 p.p.m., requiring the use of vast quantities of starting material. A total of 5 tons of celery was used in these studies! The volatile materials were recovered by vacuum distillation of the juice in a pilot-plant essence-recovery unit.

The number of compounds in each distillate fraction ranged from four to 30. Simpler fractions were submitted directly to GLC; the more complex systems were fractionated by using functional group reagents and silica gel chromatography, prior to final separation by GLC. These procedures simplified the gas chromatograms obtained, and facilitated interpretation and collection of the individual components. Much valuable information was gained by using spot-test techniques and subtractive GLC.

In most cases identification was based on comparison of infrared spectra and retention times of recovered compounds with those of authentic materials. In some instances where sufficient material was not available for detailed study, tentative identifications were made based on GLC retention times and a knowledge of the functional groups. Thirty-five compounds were positively and 11 compounds were tentatively identified.

Four additional compounds, three of which were new substances, were found to be intimately concerned with the flavor of celery (*12*). Structural elucidation of these compounds was made using, in addition to various chemical techniques, infrared, ultraviolet, and mass spectrometry (*13*). These compounds are alkylidene phthalides and dihydrophthalides—viz., 3-isobutylidene-3a,4-dihydrophthalide (I); 3-isovalidene-3a,4-

dihydrophthalide (II); 3-isobutylidene phthalide (III); and 3-isovalidene phthalide (IV) (Figure 3).

These four compounds and two others, cis-3-hexen-1-yl pyruvate and diacetyl, were found to be the ones primarily concerned with the flavor of celery. One satisfying aspect of Gold and Wilson's (12) work was that by

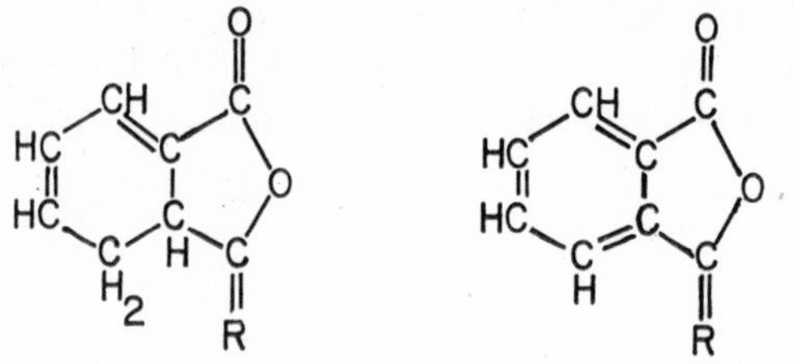

I. $R=CH \cdot CH(CH_3)_2$ III. $R=CH \cdot CH(CH_3)_2$

II. $R=CH \cdot CH_2 \cdot CH(CH_3)_2$ IV. $R=CH \cdot CH_2 \cdot CH(CH_3)_2$

Figure 3. Alkylidene phthalides and dihydrophthalides from celery (12, 13)

recombination of the isolated compounds it was possible to reproduce the flavor and odor of celery. This can be done by mixing 26 parts of I, 13 parts of II, 4 parts of cis-3-hexen-1-yl pyruvate, and 1 part of diacetyl. Small taste panels confirmed these results.

Crosby and Anderson (9) have written an extensive review of the organic constituents of celery.

Lettuce

Our lack of knowledge in vegetable chemistry is further pointed up in another review by Crosby (8), describing what is known (or really how little is known) of the chemistry of another common vegetable, lettuce. Regrettably no new work on lettuce flavor has been done in recent years.

Carrots

Off-flavors are an important aspect of flavor chemistry that is receiving more attention these days. An interesting example of the variety of off-flavors encountered in foods is provided by the study of Ayers et al. (1), who were interested in an off-flavor from dehydrated carrots stored in oxygen. The aroma encountered was reminiscent of violets. To attack this problem, diced, dehydrated carrots were extracted with ether, and the extract was distilled under high vacuum. The distillate and residue were examined by GLC, and some 24 components were evident. Further isolation revealed that nine of these had violet-like odors. Headspace analysis of the gases above stored, diced, dehydrated carrots revealed 23 components in the vapor fraction, and none of these had the odor of violets. Systematic analyses revealed that the compounds principally responsible for the violetlike aroma were α- and β-ionones and β-ionone-5,6-epoxide. Their identity was confirmed by GLC retention data, derivatization with 2,4-dinitrophenylhydrazine, and infrared spectral comparison with authentic materials.

Sauerkraut

The common aliphatic carboxylic acids are frequently associated with off-odors of many food products, and these were pinpointed as the culprits for the "cheeselike" flavor of canned sauerkraut by Vorbeck *et al.* (*38*).

Some 600 grams of sauerkraut were steam-distilled at the rate of 5 ml. per minute until 1200 ml. of distillate were collected, and the pH of the distillate was adjusted to 8.3 with NaOH. The solution was reduced to near-dryness using a rotary evaporator, made acidic, and extracted with ethyl ether. Silicic acid chromatography was used to remove the large excess of acetic acid. After removal of the ether from the column effluent, and conversion to the methyl esters using diazomethane, the material was analyzed by GLC.

Table III.   Carboxylic Acid Composition of Normal and Off-Odored Canned Sauerkraut (*38*)

Acid	Good	Off-Odor
	P.p.m.	
Propionic	0.1	6.7
n-Butyric	0.1	103.0
Isobutyric	—	3.9
Valeric	—	19.2
Isovaleric	—	9.9
n-Caproic	1.4	59.3
Enanthic	10.9	—
n-Caprylic	10.0	7.1

The major components of this fraction proved to be acetic and lactic acids and ethanol. Samples of normal sauerkraut contained rather small amounts of the lower homologs of the aliphatic carboxylic acids while there was a marked increase in *n*-butyric and *n*-caproic acid content in the off-flavored product (Table III). The materials isolated were identified by using GLC retention data and comparing two stationary liquid phases. Since this is not an ideal manner in which to confirm identity, one should look upon these results as "tentative" rather than "absolute." Some flavor panel evaluation was made using the common acids and this work is currently in progress (38).

Rutabaga

Rutabaga, a *Brassica* with a strong, characteristic aroma, is a type of turnip. Although it is not as common at the dining table as other members of this group, its flavor chemistry has recently been investigated to a limited extent. Hing and Weckel (14) extracted slurries of this vegetable and also used entrainment procedures to isolate the volatile materials from cooked rutabaga. These volatiles were analyzed by GLC, and the identities of components isolated were confirmed by chemical derivatization. The compounds reported are the usual ubiquitous components of many food products—methanal, hydrogen sulfide, methyl sulfide, methyl disulfide, and ammonia. They "detected" the presence of mercaptans and isothiocyanates, $R-N=C=S$, which is to be expected, since these are well-recognized constituents of *Brassica*.

Cucumbers

A team of Australian investigators led by Forss (11) has isolated and identified a unique group of unsaturated aliphatic aldehydes closely associated with the flavor and odor of cucumbers. These materials make up about 0.0002 to 0.002% (fresh weight) of the vegetable.

Cucumbers were diced, macerated, and distilled at 35°/20 mm. of Hg. The distillate was treated in two ways; one portion was treated with 2,4-dinitrophenylhydrazine and the phenylhydrazones were prepared. These were chromatographed using standard liquid-solid procedures to give six distinct compounds. The second portion of the distillate was extracted with petroleum ether, and the extract fractionated by GLC to give six carbonyl compounds. The carbonyl compounds isolated via these two procedures proved identical. Effluent fractions from the gas chromatograph were trapped and infrared spectra taken and compared with spectra of known compounds to establish identity. Phenylhydrazones of known compounds were likewise prepared and their chromatographic behavior and melting points compared with those isolated from the natural product. Three aliphatic aldehydes (*see* below) and three unsaturated aldehydes—nona-2,6-dienal, non-2-enal, and hex-2-enal—were found.

These authors state that typical aldehyde composition for cucumbers would consist of:

10% ethanal	15% hex-2-enal
10% propanal	20% non-2-enal
15% hexanal	30% nona-2,6-dienal

Forss *et al.* (11) investigated the stereochemical configuration of the nona-2,6-dienal using infrared spectroscopy and concluded that it had the 2-*trans*-6-*cis* configuration. Apparently the other stereoisomers are not found in cucumbers. It was also determined that the other two unsaturated aldehydes also had the 2-*trans* configuration.

To confirm the role played by these aldehydes in cucumber flavor, the investigators prepared various mixtures of these compounds and submitted them to a taste panel. Individual aldehydes were also evaluated, and these investigators concluded that the six aldehydes listed above are the principal compounds responsible for the characteristic flavor of cucumbers.

Peas

As part of a general investigation of the correlation between flavor changes and enzyme activity in unblanched frozen plant material, Bengtsson and Bosund (3) examined the formation of volatile substances in stored peas. Frozen fresh peas were held at various temperatures from $-8°$ to $-70°$ C. for 8 months and the volatiles examined by headspace techniques using GLC. The deterioration of the material was continually examined by organoleptic analysis. Material stored below $-40°$ showed little evidence of off-flavor formation, but peas stored at $-26°$ showed adverse flavor changes in as little as a single month. Three major peaks were selected for study and subsequently tentatively identified as methanal, ethanol, and hexanal. The authors state that this marks the first time hexanal has been reported as a constituent of peas. The hexanal was further identified by chemical derivatization and infrared techniques, while the other two compounds were identified solely by GLC retention data. It appears that as hexanal concentration increases, off-flavor increases, a fact which is not surprising. Bengtsson and Bosund (3) theorize that hexanal can "easily be formed in reactions following the oxidation of linoleic acid by lipoxidase."

Potatoes

Hexanal is also believed to be responsible for off-flavors of stored potato granules, according to Boggs *et al.* (5). Employing headspace sampling techniques, they report, after 60 days of storage at $22°$, that hexanal concentrations varied from 0.2 to 0.6 p.p.m. By 80 days, it had reached 1.6 p.p.m., and after 125 days 8.5 p.p.m. Taste panels were also used for concurrent organoleptic evaluations.

A number of volatile carbonyl compounds have been detected in stored potato chips. Dornseifer and Powers (10) steam-distilled 20 pounds of chips and collected 2 liters of distillate. Treatment of the distillate with 2,4-dinitrophenylhydrazine gave the phenylhydrazones, which were then converted to the free carbonyls by fusion with α-ketoglutaric acid. These carbonyls were examined by GLC and the following compounds were tentatively identified from retention time data: ethanal, propenal, 2-propanone, butanal, 2-pentenal, 2,3-butanedione, 2-hexenal, heptanal, and 2-heptenal. The only compound confirmed by infrared was 2,3-butanedione. No organoleptic evaluations were made by the authors.

Cooked Vegetables

Not content with examination of a single vegetable, Self *et al.* (*30*), in a most ambitious undertaking, examined the low boiling volatiles from 13 cooked vegetables, beef, coconut, coffee, and tea.

Using capillary column gas chromatography, 13 low-boiling compounds were identified in a volatile fraction from boiling potatoes. These include, besides methanol and acetone, six aldehydes, three sulfides, and two thiols (*31*). After boiling for 20 to 30 minutes, only seven of these volatiles appeared; the other six appeared after boiling for several hours (cf. potato samples A and B in Table IV). When the volatiles obtained after 30 minutes' boiling from a number of other foods were examined, all contained at least six of the 13 components present in the potato (Table IV). Several contained 1-propanethiol, which was not found in the potato.

It seems likely that most cooked foods will produce a similar pattern of low boiling volatiles varying only in relative quantities present. This suggests that these common volatile substances are produced by degradation of metabolites which are normally present in all biological material. Some of the components identified in Table IV have been shown to be produced from amino acids in model systems (*30*). Naturally these patterns are influenced by many factors, such as other compounds in the system, experimental conditions of degradation, etc. Great care must be exercised in evaluating flavor composition based upon this type of research. Self (*30*) is careful to point out that, although the high boiling components of cooked foods must play an important part in their over-all flavor, the low boiling volatiles obviously have an important role—a fact that seems too obvious to mention.

Tomatoes

There has been little recent work on tomato constituents, but Schormeuller and Grosch (*27*) have shown that tomato juice contains methanal, acetone, 2-pentanal, hexanal, and 2-hexenal. Juice was pressed from 27.5 pounds of tomatoes, clarified by centrifugation, and distilled in vacuo at 28° to 35°. The distillate was collected in cold traps and the phenylhydrazones were prepared. The results of this study do not appear surprising in the light of the work of Self *et al.* (*30, 31*).

Table IV. Survey of Low Boiling Volatile Components from Cooked Food Produced after Boiling for 30 Minutes (*30*)

Food	1	2	3	4	5	6	7	8	9	10	11	12
Brussels sprouts	L	S	VL	(S)		S	VL	S	O	O	O	VL
Beans (French, frozen)	S	S	S	(S)		O	M	O	Tr	O	Tr	—
Beef (rump steak)	L	S	Tr	(S)		(M)		O	O	Tr	O	—
Carrot	O	L	S	(S)		Tr	L	Tr	O	O	O	M
Cauliflower (inflorescence)	L	S	VL	(S)		S	VL	Tr	S	O	O	—
Celery	Tr	S	O	(Tr)		O	VL	O	O	O	O	VL
Coconut	L	L	S	(L)		(L)		S	S	O	O	—
Coffee (instant powder)	O	L	Tr	(M)		(S)		S	O	S	S	O
Corn (sweet, frozen)	L	L	S	(S)		S	L	O	O	O	O	S
Leek	L	S/L	L	(L)		(L)		O	VL	O	O	—
Lettuce	S	L	S	S	S	S	L	S	O	S	S	—
Onion	L	S	L	(VL and M)				O	VL	O	O	L
Parsnip	S	L	S	Tr	S	Tr	VL	O	O	O	O	VL
Peas (frozen)	L	S	S	O		Tr	M	O	Tr/S	O	Tr	S
Potato												
A. 30 min.	M	S	S	(S)		Tr	M	O	O	O	O	L
B. 5 hours	VL	VL	L	(VL)		M	S/L	M	O	M	M	VL
Swede	M	L	L	(S)		O	VL	O	O	O	O	VL
Tea (black)	S	M	Tr	(M)		(L)		S	S	S	S	—

Compound. 1, hydrogen sulfide; 2, methanal; 3, methanethiol; 4, propanal; 5, acetone; 6, ethanethiol; 7, dimethyl sulfide; 8, 2-methylpropanal; 9, propanethiol; 10, 3-methylbutanal; 11, 2-methylbutanal; 12, methanol; 13, dimethyl disulfide, present only after more than 0.5 hr. boiling; 14, acrolein detected in trace amounts in potato

Except for methanol, in order of retention time from 50 foot silicone oil on nylon capillary at 25°C. Methanol was detected using a 36 foot polyethylene glycol-200 on stainless steel capillary at 40°C.

Tr = trace; O = undetectable; S = small; M = medium; L = large; VL = very large; — = not estimated.

Values in parentheses indicate incomplete separation.

Beans

Matthews (*19*) examined snap beans, peas, and tomatoes by paper and gas chromatographic means and found the expected carbonyl compounds. These findings too are in keeping with the results reported by Self's group (*30, 31*).

Conclusions

Perhaps it is too evident to need further statement, but one is left with a single salient conclusion: We need more research in the area of vegetable flavor chemistry. Much needs to be reinvestigated, and our frontiers need to be expanded well beyond their present boundaries. We can only hope that each piece of new investigation will presage a better understanding of these complex problems.

Literature Cited

(1) Ayers, J. E., Fishwick, M. J., Land, D. G., Swain, T., *Nature* **203**, 81 (1964).
(2) Bassette, R., Ozeris, S., Whitnah, C. H., *Anal. Chem.* **34**, 1540 (1962).
(3) Bengtsson, B., Bosund, I., *Food Technol.* **18**, 773 (1964).
(4) Bernhard, R. A., Saghir, A. R., Jacobsen, J. V., Mann, L. K., *Arch. Biochem. Biophys.* **107**, 137 (1964).
(5) Boggs, M. M., Buttery, R. G., Venstrom, D. W., Belote, M. L., *J. Food Sci.* **29**, 487 (1964).
(6) Buttery, R. G., Teranishi, R., *Anal. Chem.* **33**, 1439 (1961).
(7) Carson, J. F., Wong, F. F., *J. Agr. Food Chem.* **9**, 140 (1961).
(8) Crosby, D. G., *J. Food Sci.* **28**, 347 (1963).
(9) Crosby, D. G., Anderson, L. J., *Ibid.*, **28**, 640 (1963).
(10) Dornseifer, T. P., Powers, J. J., *Food Technol.* **17**, 1330 (1963).
(11) Forss, D. A., Dunstone, E. A., Ramshaw, E. H., Stark, W., *J. Food Sci.* **27**, 90 (1962).
(12) Gold, H. J., Wilson, C. W., *Ibid.*, **28**, 484 (1963).
(13) Gold, H. J., Wilson, C. W., *J. Org. Chem.* **28**, 985 (1963).
(14) Hing, F. S., Weckel, K. G., *J. Food Sci.* **29**, 149 (1964).
(15) Jacobsen, J. V., Bernhard, R. A., Mann, L. K., and Saghir, A. R., *Arch. Biochem. Biophys.* **104**, 473 (1964).
(16) Jones, H. A., Mann, L. K., "Onions and Their Allies," pp. 24–47, Leonard Hill, London, 1963.
(17) Kohman, E. F., *Science* **106**, 625 (1947).
(18) Kuon, J., Bernhard, R. A., *J. Food Sci.* **28**, 298 (1963).
(19) Matthews, R. F., *Dissertation Abstr.* **21**, 1693 (1961).
(20) Moisio, T., Spåre, C. G., Virtanen, A. I., *Suomen Kemistilehti* **B35**, 29 (1962).
(21) Nawar, W. W., Fagerson, I. S., *Anal. Chem.* **32**, 1534 (1960).
(22) Nawar, W. W., Fagerson, I. S., *Food Technol.* **16**, 107 (1962).
(23) Oaks, D. M., Hartmann, H., Dimick, K. P., *Anal. Chem.* **36**, 1561 (1964).
(24) Parsons, P. S., McCrokle, C. O., "Statistical Picture of California's Agriculture," **459** (1963), Circ. Agr. Extension Service, Univ. of Calif., Berkeley, Calif.
(25) Saghir, A. R., Mann, L. K., *Suomen Kemistilehti* **B38**, 78 (1965).
(26) Saghir, A. R., Mann, L. K., Bernhard, R. A., Jacobsen, J. V., *Proc. Am. Soc. Hort. Sci.* **84**, 386 (1964).
(27) Schormueller, J., Grosch, W., *Z. Lebensm.-Untersuch. Forsch.* **118**, 385 (1962).
(28) Schwimmer, S., Mazelis, M., *Arch. Biochem. Biophys.* **100**, 66 (1963).
(29) Schwimmer, S., Weston, W. J., *J. Agr. Food Chem.* **9**, 301 (1961).
(30) Self, R., Casey, J. C., Swain, T., *Chem. Ind.* **21**, 863 (1963).
(31) Self, R., Holley, H. L. J., Joyce, A. E., *J. Sci. Food Agr.* **14**, 8;209 (1963).
(32) Semmler, F. W., *Arch. Pharmacol.* **230**, 434 (1892).
(33) Spåre, C.-G., Virtanen, A. I., *Acta Chem. Scand.* **15**, 1280 (1961).
(34) Stewart, G. F., *Food Technol.* **17**, 5 (1963).
(35) Stoll, A., Seeback, E., *Advan. Enzymol.* **11**, 377 (1951).
(36) Virtanen, A. I., Matikkala, E. J., *Acta Chem. Scand.* **13**, 1898 (1959).
(37) Virtanen, A. I., Spåre, C. G., *Suomen Kemistilehti* **B34**, 72 (1961); **B35**, 28 (1962).
(38) Vorbeck, M. L., Mattick, L. R., Lee, F. A., Pederson, C. S., *J. Food Sci.* **26**, 569 (1961).
(39) Wilkins, W. F., *Dissertation Abstr.* **22**, 3978 (1962).

RECEIVED April 27, 1965.

Chemistry of Bread Flavor

JOHN A. JOHNSON, LLOYD ROONEY, and ALI SALEM

Department of Flour and Feed Milling Industries, Kansas State University, Manhattan, Kan.

The compounds responsible for bread flavor sensation appear to be unstable. More than 70 different organic compounds have been identified in pre-ferments, dough, oven vapors, and bread. Those compounds, which include several organic acids, alcohols, carbonyls, and esters, arise through a complex series of reactions during fermentation and baking. Both fermentation and baking of dough are essential to develop an acceptable bread flavor. Many of the compounds formed during fermentation are volatilized during baking. Evidence suggests that reactions between free amino groups and reducing sugars predominate in crust browning and in producing bread flavor stimuli. Bread crust contains larger amounts of carbonyl compounds than the crumb. A gradual loss of carbonyl compounds from the crust parallels the staling of bread.

Freshly baked bread has a delectable flavor that is most appealing to the public. The flavor, however, is not stable, for bread loses much of its appeal after relatively short storage time. The modern trend toward mechanization and wider area of distribution increases the difficulty of maintaining acceptable bread flavor. If the fresh flavor of bread could be preserved or stabilized, increased acceptability of bread by consumers might be expected. To accomplish this, knowledge of factors that govern flavor production is necessary.

Aroma has been described as a nasal sensation derived from aromatic substances having significant vapor pressures. This definition recognizes the sensation detected through the olfactory sense organs but does not account for factors such as sweetness, saltiness, bitterness, burning, or cooling sensations sensed by the taste buds located in the tongue and back of the throat. A broader definition of flavor recognizes a complex of sensations detected by the taste buds of the tongue and throat as well as the olfactory sense. "Good taste" of a food product includes the consumer's total reaction to such factors as aroma or odor in addition to taste, color, appearance, and mechanical eating qualities.

Research on bread flavor may take the route of consumer preference tests, difference tests, flavor profile tests, or a combination of organoleptic and statistical procedures. Though such tests indicate flavor preferences, they contribute little to the basic knowledge of the specific chemical stimuli involved. Recently, progress has been made in isolating and detecting the chemical stimuli associated with bread flavor. Unfortunately, however, few correlations of such information with consumer preference data have been made.

This review is concerned with the source of bread flavor components, and methods for their isolation and identification. A number of reviews have been written on various aspects of bread flavors (*12, 13, 26, 40, 46, 64, 67, 77, 81*).

Successful research on a basic flavor problem involves isolation of the flavor components, followed by their separation and identification. Hopefully then, the compounds may be recombined into a mixture closely resembling the original flavor (*75*). Progress made in recent years toward understanding bread flavor has been due to the development of more sensitive analytical tools for separating complex organic mixtures. Paper, column, thin-layer, and gas-liquid chromatography, coupled with ultraviolet, infrared, and mass spectrometric analysis, have permitted separation and identification of trace components present in doughs, pre-ferments, oven gases, and bread. Generally, classical organic analytical methods have been used to investigate each class of organic compounds. With all procedures there have been associated dangers of alteration, deterioration, and artifact formation.

Vacuum distillation techniques at low temperatures have been used to isolate certain compounds from oven vapors or bread (*49, 76, 78*). The distillates are condensed in traps with dry ice or liquid nitrogen—a method that concentrates the most volatile components and appears to limit interactions and formation of artifacts. Subsequent removal of the flavor constituents by formation of derivatives or solvent extraction is required for further analyses. Solvent extractions of bread have been used (*34, 35, 43*), but many compounds such as lipids, proteins, and minerals are removed along with the flavor components, which further complicates subsequent analyses.

The development of sensitive ionization detector systems for use in gas-liquid chromatography permits the analysis of head space vapors of different foods (*2, 3, 38, 65, 74*). The head space gas analyses are fast, accurate, and reproducible and give a true ratio of substances present in the vapor. Alterations due to solvent action are eliminated and changes occurring in food vapors with storage time can be followed readily.

Weurman (74) indicated that the method could be made quantitative by relating chromatogram peak height with concentration of the compounds. Nawar and Fagerson (42) correlated gas chromatogram data with organoleptic data for various foodstuffs. The chromatographic data did not always indicate differences in the organoleptic properties of foodstuffs. This, presumably, indicates that organoleptic differences in food flavor may be associated with factors other than the most volatile flavor stimuli.

The "aromagram" technique using head space gas analysis, developed by scientists at the Western Regional Research Laboratory (65), consists of placing the food sample in a covered Erlenmeyer flask and after a few minutes removing samples of the vapor with a syringe and injecting them into the gas chromatograph. For samples with low vapor pressure, 100 ml. of boiling water is added to the flask before the vapor sample is removed.

Bassette et al. (6) and Ozeris and Bassette (47) devised head space gas analysis techniques for determining trace amounts of organic compounds in milk and other natural fluids. The relative peak heights of the compounds represented in the chromatograms were obtained from a sample of the vapor after the liquid was saturated with salt. Kepner et al. (30) described a method for the quantitative determination of volatile components by use of internal standards with saturated salt solutions.

The methods described above appear to have merit for use in research on bread flavor. Recently, de Figueiredo (13) obtained chromatograms of the vapor above pre-ferment, dough, and bread. Though the aromas were decidedly different, there were few differences in the chromatograms. Perhaps a method of concentrating the volatile compounds is required. It may be that isolation procedures need refinement.

Flavor Components

The extremely complex nature of bread flavor is illustrated by the fact that more than 70 compounds have been identified or implicated (12). In attempts to gain knowledge of the compounds involved in bread flavor various stages of bread production have been studied, including pre-ferments, doughs, oven vapors, and bread. Many classes of organic compounds have been found. Some of the identifications have been based solely on gas chromatographic retention times and, therefore, are to be considered only tentative. Many components have been observed but not identified—for example, Wick et al. (76) could not identify 17 of the trace components in a flavor distillate from white bread. Hunter et al. (24) did not identify 28 of 45 organic acids obtained on gas chromatograms from pre-ferments. Also it is probable that many compounds have not been isolated.

The formation of bread flavor stimuli has been attributed to fermentation and baking. Bread with acceptable flavor cannot be produced without both fermentation and baking. This was clearly shown by Baker and co-workers (*4, 5*), who found that neither a normally fermented dough baked without crust formation nor an improperly fermented dough baked with crust formation had acceptable flavor. Many of the compounds formed during fermentation are volatilized during baking and do not affect the flavor profile of the bread.

It is not known that all the compounds isolated from doughs or even from bread are responsible for bread flavor. It is generally assumed, however, that any compound isolated from bread possessing a distinct odor contributes to bread flavor. Johnson (*26*) cautioned, however, that the mere detection of an aromatic substance in bread does not necessarily mean that it is involved in bread flavor and "research combining chemical analysis with consumer preference studies is sorely needed." Rothe and Thomas (*55, 57, 67*) thought that the presence of a substance in concentrations above the threshold of human perception must be established before it can be assumed to be a component of bread flavor. They also indicated that interaction between compounds may alter the threshold level. Some compounds present in subthreshold levels may produce a detectable odor or aroma when mixed.

ORGANIC ACIDS. In general, organic acids are extracted from pre-ferments, doughs, and bread with water, steam, or organic solvents or by vacuum distillation (*10, 32*). After extraction and conversion to their sodium salts, they are concentrated under vacuum. The acid salts may be separated by paper, column, or gas-liquid chromatography. Johnson *et al.* (*29*) measured the organic acids in pre-ferments by means of paper and column chromatography. The sodium salts of the acids were separated by paper chromatography using diethyl ether–acetic acid–H_2O (13:1:1) or water-saturated butanol–formic acid solvents. Buffered silicic acid columns were used to separate the organic acids. Positive identification was made by melting points and infrared spectra of the *p*-bromophenacyl derivatives. Wiseblatt (*79*) studied the volatile acids of dough and bread by isolating the acids from a steam distillate as barium salts. The regenerated acids were extracted with diethyl ether, concentrated, and determined quantitatively by gas-liquid chromatography.

Hunter *et al.* (*24*) obtained 45 different peaks on gas chromatograms of ethyl esters of organic acid concentrates by use of a flash exchange procedure. The method involved drawing a water solution of the sodium salts of the organic acids and potassium ethyl sulfate (approximately equal concentration) into a hypodermic syringe containing diatomaceous earth (*23*). The ethyl esters of the acids were formed by an exchange reaction and swept into the column by an argon gas stream. Unfortu-

Table I. Organic Acids Isolated from Pre-ferments, Doughs, and Bread

Organic Acids	Pre-ferments	Doughs	Bread	References
Formic	X	—	X	(24, 49)
Acetic	X	X	X	(5, 24, 29, 49, 50, 78, 79, 82)
Propionic	X	—	X	(24, 50, 82)
n-Butyric	X	X	X	(24, 27, 50, 79)
Isobutyric	X	—	X	(24, 50)
Valeric	X	—	X	(24, 50)
Isovaleric	X	X	X	(24, 50, 79)
Caproic	X	X	X	(24, 50, 79)
Isocaproic	X	—	X	(24, 50)
Heptanoic	X	—	X	(24, 50)
Caprylic	X	—	X	(24, 50)
Pelargonic	X	—	X	(24, 50)
Capric	X	—	X	(24, 50)
Lauric	X	—	—	(24)
Myristic	X	—	—	(24)
Palmitic	X	—	—	(24)
Lactic	X	X	X	(29, 81)
Succinic	—	—	X	(81)
Crotonic	X	—	—	(24)
Pyruvic	X	—	X	(10, 81)
Hydrocinnamic	—	—	X	(81)
Benzilic	—	—	X	(81)
Itaconic	—	—	X	(81)
Levulinic	—	—	X	(81)

nately, the exchange reaction did not go to completion (23); therefore, quantitative results were impossible.

Table I shows 23 organic acids isolated from pre-ferments, doughs, and bread. Quantitative data are scarce. Johnson *et al.* (29) analyzed pre-ferments and found acetic and lactic acids to predominate (Figure 1). These acids are developed during the first hours of fermentation. Lactic acid continues to develop slowly while acetic acid production ceases with extended fermentation. Cole *et al.* (10) found that total acid production in pre-ferments reached maximum values within 3 to 5 hours and depended on available sugar and yeast concentration (Figure 2). Wiseblatt (79) estimated the quantity of acetic, n-butyric, isovaleric, and n-caproic acids in dough, oven gases, and bread. He found that amounts in bread and oven gases did not equal the concentration found in dough. In addition to yeast fermentation, acids are produced by bacterial action on sugar and amino acids and by enzymatic action on lipids. Some acids, like levulinic, probably are produced by reactions during oven baking.

Ronnebeck (53) and Thomas and Ronnebeck (66) determined volatile and nonvolatile acid content of rye breads but could not establish a positive correlation between acidity and organoleptic tests. Conversely, Stone and Bayfield (63) compared white breads made by various pre-ferment processes and found that taste and aroma were "in direct agreement with acid production and decrease in pH."

The significance of the organic acids in the bread flavor profile is not known. It has been postulated that their effects may be mainly on physical properties of the crumb (*26*). Hunter *et al.* (*24*) thought the higher

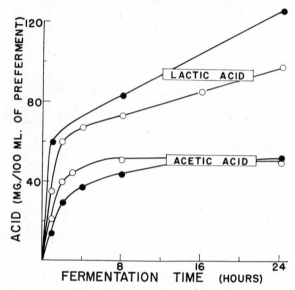

Figure 1. *Effect of fermentation time on amount of acetic and lactic acids produced in different pre-ferments (29)*

● *ADMI pre-ferment (milk buffered)*
○ *Fleischmann pre-ferment (salt buffered)*

acids might function by retarding evaporation of the lower boiling components. They also found that a mixture of organic acids, when heated, produced an odor resembling bread aroma. The purity of the acids, however, was not established; so the odor could have been due to other reactants. The extremely acrid smell of the four to ten carbon acids leads to the hypothesis that even trace quantities have significant effects on the flavor profile.

ALCOHOLS. Alcohols found in pre-ferments, oven vapors, and bread are summarized in Table II. As might be expected, the primary product of bread-dough fermentation is ethanol. Cole *et al.* (*10*) found that the ethanol content of pre-ferments reached a maximum within 3 to 5 hours of fermentation and remained constant during 23 hours of storage (Figure 3). The total ethanol produced depended on sugar and yeast concentration. Coffman *et al.* (*9*) found that compounds in bread oven volatiles did not differ qualitatively but that the quantity of amyl alcohols appeared to be related to increased aroma intensity.   Wick *et al.* (*76*) indicated that ethanol, l-propanol, isobutyl alcohol, isoamyl alcohol, and acetoin were major components of the distillate from white bread, while ethanol and water were the major components of oven vapors.   Smith and Coffman (*61*) believed that lower alcohols from pre-ferments were not involved in flavor, but that the higher alcohols, present only in trace amounts, tended to be stable during baking and remained in bread as flavor constituents.

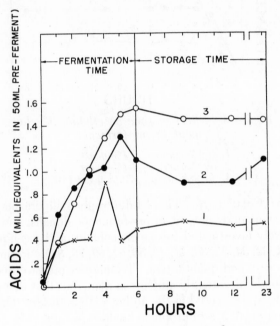

Figure 2.   Changes in organic acids in pre-ferments with time

1. *3.2% sucrose, 2.4% yeast*
2. *6.6% sucrose, 4.4% yeast*
3. *11.9% sucrose, 7.0% yeast* (10)

Table II. Alcohols Isolated from Pre-Ferments, Oven Vapors, and Bread

Alcohols	Pre-ferments	Oven Vapors	Bread	References
Ethyl	X	X	X	(*9, 10, 11, 61, 76, 78*)
n-Propyl	X	—	—	(*61, 76*)
Isobutyl	X	—	—	(*61, 76*)
Amyl, isoamyl	X	X	X	(*5, 61, 76*)
2,3-Butanediols	X	—	—	(*61*)
2-Phenylethyl	X	—	—	(*61*)

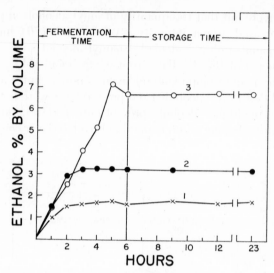

*Figure 3. Effect of time on ethanol develop-
ment in pre-ferments*

1. 3.2% sucrose, 2.4% yeast
2. 6.6% sucrose, 4.4% yeast
3. 11.9% sucrose, 7.0% yeast (10)

CARBONYL COMPOUNDS. The 2,4-dinitrophenylhydrazone derivatives
of carbonyl compounds present in pre-ferments, doughs, and bread have
been extensively investigated by paper, column, and gas-liquid chromatography (11, 32, 34, 35, 36, 41, 43, 56, 61, 69, 78, 82). Formation of the
derivatives is easy and quantitative. Techniques used to investigate carbonyl compounds vary greatly and are so numerous that this discussion is
limited mainly to those used in the author's laboratories. These methods
included formation of 2,4-dinitrophenylhydrazones and subsequent separation by paper, column, or flash exchange gas-liquid chromatography (34,
35, 36, 42).

For analysis of the pre-ferments, the gases escaping from fermentation
are bubbled through a 1% solution of 2,4-dinitrophenylhydrazine in 5N
sulfuric acid. The hydrazone derivatives are extracted with several portions of chloroform and after being dried with anhydrous sodium sulfate
and concentrated, the extracts are used for chromatographic separations.
In some cases, it is desirable to separate larger quantities of the hydrazones. The most useful technique is a partial separation using a Celite
545 column with a *n*-hexane–chloroform solvent mixture. The hydrazones are separated into seven groups that could then be further separated
by paper or gas-liquid chromatography.

The liquid pre-ferments are analyzed for carbonyl compounds by
first inactivating the yeast with mercuric chloride, then saturating with

sodium chloride and extracting the carbonyl compounds with a continuous liquid-liquid extractor using diethyl ether. Chloroform may also be used as an extractant. The receiving flask of the extractor contains a 1% solution of 2,4-dinitrophenylhydrazine reagent and ether. After removal of the ether, the hydrazones are extracted with chloroform, and separated by chromatographic methods. Bread crumb and crust are analyzed similarly by liquid-liquid extraction and chromatography.

The method of Piha *et al.* (*51*) is most suitable for separating the hydrazones by paper chromatography. Whatman No. 4 paper is spotted with the hydrazones and immersed in a 1 to 1 mixture of *N,N*-dimethylformamide and absolute ethanol to within 0.5 cm. of the spots. The paper is equilibrated in the presence of cyclohexane and *N,N*-dimethylformamide vapor for 5 hours in the chromatography chamber. The paper is developed for 5 hours at 23°C. in a 6 to 1 mixture of cyclohexane and *N,N*-dimethylformamide. Where separation is not complete with one solvent system, the method of Nonaka *et al.* (*44*), using *n*-hexane saturated with 2-phenoxyethanol as solvent, is used. When the hydrazones are not separated by these methods, the partially separated hydrazones may be extracted from the paper with absolute methanol, evaporated to dryness, and resolved by gas-liquid chromatography.

Quantitative estimations of the carbonyl compounds are obtained by extracting the hydrazones from the paper for 20 minutes with 5 ml. of 95% ethanol. Absorbance of ethanol extracts is determined with a Beckman DU spectrophotometer at maximum absorbance wavelength for each of the compounds, and related to standard curves. In case the compounds are not completely separated, the maximum absorption wavelength of the most prevalent compound is used, or the compounds are further separated using gas-liquid chromatography.

Determination of the carbonyl compounds by gas-liquid chromatography is accomplished by flash exchange of their hydrazone derivatives according to a slight modification of the procedure of Stephen and Teszler (*62*). One milligram of a 2 to 1 mixture of alpha-ketoglutaric acid and the hydrazone derivative of formaldehyde is placed in a glass capillary tube. Eight milligrams of Celite 545 mixed intimately with 250 μg. of the mixed hydrazone derivatives and 1 mg. of alpha-ketoglutaric acid are added to the tube. The open end of the bent capillary is inserted through the rubber septum and flash exchange is achieved by carefully heating the tube in a silicone oil bath at 250°C. for 30 seconds. This method is employed to separate the groups of hydrazone derivatives obtained by column or paper chromatography. Identification is by retention times with reference to known compounds.

Table III summarizes the aldehydes and ketones isolated from preferments, doughs, oven vapors, and bread. The carbonyl compounds are very aromatic and it is believed that they are important in the production of flavor. Visser't Hooft and De Leeuw (73), in an early investigation of bread flavor, thought diacetyl was the most important constituent. They found that acetoin was slowly converted to diacetyl, which did not accumulate in bread because of its high volatility. Attempts to fortify bread flavor by adding acetoin or diacetyl to doughs have failed (39). Cole *et al.* (10) studied the production of carbonyl compounds in pre-ferments. They found the total carbonyl content increased rapidly during the first 4 hours of fermentation and then decreased slightly as the pre-ferment was stored for periods up to 23 hours (Figure 4). Linko *et al.* (36) performed quantitative analysis of carbonyl compounds in pre-ferments and found that acetaldehyde was the major component. Other carbonyl compounds included acetone, propionaldehyde, formaldehyde, isobutyraldehyde, 2-butanone, iso- and *n*-valeraldehyde, 2-methylbutanal, and *n*-hexaldehyde.

Thomas and Rothe (67, 68) related the flavor of different types of bread to the amount of carbonyl compounds. Furfural appeared to be the most prevalent aldehyde in rye breads. The aldehyde content was

Table III.   Carbonyl Compounds Isolated from Pre-ferments, Doughs, Oven Vapors, and Bread

Aldehydes	Pre-ferments	Doughs	Oven Vapors	Bread	References
Formaldehyde	X	—	—	X	(35, 36, 41, 43, 60, 76)
Acetaldehyde	X	X	X	X	(5, 32, 36, 41, 43, 57, 61, 82)
Propionaldehyde	—	—	—	X	(35, 36, 76)
n-Butyraldehyde	X	X	—	—	(32, 41)
Isobutyraldehyde	X	—	X	X	(35, 36, 41, 43, 54, 57, 76)
n-Valeraldehyde	X	—	X	X	(35, 36, 41, 43, 76)
Isovaleraldehyde	X	X	—	X	(32, 36, 41, 54, 57, 76)
2-Methylbutanal	X	—	—	X	(35, 41, 43, 54)
n-Hexaldehyde	X	X	—	X	(32, 35, 36, 43)
Crotonaldehyde	—	—	—	X	(82)
Benzaldehyde	—	X	—	—	(32)
Phenylacetaldehyde	—	—	—	X	(54, 56)
Pyruvaldehyde	—	X	X	X	(5, 32, 54, 57, 82)
Furfural	—	X	X	X	(5, 35, 43, 57, 82)
Hydroxymethylfurfural	—	—	—	X	(35)
Methional	—	—	—	X	(54)
Ketones					
Acetone	X	X	X	X	(5, 32, 35, 36, 41, 43, 82)
2-Butanone	X	X	—	X	(5, 32, 35, 36, 41, 43)
2-Hexanone	—	X	—	X	(32, 82)
3-Heptanone	—	—	—	X	(82)
Diacetyl	X	X	X	X	(5, 61, 73, 76)
Acetoin	X	—	—	X	(5, 61, 73, 76)

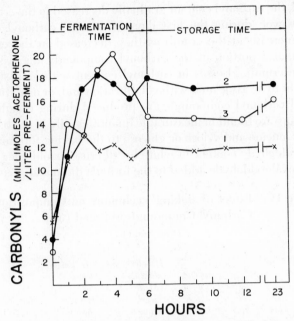

*Figure 4.   Effect of fermentation and holding
time on carbonyl compounds in pre-ferments*

1. *3.2% sucrose, 2.4% yeast*
2. *6.6% sucrose, 4.4% yeast*
3. *11.9% sucrose, 7.0% yeast* (*10*)

influenced by baking time and temperature. Quantitative values for eight carbonyl compounds were determined by Rothe and Thomas, for crust and crumb separately, of white, gray rye, whole grain rye, and pumpernickel breads (*57*). The aldehyde content increased with increasing darkness of the bread, which roughly corresponded to the organoleptic flavor intensity. Hydroxymethylfurfural rather than furfural was shown by Linko *et al.* (*35*) to be prevalent in the crust of white bread made with glucose. A bisulfite binding method for the determining aldehydes has been recommended as an index of bread flavor (*71, 72*).

Quantitative data comparing the amount of certain carbonyl compounds formed when different methods of bread production are used are shown in Table IV (*35*). The different methods did not greatly affect the carbonyl content of the crust or crumb of white bread. Comparative values for crust and crumb indicated that carbonyl compounds were produced mainly in the crust, as would be expected to result from the browning reaction. Since dextrose was used in the breads, hydroxymethylfurfural concentration exceeded that of furfural.

Changes in the carbonyl content of bread crumb and crust during storage are shown in Table V (*35*). Whether the bread was wrapped or unwrapped, the carbonyl content gradually decreased in the crust as bread aged. However, during the first days of storage, carbonyl compounds tended to increase in the crumb as they decreased in the crust, which suggested that a portion of the carbonyl compounds migrated from the crust to the crumb. Losses in carbonyl content with long storage time were thought to be associated with volatilization and/or oxidation.

Several carbonyl compounds are produced during dough fermentation, but many are found in measurable quantities only in the baked bread. Addition of leucine and xylose or glucose to the baking formula increased the isovaleraldehyde content in white bread crust sixfold over that of the control. Isovaleraldehyde added to the formula did not appreciably affect

Table IV. Effect of Baking Technique on Composition of Carbonyl Compounds in Bread (35)

(Mg./100 G.)

Method of Baking	Form-alde-hyde	Acet-alde-hyde	Acetone (Propion-alde-hyde)	Isobutyr-aldehyde (Methyl-ethyl ketone)	Isovaleralde-hyde (n-Valer-aldehyde 2-Methylburanal n-Hexalde-hyde)	Fur-fural	HMF	Total Car-bonyl Com-pounds
				CRUST				
Straight dough	0.99	2.20	12.8	0.82	2.02	0.16	3.19	22.2
Sponge dough	0.98	2.17	17.1	0.97	1.60	0.34	6.65	29.8
No-time dough	0.86	1.65	10.7	1.47	1.18	0.31	5.43	21.7
Pre-ferment dough	1.02	1.82	15.6	0.70	3.23	0.04	3.29	25.7
				CRUMB				
Straight dough	0.20	0.32	0.75	0.14	0.51	—	0.65	2.57
Sponge dough	0.20	0.35	0.85	0.15	0.76	—	0.72	3.02
No-time dough	0.17	0.29	0.81	—	0.86	—	0.59	2.83
Pre-ferment dough	0.14	0.35	2.11	0.23	0.62	—	0.56	3.99

Table V. Changes in Total Carbonyl Compounds as Bread Ages (35)

Days of Storage	Wrapped, Mg./100 G.		Unwrapped, Mg./100 G.	
	Crust	Crumb	Crust	Crumb
0	29.2	2.8	29.2	2.8
1	25.3	3.9	26.7	4.5
2	26.3	6.0	23.9	4.3
3	27.8	5.7	18.7	5.2
5	24.1	2.7	18.4	2.2
7	13.3	2.5	17.4	2.3

Table VI. Organic Esters Isolated from Pre-ferments and Bread

Esters	Pre-ferments	Bread	References
Ethyl formate	X	—	(61)
Ethyl acetate	X	—	(5, 29, 41)
Ethyl lactate	X	X	(61, 80)
Ethyl pyruvate	—	X	(81, 82)
Ethyl levulinate	—	X	(81, 82)
Ethyl succinate	—	X	(80)
Ethyl hydrocinnamate	—	X	(80)
Ethyl benzilate	—	X	(80)
Ethyl itaconate	—	X	(80)
1,3-Propanediol monoacetate	X	X	(61)

the isovaleraldehyde content of the crust (35). This suggests that many of the compounds produced during fermentation may be volatilized during baking, and that crust formation and the browning reaction are important in producing bread flavor.

ESTERS. Since both alcohols and organic acids are produced during dough fermentation, certain esters might be present. Several organic esters have been identified in pre-ferments or bread (Table VI). Probably because of the predominance of ethyl alcohol, nearly all the esters found are ethyl esters. Johnson *et al.* (29) measured the amount of ethyl acetate and lactate by differences in total free acids in pre-ferments adjusted to pH 7.2 and 10.0. They found that a maximum concentration of esters was reached after 6 to 8 hours of fermentation and decreased to zero after 48 hours. Ethyl acetate is volatilized during baking and little remains in the bread. A few of the esters of higher molecular weight may remain as flavor constituents in bread.

MISCELLANEOUS COMPOUNDS. Other compounds such as methyl mercaptan (56, 59, 60), hydrogen sulfide (59, 60), isomaltol, maltol (1), and melanoidins have been isolated from bread. Rotsch and Dorner (60) believed that methyl mercaptan originates during baking from sulfur-containing amino acids of flour and yeast proteins. Both isomaltol and maltol have a caramel-like flavor and aroma (21, 22). It is not known whether the traces of maltol and isomaltol found in bread are important flavor contributors. Melanoidins, the brown polymers formed during the browning reaction, are perhaps not as important to the bread flavor profile as the intermediates of browning.

Fermentation and Bread Flavor

It is generally assumed that bread implies a product produced by yeast fermentation and that such a process is essential to developing an acceptable bread flavor. Lüers (37) believed that knowledge of bread flavor could be obtained by studying alcoholic fermentation. A host of compounds are formed by anaerobic yeast fermentation of sugars. The Embden-Meyerhoff-Parnas scheme (15) indicates that ethanol, acetaldehyde, pyruvic acid, and carbon dioxide are the predominant compounds involved, but small quantities of other compounds are formed.

Yeast has the ability to utilize amino acids as a source of nitrogen. The amino acids are oxidized to imino acids, which react with water to yield alpha-ketocarboxylic acids and ammonia. The carboxylic acids may be cleaved to form an aldehyde and carbon dioxide. Alcohols and acids may be formed by reduction or oxidation of the aldehyde (37).

Microorganisms other than yeast may play an important role in producing flavor compounds during fermentation. Grunhut and Weber (18) found that bacterial degradation of amino acids was involved in forming organic acids, alcohols, and aldehydes. Robinson et al. (52) isolated several bacteria from pre-ferments and studied their individual effects on production of bread flavor. Several bacteria were found that contributed significantly to acceptable bread flavor. Carlin (8) also studied selected microorganisms and found that certain microorganisms improved bread flavor. Linko et al. (36) studied the effect of different microorganisms on the quantity of several carbonyl compounds produced in pre-ferments. Only *Pediococcus cerevisiae* had a significant effect, increasing acetone production. In normal bread dough fermentation, the bacterial population responsible for characteristic "sour dough" flavors do not predominate.

While many investigations have identified numerous organic compounds with fermentation of bread dough, it is not known whether the compounds remain in significant concentration in the bread to be detected by the consumer, or whether the compounds react during baking to form new products that contribute to flavor. The fact remains, however, that the products of fermentation appear essential for production of good bread flavor.

Oven Browning and Bread Flavor

The importance of crust formation and browning in producing acceptable flavor in bread has been cited. Most of the early literature (16, 25, 48) described crust browning as caramelization. More recent evidence suggests the predominance of Maillard-type browning (28). Caramelization reactions require higher temperatures for activation and involve only the sugars, whereas Maillard-type browning occurs at lower temperatures and involves reactions between free amino groups and reducing sugars. Both produce brown polymers, but the flavor and aroma of the products are distinctly different.

Hodge (20), in an excellent review of the browning reaction, integrated the various theories and facts into a general reaction scheme. The initial reaction in Maillard browning is a condensation of the free amino

$$\begin{array}{ccc}
\begin{array}{c}
HC\colon O \\
| \\
(CHOH)n \\
| \\
CH_2OH
\end{array}
&
\xrightarrow{+RNH_2}
&
\begin{array}{c}
RNH \\
| \\
CHOH \\
| \\
(CHOH)n \\
| \\
CH_2OH
\end{array}
&
\xrightarrow{-H_2O}
\end{array}$$

$$\begin{array}{c}
RN \\
\| \\
CH \\
| \\
(CHOH)n \\
| \\
CH_2OH
\end{array}
\quad \Longleftrightarrow \quad
\begin{array}{c}
RNH \\
| \\
HC \!-\!\!-\!\!-\! \\
| \\
(CHOH)n\!-\!1 \quad O \\
| \\
HC \!-\!\!-\!\!-\! \\
| \\
CH_2OH
\end{array}$$

Figure 5. Initial reactions of Maillard-type browning (20)

group with the reducing carbohydrate, which loses a molecule of water and rearranges to form an *N*-substituted glycosylamine (Figure 5). The *N*-glycosylamine undergoes the Amadori rearrangement to form an *N*-substituted 1-amino-1-deoxy-2-ketose (Figure 6) (20), which can undergo subsequent dehydration, fission, and polymerization reactions, to produce the complex melanoidins and other compounds (Figure 7). The compounds produced depend on temperature, moisture, pH, and form of amine present. By this scheme, it is possible to account for the origin of

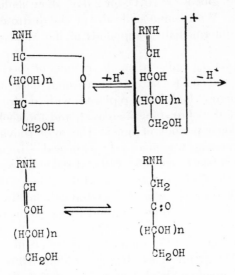

Figure 6. Amadori rearrangement to form 1-amino-1-deoxy-2-ketose (20)

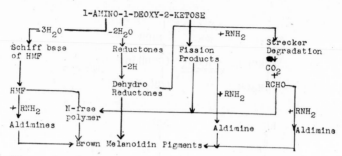

Figure 7. Formation of intermediates of browning reaction (20)

many compounds found in bread, such as furfural, hydroxymethylfurfural, and various aldehydes.

Many investigators now believe that Maillard-type browning is the most important reaction responsible for flavor formation (*5, 14, 28, 33, 45*). The reactants and favorable conditions of pH, moisture, and temperature for the reaction are present during baking. Bertram (*7*) was one of the first to show that caramelization of sugar did not adequately explain crust browning. Certain Dutch, low protein flours that produced grayish bread crusts were notably improved by adding gluten protein or egg white while addition of glucose alone did not increase the crust color.

The ultraviolet absorption curves of an aqueous extract of bread crust and certain aqueous model systems in which lysine, glycine, and tryptophan reacted with glucose at 70°C. for 2 days show similar characteristics (Figure 8) (*19*). With amino acids absent, the dextrose solution did not brown, and the intermediate compounds of the Maillard reaction were not present.

When Haney (*19*) replaced small amounts of sucrose with dextrose in sugar cookies, the cookies became increasingly dark and flavorful until 5.0% of the sucrose had been replaced with dextrose. Flavor was markedly improved as browning increased, and the cookies appeared to stay fresh for longer periods of time. The most convincing proof that Maillard-type browning was involved was provided by using methylated derivatives of dextrose (Figure 9) (*19*). Cookie 1 prepared with 5.0% dextrose was distinctly brown and flavorful. When 5.0% dextrose was replaced with 5.0% of methylglucoside, tetramethylmethylglucoside, tetramethylglucose, or sucrose, browning and flavor production were practically inhibited.

Griffith and Johnson (*17*) found that the shelf life of sugar cookies could be extended as much as 70% by adding 5.0% dextrose to the formula. Cookies made without dextrose and stored at room temperature in 11% relative humidity were rancid within 64 days while cookies baked with added dextrose were judged rancid after 94 days. The extended shelf life was attributed to formation of reductones during browning. The reductones are oxygen acceptors and may function as fat antioxidants.

Thomas and Rothe (*67, 68, 69*) listed ten aldehydes found in rye bread as by-products of the Maillard reaction. Each was specifically associated with an amino acid or sugar. The aldehydes formed along with the amino acid precursor are listed in Table VII. The amino acid undergoes the Strecker degradation, in which it loses the carboxyl and amino groups

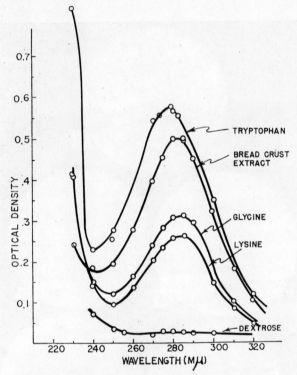

Figure 8. Absorption of ultraviolet by aqueous solutions of reactants of dextrose with amino acids and flour proteins (19)

and an aldehyde with one less carbon atom is formed. Linko and Johnson (*34*) showed that the concentration of amino acids in crust was markedly lower than in crumb of the same bread. That, along with the evidence showing the marked increase of carbonyl compounds in crust, indicates the importance of Maillard browning in bread flavor.

A favorite means of studying browning has been to use model reaction systems in which amino acids and sugars react under carefully controlled conditions. Kiely *et al.* (*31*) found that the sugar affected the rate of reaction during browning while the amino acid primarily determined the aroma. These investigators, using a flavor profile technique, found the leucine, histidine, or arginine reacting with a reducing sugar produced a bread-like aroma. Nonreducing sugars did not brown nor create the bread-like aroma.

Rothe and Voight (58) studied the reaction of 21 different amino acids with xylose under nearly dry conditions. They measured browning intensity and determined the amount of aldehydes formed. Browning intensity was inversely correlated with the amount of aldehydes produced,

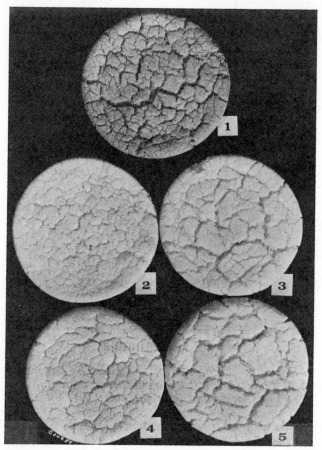

Figure 9. Effect of dextrose, methylated sugars, and sucrose on cookie color (19)

1. *5% dextrose*
2. *5% methyl glucoside*
3. *5% tetramethyl methyl glucoside*
4. *5% tetramethyl glucose*
5. *Sucrose*

Table VII.   Aldehydes Formed from Amino Acids during Strecker Degradation (67, 68, 69)

Amino Acid	Aldehyde
Alanine	Acetaldehyde
Glycine	Formaldehyde
Isoleucine	2-Methybutanal
Leucine	Isovaleraldehyde
Methionine	Methional
Phenylalanine	Phenylacetaldehyde
Threonine	2-Hydroxypropanal
Serine	Glyoxal

which led them to postulate that in natural systems, browning and flavor production may not necessarily be correlated. Wiseblatt and Zoumut (38) reported that proline, valine, and isolucine reacting with dihydroxyacetone gave the most significant bread-like aromas.

Summary

Bread flavor continuous to intrigue man. The many investigations of bread flavor have advanced knowledge of the factors which contribute to flavor. It is believed today that both fermentation and baking are essential. Microbiological fermentation gives rise to a host of compounds, some of which are mainly volatilized during oven baking and perhaps contribute little to bread flavor. The less volatile flavor stimuli remain in baked bread and in certain combinations contribute materially to acceptability.

Perhaps more important to bread flavor than the products of fermentation are the products resulting from the browning reaction during baking. Numerous flavor compounds are formed as the result of browning and are concentrated in the crust. The compounds are not necessarily stable since their concentration changes while bread is stored. Stabilization of the flavor stimuli would do much to cause bread to have wider public appeal.

While research has established that many possible bread flavor stimuli are present in freshly baked bread, there is a dearth of information correlating the stimuli with consumer preference. Systematic investigation of the relationship of the concentration of bread flavor components with organoleptic tests of consumer preference should be performed. Further research is needed to determine the specific role of amino acids and proteins as precursors of bread flavor.

Literature Cited

(1) Backe, A., *Compt. Rend.* **150**, 540–3 (1910).
(2) Bailey, S. D., Bazinet, M. L., Driscoll, M. L., McCarthy, A. I., *J. Food Sci.* **26**, 163–70 (1961).

(3) Bailey, S. D., Mitchell, D. G., Bazinet, M. L., Weurman, C., *Ibid.*, **27**, 165–70 (1962).
(4) Baker, J. C., Mize, M. D., *Cereal Chem.* **16**, 295–7 (1939).
(5) Baker, J. C., Parker, M. K., Fortmann, K. L., *Ibid.*, **30**, 22–30 (1953).
(6) Bassette, R., Ozeris, S., Whitnah, C. H., *Anal. Chem.* **34**, 1540–3 (1962).
(7) Bertram, G. L., *Cereal Chem.* **30**, 127–39 (1953).
(8) Carlin, G. T., *Proc. Am. Soc. Bakery Engrs.* **1958**, 56–63.
(9) Coffman, J. R., Meisner, D. F., Terry, D. E. *Cereal Sci. Today* **9**, 305–8 (1964).
(10) Cole, E. W., Hale, W. S., Pence, J. W. *Cereal Chem.* **39**, 114–22 (1962).
(11) *Ibid.*, **40**, 260–5 (1963).
(12) Collyer, D. M., *Bakers Dig.* **38**, 43–54 (February 1964).
(13) de Figueiredo, M. P., *Ibid.*, **38**, 48–51 (1964).
(14) Deschreider, A. R., *Bull. Ecole Meunerie Belge* **19**, No. 2, 18–28 (1957).
(15) Fruton, J. S., Simmon, D. S., "General Biochemistry," New York, 1960.
(16) Geddes, W. F., Winkler, C. A., *Can. J. Res.* **3**, 543–59 (1930).
(17) Griffith, T., Johnson, J. A., *Cereal Chem.* **34**, 159–69 (1957).
(18) Grunhut, L., Weber, J., *Biochem. Z.* **121**, 109–19 (1921).
(19) Haney, H. N., "Browning Reaction in Baked Products," master's thesis, Kansas State University, Manhattan, Kan., 1952.
(20) Hodge, J. E., *J. Agr. Food Chem.* **1**, 928–43 (1953).
(21) Hodge, J. E., Moser, H. A., *Cereal Chem.* **38**, 221–8 (1961).
(22) Hodge, J. E., Nelson, E. C., *Ibid.*, **38**, 207–20 (1961).
(23) Hunter, I. R., *J. Chromatog* **1**, 288–92 (1962).
(24) Hunter, I. R., Ng, H., Pence, J. W., *J. Food Sci.* **26**, 578–80 (1961).
(25) Jago, W., Jago, W. C., "The Technology of Bread Making," p. 428, American ed., Bakers' Helper Co., Chicago, Ill.
(26) Johnson, J. A., *Proc. Amer. Soc. Bakery Engrs.* **1963**, 78–83.
(27) Johnson, J. A., Miller, B. S., *Baker's Dig.* **31**, 29–32, 35, 76 (June 1957).
(28) *Ibid.*, **35**, 52–9 (October 1961).
(29) Johnson, J. A., Miller, B. S., Curnutte, B., *J. Agr. Food Chem.* **6**, 384–7 (1958).
(30) Kepner, R. E., Maarse, H., Strating, J., *Anal. Chem.* **36**, 77–82 (1964).
(31) Kiely, R. J., Nowlin, A. C., Moriarity, J. H., *Cereal Sci. Today* **5**, 273–4 (1960).
(32) Kohn, F. E., Wiseblatt, L., Fosdick, L. S., *Cereal Chem.* **38**, 165–9 (1961).
(33) Larsen, R. H., Koch, R. B., McMullen, J. J., *Food Technol.* **8**, 355–7 (1954).
(34) Linko, Y., Johnson, J. A., *J. Agr. Food Chem.* **11**, 150–2 (1963).
(35) Linko, Y., Johnson, J. A., Miller, B. S., *Cereal Chem.* **39**, 468–76 (1962).
(36) Linko, Y., Miller, B. S., Johnson, J. A., *Ibid.*, **39**, 263–72 (1962).
(37) Lüers, H., *Brewer's Dig.* **23**, 45–9, 53 (1948).
(38) Mackay, D. A. M., Lang, D. A., Berdick, M., *Anal. Chem.* **33**, 1369–74 (1961).
(39) Maiden, A. M., *Chem. Ind. (London)* **55**, 143–5 (1936).
(40) Miller, B. S., Johnson, J. A., *Wallerstein Lab. Comm.*, **21**, 115–32 (1958).
(41) Miller, B. S., Johnson, J. A., Robinson, R. J. *Cereal Chem.* **38**, 507–15 (1961).
(42) Nawar, W. W., Fagerson, I. S., *Food Technol.* **15**, 107–9 (1962).
(43) Ng, H., Reed, D. J., Pence, J. W., *Cereal Chem.* **37**, 638–45 (1960).
(44) Nonaka, M., Pippen, E. L., Bailey, G. F., *Anal. Chem.*, **31**, 875–7 (1959).
(45) Nordin, P., Johnson, J. A., *Cereal Chem.* **34**, 170–8 (1957).
(46) Otterbacker, T. J., *Baker's Dig.* **33**, 36–8, 40, 42 (June 1959).
(47) Ozeris, S., Bassette, R., *Anal. Chem.* **35**, 1091 (1963).
(48) Pelshenke, P., "Handbuch der Neuzeitlichen Baeckerei," Hugo Matthaes Verlag, Stuttgart, Germany, 1950.
(49) Pence, E. A., "A Study of Baking Oven Vapors," master's thesis, Kansas State University, Manhattan, Kan., 1952.

(50) Pence, J. W., Kohler, G. O., *Brot Gebaeck* **15**, 129–35 (1961).
(51) Piha, P. Kitunen, M., Holmberg, A. M., Suomalainen, H., Z. *Lebensm. Untersuch. Forsch.* **113**, 134–43 (1960).
(52) Robinson, R. J., Lord, T. H., Johnson, J. A., and Miller, B. S., *Cereal Chem.* **35**, 295–306 (1958).
(53) Ronnebeck, H., *Ernährungsforsch.*, **2**, 527–39 (1957). *C.A.* **52**, 66566 (1958).
(54) Rothe, M., *Ernährungsforsch.* **5**, 131–142 (1960).
(55) *Ibid.*, **7**, 639–46 (1963).
(56) Rothe, M., Thomas, B., *Nährung* **3**, 1–17 (1959).
(57) Rothe, M., Thomas, B., Z. *Lebensm. Untersuch. Forsch.* **119**, 302–10 (1963).
(58) Rothe, M., Voigt, I., *Nährung* **7**, 50–9 (1963).
(59) Rotsch, A., Dörner, H. *Brot. Gebaeck* **11**, 173–7 (1957).
(60) *Ibid.*, **12**, 138 (1958).
(61) Smith, D. E., Coffman, J. R., *Anal. Chem.* **32**, 1733–7 (1960).
(62) Stephen, R. L., Teszler, A. P., *Ibid.*, **32**, 1047 (1960).
(63) Stone, C. D., Bayfield, E. G., *Bakers' Dig.* **34**, 34–40, 43–46, 48, 89 (April 1960).
(64) Sykes, H. D., *Ibid.*, **33**, 48–51 (1959).
(65) Teranishi, R., Buttery, R. G., Lunden, R. E., *Anal. Chem.* **34**, 1033–5 (1962).
(66) Thomas, B., Ronnebeck, H., *Ernährungsforsch.* **5**, 478–498 (1960); *C.A.* **44**, 1956h (1961).
(67) Thomas, B., Rothe, M., *Baker's Dig.* **34**, 50, 53–6 (August 1960).
(68) Thomas, B., Rothe, M., *Ernährungsforsch.* **1**, 362–71 (1956); *C.A.* **51**, 10, 780c (1957).
(69) Thomas, B., Rothe, M., *Ernährungsforsch.* **2**, 427–43 (1957).
(70) *Ibid.*, pp. 751–7.
(71) Tokareva, R. R., Kretovich, V. L., *Khlebopekar i. Konditer. Prom.* **5**, 11–13 (1961);*C.A.* **55**, 21405 (1961).
(72) Tokareva, R. R., Kretovich, V. L., *Khlebopekar. i Konditer. Prom.* **6**, 5–8 (1962); *C.A.* **56**, 15887a (1962).
(73) Visser't Hooft, F., De Leeuw, F. J. G., *Cereal Chem.* **12**, 213–29 (1935).
(74) Weurman, C., *Food Technol.* **15**, 531–534 (1961).
(75) Wick, E. L., *Cereal Sci. Today* **5**, 240–1, 258 (1960).
(76) Wick, E. L., de Figueiredo, M. P., Wallace, D. H., *Cereal Chem.* **41**, 300–15 (1964).
(77) Wiseblatt, L., *Baker's Dig.* **35**, 60–3, 174, 176 (October 1961).
(78) Wiseblatt, L., *Cereal Chem.* **37**, 728–33 (1960).
(79) *Ibid.*, pp. 734–9.
(80) Wiseblatt, L., 41st Annual Meeting, American Association of Cereal Chemists, 1956.
(81) Wiseblatt, L., *Northwestern Miller* **258**, (11), la (1957).
(82) Wiseblatt, L., Kohn, F. E., *Cereal Chem.* **37**, 55–66 (1960).
(83) Wiseblatt, L., Zoumut, A. F., *Ibid.*, **40**, 162–8 (1963).

RECEIVED April 27, 1965.   Contribution 524, Department of Flour and Feed Milling Industries, Kansas Agricultural Experiment Station, Manhattan, Kan.

10

Beverage Flavors

KURT S. KONIGSBACHER and MARY ELLEN DONWORTH

Evans Research and Development Corp., New York, N.Y.

Beverage flavors are derived from different starting materials and/or developed by different reaction mechanisms. These variations in origin and/or biogenesis result in differences in components or in proportions thereof which are perceived as flavor differences. Two general natural pathways are possible for flavor formation: unique—developed from metabolites indigenous to one or a few natural products, or widely distributed—produced by degradation of common metabolites. Research shows examples especially of the unique compounds. Evidence of at least 30 common flavor components supports the idea of beverage flavor generation from common metabolites. Flavorants common to all or a majority of the beverage types studied include alcohols, acids, carbonyls, and sulfur-containing compounds. Individual beverages are categorized as natural, processed, and compounded flavors.

The aim of this paper is not simply to enumerate the beverage flavor constituents isolated and identified by different approaches, methods, and results reported in the literature. Rather it is to look at the origin and biogenesis of beverage flavors and to tie together some of the disjointed information to see whether common reaction mechanisms are involved or whether each product represents a unique case.

Background

Beverage flavors are, generally speaking, a heterogeneous lot, perhaps more so than those of most other types of foods. The reason is, of course, that the term "beverage" includes a variety of items imbibed at various times and at different stages of life: from mother's milk for the very young to soft drinks during early adolescence, and finally to the sophisticated, physiologically-stimulating beverages of the mature adult.

There can be little argument that different beverages have different effects—soporific, stimulating, diuretic are a few—on the human body and mind. However, there is considerable argument about the flavors of these beverages, their origin, their synthesis by nature, and their chemical composition.

Learned dissertations have been written on the chemical nature of beverage flavors and differences between them. Indeed, we all know that such differences exist; after all, who could fail to differentiate between orange juice and tea? Neither can the fact that flavors vary not only between types of beverages, but also within each type, be overlooked, since it is incessantly stressed in advertising. That it is really so, is probably obvious to most anybody who has ever compared Scotch and Bourbon or grapefruit and tangerine juice, and it does not take a connoisseur to differentiate between a Moselle and a Sauterne wine.

Information on the origin and biogenesis (the development of flavor in a living organism from precursors as part of the normal metabolism) of beverage flavors is less positive and clear-cut. Yet, they represent the key which we hope will some day open the door to an understanding of the relationship between flavor and chemical structure.

Biogenesis of Flavors

Even a cursory examination of beverage flavors and their origin indicates that they are derived from widely different starting materials and are developed by different reaction mechanisms. However, the same cursory examination would also indicate startling similarities in the composition of those flavors (*12, 25, 27, 30*). Actually, there is no discrepancy between the two statements, because flavors are complex chemical mixtures, so that flavor differences can be perceived by the human senses either because of differences in chemical composition or because of differences in relative quantities of the same components.

It is our thinking that both types of flavor differentiation exist, often at the same time. The reasons for this can be found in the origin and biogenesis of the flavors. It could be said that the differences are metabolically conditioned. Theoretically, at least two general natural pathways appear possible for the formation of flavor: one where unique flavor compounds are developed from metabolites indigenous to one or a few natural products, the other where widely distributed flavor constituents are produced by the degradation of common metabolites.

Flavor research programs conducted in our laboratories have shown examples of both, but particularly of the former. In processed green beans, for instance, enzymatic odor formation was found to play a major role, as shown by the increase in 2-*trans*-hexenal, believed to be the

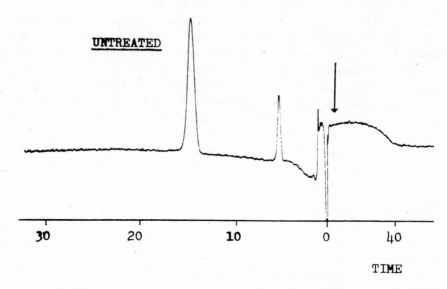

Figure 1. Pye argon chromatograms

Column. 10% di-n-decyl phthalate on firebrick, 100/120-mesh
Temperature. 100°C.
Pressure. 12 p.s.i.
Flow rate. 60 ml. of argon per minute

major odor component after the application of a suitable enzyme preparation (*14*).   Figure 1 compares a chromatogram of the volatiles from enzyme-treated string beans with one for string beans which were not enzyme-treated. The two elongated peaks in the enzyme-treated beans are present in the untreated beans but in much smaller amounts. The enzymes are not producing new compounds but increasing ones already present.

Brunet and Kent (*5*) found that the *o*-quinone produced as a defense secretion by the glands of *Periplaneta americana* is formed from the β-glucoside of its phenolic precursor. The reaction mechanism is believed to be hydrolysis of the β-glucoside by a β-glucosidase, followed by the oxidation of the phenol to the quinone, catalyzed by phenol oxidase. A

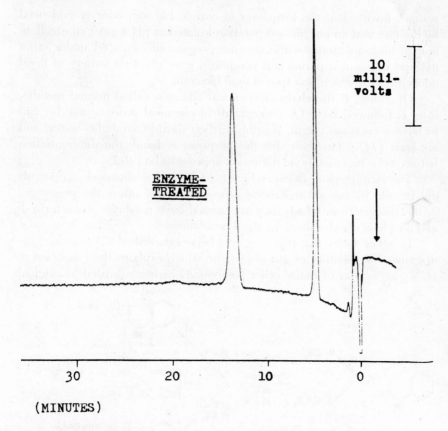

10
milli-
volts

30   20   10   0

(MINUTES)

of volatiles from rehydrated string beans

Voltage. 1750 volts
Recorder. 10-mv.
Attenuation. 5 ×

β-glucosidase and a polyphenol oxidase were shown to be present in the tracheal glands of Diploptera by Roth and Stay although no β-glucoside was identified in ethanolic and aqueous extracts of the glands.

A case of particular interest is reported by Schildknecht and Holubek (*24*). In *Brachinus* spp. the final synthesis of the quinones takes place at the very moment of discharge, where the hydroquinones are oxidized by hydrogen peroxide in an enzyme-catalyzed, explosive reaction.

Another interesting example is experiments conducted in our laboratories with orange blossoms (*15*). The addition of enzyme preparations to inactive, odorless substrates consisting of orange blossom odor precursors resulted in a definite odor development. The complexity of the systems involved in the formation of orange blossom odor is evidenced by the fact that an enzyme preparation isolated at pH 4 gave an excellent orange blossom aroma while enzyme preparations isolated under other pH and different experimental conditions gave rise to a variety of floral odors, none of which was true orange blossom.

Of course, if the chain of chemical changes, called normal metabolism, is followed back far enough, all biochemical process may be said to have a common origin, possibly carbon dioxide, sunlight, water, and minerals (14). However, for the purposes in hand, the differentiation between the two metabolic pathways appears to be valid.

The characteristic flavors which exist as unique chemical compounds are formed by normal metabolic processes. Most often, the precursors or metabolites from which they are formed have not been characterized, and the chain of substances involved is unknown.

In other cases the pathway has been established. Virtanen (29) describes the isolation of glucobrassicin, which explains the formation of SCN⁻ as well as of many other compounds earlier regarded as original

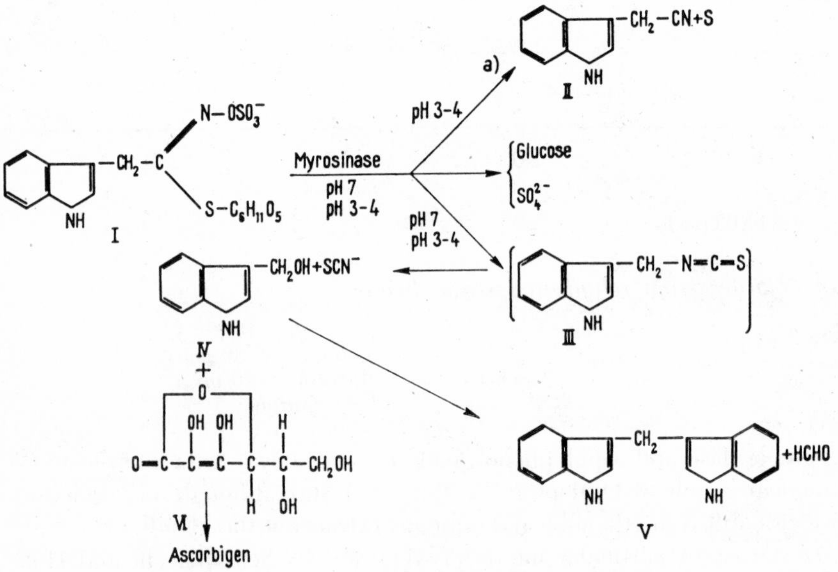

Figure 2. Development of flavor compounds from glucobrassicin

plant substances. Figure 2 summarizes the development of 3-indolacetonitrile (a plant growth hormone), Ascorbigen, and other compounds from glucobrassicin, which itself appears only when cabbage is crushed. The isothiocyanate (III) which should be formed from glucobrassicin, in analogy with other mustard oil glucosides, is so unstable because of its indole group that it is immediately split into SCN⁻ and 3-hydroxymethylindole (IV). The formation of SCN^- is quantitative at a neutral reaction, which makes it possible to determine glucobrassicin quantitatively in cabbage plants. Because some Brassica plants contain smaller amounts of N_1-methylglucobrassicin too (9), the SCN^- formed from these plants corresponds to both thioglucosides. When cabbage is boiled, SCN^- is also formed, but only half the amount formed enzymically (10). This is because glucobrassicin is then decomposed in two different ways.

But no matter what the reasons for flavor production or the path of development, the reactions, as part of the metabolic process, are enzyme-catalyzed. These enzymes are often highly specific for bringing about the chemical changes in each step of the complicated process whereby flavor precursors are built up and then converted into the flavors themselves (14). For example, succinic acid dehydrogenase catalyzes the transformation of succinic acid to fumaric acid, but will not dehydrogenate any other substance. However, if malonic acid is added to the substrate, it will compete with the succinic acid because of the similarity in structure and hence make the enzyme unavailable for dehydrogenating succinic acid. Yet the malonic acid itself is not dehydrogenated (4).

The second hypothesis, that beverage flavors, or at least flavor components, are derived from common metabolites, particularly amino acids, is supported by considerable evidence. Since this is also a metabolic process, it must be catalyzed by enzymes unless it involves a thermally induced chemical degradation. It would then be assumed that flavor differences are due to variations in relative quantities of the degradation products which, in turn, depend on the amounts of metabolites present, on the activation energy of each breakdown product, and on such extraneous factors as temperature, pH, and ionic strength (71). Indeed, the mere presence of an enzyme will not start a reaction since the molecules entering the reaction must be in an activated state for the reaction to proceed. The relationship among reaction rate, activation energy, and temperature are expressed by Arrhenius' equation

$$K = Ae^{-Ea/RT}$$

where K = rate of reaction quotient, A = constant, e = natural logarithmic base, E_a = activation energy, R = gas constant (1.99 cal. per mole), and T = absolute temperature.

This means that slight changes in the activation energy or temperature will influence the rate of reaction enormously—for instance, a rise of 10° C. may double or triple the rate of the reaction. For invertase (β-fructosidase) K, the velocity constant between 0° and 20° C., will be (4):

$$\frac{K_t + 10}{K_t} = 2.0$$

Probably the most important conversion of common metabolites to flavor is the degradation of amino acids resulting from the hydrolysis of proteins. Typical examples of this type of natural flavor generation are the formation of fusel oils during fermentation and the Strecker degradation.

Alcoholic beverage fermentation involves primarily the conversion of fermentable grain sugars, produced by the action of amylases on starch, into about equal parts of ethanol and carbon dioxide. Of the starch converted to sugar and subsequently fermented, 5 to 6% is consumed in side reactions (20). These side reactions then lead to secondary products, called "congeners," which determine the characteristic flavor of the final product when retained in the distillate. A major group of constituents formed during this process consists of higher alcohols and is collectively called "fusel oils." These fusel oils are the result of the deamination of amino acids (13). The conversion of leucine to isoamyl alcohol will serve to demonstrate the type of reaction involved:

$$(CH_3)_2-CH-CH_2-CH(NH_2)COOH + H_2O \rightarrow$$
$$(CH_3)_2-CH-CH_2-CH_2(OH) + CO_2 + NH_3$$

Other alcohols are derived similarly from their amino acid precursors. Since the reaction takes place in yeast cells only, the ammonia formed is available to form new yeast cells and hence does not appear to influence flavor.

Another pathway for flavor formation from amino acids is the above-mentioned Strecker degradation, first established in 1861, which consists of the conversion to carbonyls by oxidation, deamination, and decarboxylation. The reaction is believed to proceed as follows:

$$R-\underset{\underset{NH_2}{|}}{CH}-COOH \rightarrow R-\underset{\underset{NH}{\|}}{C}-COOH \rightarrow R-\underset{\underset{O}{\|}}{C}-COOH \rightarrow R-\underset{\underset{O}{\|}}{C}-H$$

Using leucine again as the model, it can be seen readily that it would be converted to isovaleraldehyde, which has, for instance, been isolated from cocoa beans.

Of course, other natural processes besides the two mentioned originate from common metabolites. Suffice it to mention the biosynthesis of terpenes from isoprene groups.

Common Flavors

If the generation of beverage flavors from common metabolites represents a valid biochemical concept, it would mean that different beverages should contain the same flavor components, albeit in different proportions. The answer is that they do and that there are, indeed, flavor components common to all or the majority of the beverages under consideration. The flavorants include alcohols, acids, carbonyls, and sulfur-containing compounds (*31*). Beyond that, many flavors are partially composed of terpene hydrocarbons, which have been omitted, since they are not flavor components, but rather carriers for oxygenated compounds such as alcohols, aldehydes, ketones, acids, and esters.

In the search for common flavor constituents, the beverages were classified into four categories for the sake of convenience: citrus fruits, milk, coffee-tea-cocoa, and fermented beverages. This classification is patently incomplete, as is the compilation of common flavor components, but then the reason was to demonstrate rather than to enumerate.

Evidence has been collected of at least 30 common flavor components (*31*). Of these, 9 have been found in all four categories, and an additional 14 in at least three of the four.

Compounds Found in All 4 Categories:

Ethanol	2-Hexenal
Propionaldehyde	Acetaldehyde
n-Valeraldehyde	Acetic acid
Furfural	Acetone
2-Butanone	

Compounds Found in 3 Categories:

Methanol	Formic acid
Iso-amyl Alcohol	Propionic acid
n-Butyraldehyde	n-Butyric acid
Iso-valeraldehyde	Iso-valeric acid
Diacetyl	Hydrogen sulfide
Acetoin	Methyl sulfide
Hexanal	Acetyl methyl carbinol

Other Common Constituents:

Propanol	Formaldehyde
2-Propanol	Iso-butyric acid
n-Valeric acid	Caproic acid

The list is rather interesting, and there can be little doubt that the common flavor constituents above are important to beverage flavors. The presence of such compounds as 2-hexenal or valeraldehyde could even be said to be unexpected.

Individual Beverages

The importance of origin and biogenetic formation of beverage flavors has been indicated. It would now seem to be in order to discuss briefly the flavors of individual types of beverages. To do this in an orderly manner, it is necessary to classify the major beverages. Our own system consists of classifying beverage flavors in broad categories on the basis of their origin.

On this basis, three fundamental classes of beverage flavors can be established: natural flavors, processed flavors, and compounded flavors. Like most attempts to classify complex and diverse materials, this is far from perfect and many beverages cannot be put into a single slot. Nevertheless, the system appears to have certain merits.

Natural Flavors. Natural flavors are defined as flavors in beverages which are derived from pre-existing components. They can be both lipophylic, as in the case of essential oils, or hydrophylic, as in apples.

Beverages in this class today are usually processed before they reach the consumer to increase shelf life and convenience. Flavor changes can and do take place during processing. However, these changes are incidental to the reasons for processing and are generally undesirable. They happen because processing techniques are imperfect with respect to flavor. A typical example is milk. Although pasteurization or spray-drying modifies the flavor of raw milk, the flavor is still a natural milk flavor. Buttermilk, on the other hand, has a flavor which would be classified as processed because it results from the deliberate addition of lactic acid organisms.

Another example is orange juice, the flavor of which after processing should be as close to that of freshly squeezed orange juice as possible. Temperatures as low as 80° F. may alter the flavor of orange juice (1). The effects of high processing temperatures are very evident when considering the flavor of canned orange juice. With the advent of vacuum concentration, the industry was able to overcome most of the effects of high temperatures and produce a product similar in flavor to the fresh juice. However, even in this process the volatiles that add much to the flavor are lost in the condensate. To compensate for this, the juice is evaporated to a high sugar content and is then "cut back" with fresh juice. In may cases, peel oil is also added to the final product.

More recently, many manufacturers have installed "volatile recovery" systems which trap the volatiles previously lost in the condensate. These volatiles are then added back into the juice before freezing.

To give the juice cloud and body, it is necessary to add a certain amount of pulp. The pulp is made up mainly of juice sacs and rag. These two components contain the largest amounts of pectin and pectin esterase (23). If the enzyme, pectinesterase, is not inactivated to a large degree, it will hydrolyze the pectin, resulting in a separation of the "cloud" in the juice. Even though the "stabilizing" of the juice requires elevated temperatures—(e.g., 145° to 165°)—for a matter of seconds, it is enough to cause some browning or flavor deterioration of the juice.

The principal beverages in the "natural flavor" category are fruit juices, milk, green tea, liqueurs or cordials, and gin.

FRUIT JUICES. Since fruit juices, in their simplest form, are made by expressing fruit, their flavor is that of the ripe fruit from which they are derived. Depending on the type of fruit, the outer layers may or may not be removed before juicing. This is particularly important with citrus fruit.

Generally, the flavor components in fruit juices, especially citrus fruit juices, are terpene hydrocarbons, oxygenated terpenes, and similar compounds. Some of the more recently identified flavor constituents in orange juices are (*25*):

> *n*-Butyraldehyde
> Methyl ethyl ketone
> 2-Methyl-3-buten-2-ol
>
> Ethyl *sec*-butyl ether
> 4-Methyl-2-pentanone
> 2-Hexen-1-ol
> Ethyl hexanoate
> Methyl 3-hydroxyhexanoate
> Ethyl 3-hydroxyhexanoate
> Perillaldehyde

From grapefruit juice, a new sesquiterpene ketone, nootkatone, was isolated (*18*). It is also found, incidentially, in lemon, lime, orange, bergamot, and tangerine oils.

MILK. The flavor components in milk cannot be discussed in detail. Suffice it to say that they originate not only from the metabolism of the cow, but are also influenced by what the cow feeds on, as evidenced by the appearance of onion off-flavors at certain times of the year.

GREEN TEA. The origin of the flavor of green tea is not completely understood. Since green tea is not fermented, the flavors other than those derived from the tannins and alkaloids present pre-exist in the harvested leaves. They are sometimes called tea "spirit" (*11*).

LIQUEURS AND CORDIALS. Liqueurs and cordials are usually made from rectified ethyl alcohol, sugar, and flavorants extracted from fruits, herbs, seeds, and roots by the distillation, infusion, or essence process. Their flavor is that of the botanicals, but it is, of course, modified by the presence of the sugar and the alcohol.

Typical examples are Cassis from black currants, Guignolet from black cherries, Curaçao from oranges, and Kuemmel from caraway.

GIN. Most distilled spirits fall into the category of processed flavors. Gin is different. It derives its flavor mostly from pre-existing natural essential oils rather than from products of fermentation. The principal flavorants are juniper berries, which are distilled with ethyl alcohol in a gin-head. In the United States other flavoring agents, such as angelica, anise, caraway seed, coriander, cassia bark, grains of paradise, orris root, licorice, and bitter orange peel are sometimes used. Turpentine has been employed occasionally in lieu of juniper oil, and a small quantity of sulfuric acid has been added at times before distillation to give a special ethereal bouquet (*13*).

Incidentally, the gin which makes those delightful martinis is not to be confused with the so-called "bathtub" or "synthetic" gin, the flavorants of which best remain buried.

Processed Flavors. The term "processed flavors" as used here is a generic term. It can be defined as the flavor of a finished beverage which is deliberately processed to create the flavor. This category of flavor has several subdivisions, based on the processes involved.

BREAKDOWN FLAVORS. In this subclass, the flavors are breakdown products of more complex chemical compounds. This breakdown is a direct and desired function of the specific process used.

The most typical examples of beverages in this category are coffee and cocoa, in each case, the breakdown being achieved by roasting, a thermal process.

Coffee. The flavor of coffee is still not completely understood, possibly because it is so complex, involving carbohydrates, proteins, lipids, acids, phenols, and almost every other class of organic compounds.

The phenolic acids, mainly chlorogenic acid, decompose and condense. Such decomposition products are said to contribute to the flavor.

Degradation and interaction products of the amino acids are also probably sources of much of the roasted coffee flavor (*19*).

From the lipids, such flavor components as aldehydes, ketones, and short-chain fatty acids are formed by oxidative and hydrolytic reactions (*19*).

Coffee is, of course, a collective term, and many kinds of coffee are known. They are generally classified as to where they are grown, and every coffee lover is well aware that they can differ greatly in flavor. Our own gas chromatographic studies have indicated that many of the flavor differences perceived by the human senses are due to variations in the quantities of flavorants present rather than to the presence of different flavor components.

For instance, gas chromatographs of Brazilian, Colombian, and African coffees show the same constituents present but not in the same ratios.

Whether our sense of olfaction is capable of directly interpreting changes in component ratios or whether it is simply a matter of suprathreshold stimulation by only the major components, is a question which to the best of our knowledge still waits to be answered.

Cocoa. Cocoa flavor also is composed of breakdown products which originate during roasting. However, in contrast to coffee, the roasting has to be preceded by fermentation which yields suitable flavor precursors.

Chromatograms have shown that roasted and unroasted cocoa beans contain essentially the same volatile constituents (*2*). After roasting, however, a large increase in isovaleraldehyde and isobutyraldehyde was found although the flavor of cocoa perceived by the sense of olfaction does not appear to contain those carbonyls in appreciable quantities.

FERMENTATION FLAVORS.   The desirable flavors in this broad category are created by and originate from fermentation processes.

Black Tea.   Black tea is a typical example of a beverage flavor in this class.   This flavor is due principally to oxidative fermentation of the polyphenols.

Of the 20 or so phenolic substances present, only the (—) epigallocatechin and the (—) epigallocatechin gallate appear to undergo an appreciable change during fermentation (21).   They are oxidized to theaflavin, which can be further oxidized to thearubigins.   Recent work has shown a direct correlation between flavor quality and the quantity of theaflavin (22).

Wickremasinghe and Swain (33) recently did comparative qualitative and quantitative studies of the polyphenols, amino acids, and low-boiling volatile compounds in two specially prepared samples of Ceylon tea, and those in 20 commercial samples of black tea.

Their work showed that the highest amounts of polyphenols are found in the unprocessed leaf, with a decrease on fermentation and slight rise on "firing."   The phenols reacting with vanillin, on the other hand, decreased in an absolute methanol extract and increased in the aqueous methanol extract, thus reflecting the effects of polymerization.

The polyphenol content of the aqueous methanol extracts in the various samples is relatively constant.   This may indicate that the enzymic polymerization of the polyphenols in different teas results in the formation of a relatively fixed quantity of a similar, or closely related, group of compounds which is sufficient to inhibit the enzyme systems responsible for their formation.

Researchers had previously indicated that the quinones formed by oxidizing the catechins are material for the degradation of amino acids present (3).   Wickeremasinghe and Swain (33) analyzed quantitatively the low-boiling volatiles from 10 samples of black tea.   A comparison of the amounts of 2- and 3-methylbutanols and isobutyl alcohol (2-methyl-1-propanol) with the amounts of the corresponding free amino acids showed no direct correlation between the two.   The relative efficiency of the amino acid oxidants was investigated by examining quantitatively the production of aldehydes from valine—leucine and isoleucine—by heating them with (+)-catechin, autoxidized (+)-catechin, and D-glucose. While (+)-catechin at first proved to be completely ineffective, after autoxidation it became a better oxidant than D-glucose.

In later experiments (1965) (32) these workers demonstrated the inhibition of tyrosinase activity by the condensation products obtained by the autoxidation of (+)-catechin.   A linear relation was found between the level of polyphenols and theaflavin with the lower levels of phenols, but not in the samples containing over 30 mg. per gram dry weight of phenols. The above hypothesis might account for this since it can be assumed that the enzyme systems are not a limiting factor. Thus, a low initial substrate concentration would *per se* limit the theaflavin level while a high concentration would favor the rapid formation of enzyme-inhibiting compounds, which then interfere with the further formation of theaflavin.

The total amino acid content decreased during fermentation concomitant with the production of aldehydes while appreciable amounts of ammonia were found in black tea.

Among the low-boiling volatile compounds, the presence of acrolein, n-valeraldehyde, methyl ethyl ketone, acetone, and diacetyl is reported for the first time. The detection of n-butyraldehyde and n-valeraldehyde cannot be explained as being derived from amino acids since norvaline and norleucine were not detected. Furthermore diacetyl, acetone, and methyl ethyl ketone probably arise from precursors other than amino acids.

Equally well known beverages in this class have flavors produced during the fermentation of carbohydrates to alcohol: the wines and distilled spirits and, in part, beer.

The fermentation of sugars to alcohol is unique in the beverage field, because it is both a nonspecific and a specific process. Both of these aspects have been discussed before, but it should be repeated that it is the specific congeners formed which determine directly the flavor of the finished products.

Wines. The congeners in wine, which determine the type and quality of the wine, depend in part on the grapes used (cf. Muscatel, Dezaley), in part on the composition of the "must" which contains sugars, organic acids, tannins, flavors, proteins, mineral salts, and pectin, and in part on the large variety of favorable and unfavorable yeasts, bacteria, and fungi.

Among the more recently identified flavor congeners are (30):

> Diethyl succinate
> γ-Butyrolactone
> Isoamyl lactate
> Ethyl pelargonate
> Ethyl pentadecanoate
> Diacetyl
> Diethyl malate

Distilled Spirits. Freshly distilled spirits, particularly whiskey, are raw and unpleasant in taste, and have a somewhat disagreeable odor. Present are primarily higher alcohols, acids, and aldehydes.

The specific flavors depend on the raw materials used for the mash, which might be corn, wheat, potatoes, barely, or rye.

FLAVORS BY AGING. In distilled spirits particularly, but also to some extent in cordials, wine, and beer, many of the desired flavor components are developed during aging.

As indicated above, for example, the flavor of raw whiskey is rather unpleasant. The smooth, mellow taste and rich bouquet the consumer expects develop only during aging in wood, with maximum flavor reached after about 5 years.

During storage, secondary congeners are formed by the extraction of wood constituents, the oxidation of original congeners, and the reaction between flavor components. Principally, there is an increase in acids, esters, and solids. The specific compounds involved have been described in detail by Crampton and Tolman (8), Liebman and Rosenblatt (16), Liebman and Scherl (17), and Valaer and Frazier (28).

Compounded Flavors. The principal type of beverage that can be classified under this heading is soft drinks. To a much lesser degree, cordials can be made with compounded flavors.

In contrast to the previously described beverages, products in this category are wholly manufactured products, and the only absolutely required raw material is water.

The formulation of soft drink flavors is an art rather than a science and will remain an art until the mystery of the relationship between structure and flavor is solved. The flavor can consist of pure synthetic flavorants, natural oils, essences, and tinctures, or of combinations of all of those. The flavors are generally complex. For instance, an imitation cherry beverage flavor formulated in our laboratories contained as major constituents ethyl enanthate, tolyl aldehyde, benzaldehyde, eugenol, anisyl acetate, anisyl aldehyde, absolute of jasmine, vanillin, ethyl tolylglycidate, and amylcinnamic aldehyde.

Other soft drink components which affect the flavor are the sugar or synthetic sweeteners used, the carbon dioxide added, and the water. Acidulants, in our opinion, do not contribute appreciably to the flavor and are used primarily as preservatives.

Since synthetic sweeteners are increasing in popularity because of the emphasis on reducing caloric intake, they present new flavor problems. However, these flavor problems can be overcome by the judicious formulation of the specific flavorants.

Mixed Flavors. Some beverages are difficult to classify under the suggested system because they contain flavors from several origins. A typical example of such a complex material is beer.

The flavor of beer is derived from components pre-existing in the barley and other grains used, from the hops, and from the fermentation process. There are, of course, many types of beer with distinct differences in flavor.

First, beers are divided into bottom-fermented and top-fermented brews. The former include the lagers, and the latter ales, porter, and stout. The lager beers, such as the Pilsener, Dortmund, and Munich types, are characterized by heavy body and flavor with relatively few hop notes.

Bock beer is a lager made from highly roasted malts and identified by a caramelized flavor. Porter is a full-bodied beer with a heavy foam. Stout is dark sweet, with strong malt and hop flavors.

The complexity of a "mixed flavor," such as beer, is apparent when one studies not even the whole flavor, but only the flavor constituents derived from hops, an important—but in quantity—minor ingredient.

Hop oil, which contributes to the aroma of beer, was investigated by means of capillary gas chromatography, and over 50 individual chemical compounds, primarily monoterpenes and sesquiterpenes, were isolated (6). The soft hop resins or so-called hop acids are the principal bittering agents in beer, although they are present only to the extent of 15 to 25 p.p.m. in most beers. Recent studies have shown that these bittering agents, which at one time were thought to be one individual compound, are a mixture of several isomers (26).

Conclusions

The subject of beverage flavors is complex and controversial. It is complex because many different metabolites or precursors are involved and because flavors are developed by a variety of biogenetic pathways. It is controversial because flavors are generally composed of volatile, labile chemical compounds and because flavors are perceived and judged subjectively rather than scientifically.

Yet, the study of beverages and beverage flavors is of great importance since mankind cannot exist without the continuous replenishment of body fluids.

Literature Cited

(1) Atkins, C. D., Wenzel, F. W., Moore, E. L., *Food Inds.* **22**, 1353 (1950).
(2) Bailey, S. D., Mitchell, D. G., Bazinet, M. L., Weurman, C., *J. Food Sci.* **27**, 165 (1962).
(3) Bokuchava, M. A., Popov, V. R., *Dokl. Akad. Nauk S.S.S.R.* **99**, 145 (1954); *Chem. Abstr.* **49**, 3439.
(4) Braverman, J. B. S., *"Introduction to the Biochemistry of Foods,"* 162–79, Elsevier, Amsterdam/London/New York, 1963.
(5) Brunet, P. C. J., Kent, P. W., *Proc. Roy. Soc.* (*London*) **B 144**, 259–74 (1955).
(6) Buttery, R. G., McFadden, W. H., Lundin, R. E., Kealy, M. P., *J. Inst. Brewing* **70**, 396 (1964).
(7) Casey, J. C., Self, R., Swain, T., *J. Food Sci.* **30**, 33 (1965).
(8) Crampton, C. A., Tolman, L. M., *J. Am. Chem. Soc.* **30**, 97 (1908).

(9) Gmelin, R., Virtanen, A. I., *Acta Chem. Scand.*, in press.
(10) Gmelin, R., Virtanen, A. I., *Ann. Acad. Sci. Fennicae* **A II**, No. 107 (1961).
(11) Harler, C. R., "The Culture and Marketing of Tea," Oxford University Press, London, 1933.
(12) Harrison, G. A. F., *European Brewery Conv. Proc. Congr.* 9, 247 (1963) (pub. 1964).
(13) Herstein, M., Gregory, C., "Chemistry and Technology of Wines and Liquors," p. 23, Nostrand, New York, 1935.
(14) Hewitt, E. J., Mackay, D. A. M., Konigsbacher, K., Hasselstrom, T., *Food Technol.* 10, 487 (1956).
(15) Konigsbacher, K. S., Hewitt, E. J., *Ann. N. Y. Acad. Sci.* 116, Art. 2, 705–10 (1964).
(16) Liebman, A. G., Rosenblatt, M., *Ind. Eng. Chem.* 35, 994 (1943).
(17) Liebman, A. G., Scherl, B., *Ibid.*, 41, 534 (1949).
(18) MacLeod, W. D., Jr., Buiques, N. M., *J. Food Sci.* 29, 565 (1964).
(19) Moores, R. G., Stefanucci, A., "Coffee," in Kirk-Othmer "*Encyclopedia of Chemical Technology*, 2nd ed., Vol. 5, p. 748, Interscience, New York, 1964.
(20) Packowski, G. W., Kirk-Othmer "Encyclopedia of Chemical Technology," 2nd ed., Vol. I, p. 501, Interscience, New York, 1963.
(21) Roberts, E. A. H., *Chem. Ind. (London)*, 1957, 1354.
(22) Roberts, E. A. H., Smith, R. F., *J. Sci. Food Agr.* 14, 689 (1963).
(23) Rouse, A. H., *Food Technol.* 7, 360 (1953).
(24) Schildknecht, H., Holubek, *Angew. Chem.* 73, 1–7 (19??).
(25) Schultz, T. H., Teranishi, Roy, McFadden, W. H., Kilpatrick, P. W., Corse, Joseph, *J. Food Sci.* 29, 790 (1964).
(26) Spetsig, L. O., *J. Inst. Brewing* 70, 440 (1964).
(27) Stahl, W. H., *Advan. Food Res.* 11, 202 (1962).
(28) Valaer, P., Frazier, W. H., *Ind. Eng. Chem.* 28, 92 (1936).
(29) Virtanen, A. I., *Arch. Biochem. Biophy.* Vol. Suppl. 1, 200–8 (1962).
(30) Webb, A. D., *Food Technol.* 16, 56 (1962).
(31) Weurman, C., "Lists of Volatile Compounds in Food," Central Institute for Nutrition and Food Research T.N.O., Utrecht, The Netherlands, R-1687 (1963).
(32) Wickremasinghe, R. L., Swain, T., *Chem. Ind. (London)* 37, 1574 1964.
(33) Wickremasinghe, R. L., Swain, T., *J. Sci. Food Agr.* 16, 57 (January 1965).

RECEIVED May 20, 1965.

11

Flavor of Flesh Foods

H. L. A. TARR

Vancouver Laboratory, Fisheries Research Board of Canada,
Vancouver 8, B. C., Canada

Present research indicates that flesh foods owe their characteristic flavors to complex blends of compounds including lipids, free fatty acids, lactic and certain other organic acids, carbonyl compounds, peptides, amino acids, sugars, sugar phosphates, sulfur compounds of low molecular weight including hydrogen sulfide, amines, betaines, nucleotides and related compounds, and possibly glycoproteins. Considerable progress has been made in linking flavor of poultry, red meats, and fish with certain of these compounds. However, since the manner of rearing animals and of preparing flesh foods is so variable, and the number of compounds involved in flavor is so large, much research will be necessary before it will be possible to define a flesh food flavor in terms of a defined chemical pattern.

In flesh food flavor and odor research we are dealing with dynamic rather than static problems, for a variety of influences, some predictable and others unpredictable, may affect flavor. Feed, age, sexual development, season, species, and varieties within species may alter flavor of animal flesh. At present there are really no flavor standards other than those that are loosely defined as typical of beef, pork, lamb, chicken, turkey, fish, etc. The association of flavors with known chemical compounds may require skilled tasting panels at all stages until clarification is complete. Reasonable progress has been made in a comparatively short time in this complex area of chemical research, and the application of techniques such as those of gas chromatography, mass spectrometry, and nuclear magnetic resonance is almost certain to accelerate this progress. It is to be hoped that reasonable financial assistance will be made available in the near future so that this important work can be prosecuted with increasing vigor.

Flesh foods, other than visceral organs such as liver and kidney, are composed of skeletal muscle, which in all species is largely made up of proteins: actomyosin, myogens, collagen, and elastin. It would seem probable that most of the proteins themselves do not contribute directly to flavor, since flesh dialyzed against water is usually reported to be flavorless. At any rate, research on flesh foods has so far implicated the following compounds, or classes of compounds, in flavor production: peptides, amino acids, lipids, carbonyl compounds, nucleotides and related compounds, nitrogenous compounds of low molecular weight (other than amino acids), and the various carbohydrates, acids, and alcohols that are intermediates in intermediary metabolism. Post-mortem changes are, of course, very important, since enzymic degradation may affect flavor favorably or unfavorably. To add to the difficulties many substances may be very important in causing flavor and yet be present in extremely small amounts. Finally, some flesh foods are consumed after cooking, others are consumed raw, and some undergo an aging period, and this of course introduces further complications.

Flavor research, so far as flesh foods are concerned, is in its infancy, and attempts to compare the various foods, with the small amount of information available, are obviously premature. Nevertheless, some similarities are evident, as are also outstanding differences. I propose to discuss the different classes of flesh foods separately and to attempt to correlate the findings insofar as this can be done.

Poultry

In some ways the problem of flavor in poultry is somewhat less complicated than is that of red meats or fish, for there are not the marked differences associated with the latter. There is a general similarity in flavor of turkey, chicken, pheasant, etc., that is not found among beef, pork, lamb, and the large variety of edible fish and marine invertebrates. However, even with poultry there are subtle differences in flavor that so far have not been distinguished chemically. The whole subject was reviewed in 1961 from somewhat different standpoints by Lineweaver and Pippen (16) and Kazeniac (13).

According to Lineweaver and Pippen, variety, sex, size, and age (within reason) do not greatly affect poultry flavor, and the flavor chemist has a comparatively uniform material with which to work. These investigatiors tend to discredit the opinion that is often voiced regarding the tastelessness of much of the broiler meat that is at present marketed, as compared with chicken meat available in years past. They have substantiated this claim by certain taste panel and related data and believe that evidence to the contrary has no reliable scientific basis. If differences do exist, it may be that older methods of handling resulted in visceral flavors which are still considered desirable only by a very limited group: This is a preference for the "game" flavor of the "hung" bird. There is no doubt that modern feeding and handling methods usually result in mild flavored poultry, of reasonably satisfactory bacteriological quality, and the very great increase in consumption during the past decade must indicate that in general satisfactory products are reaching the consumer.

According to Lineweaver and Pippen, available evidence indicates that the lean muscle possesses most of the desirable flavor precursors of poultry, though the lipid fraction contributes to desirable aroma of chicken broth. Since the water-soluble extract of the muscle seems to possess the flavor precursors, this has been employed in most studies. The volatile fraction of such extracts has been accounted for practically entirely as nitrogen, sulfur, and carbonyl compounds. The volatile nitrogen fraction appears to contain only ammonia, and this does not exert a significant effect on flavor. The volatile sulfur is accounted for entirely by hydrogen sulfide, and no other volatile sulfur compounds have been detected. Hydrogen sulfide in concentrations between 0.25 and 0.50 p.p.m. increases intensity of aroma in chicken broth. It has been suggested that it may be formed from glutathione.

The carbonyl compounds of the volatile flavor have been studied fairly extensively, and as might be expected, the amount was low when heating was carried out in a nitrogen atmosphere, intermediate under normal cooking conditions and very high in oxygen. Acetaldehyde, 1-hexanal, C_{16} and C_{18} aldehydes, 1-deca-2,4-dienal, and diacetyl and/or acetoin were the principal compounds isolated under normal cooking conditions. Some 14 carbonyl compounds present in comparatively low concentrations were identified by micromethods. These included acetone and 4 to 10 carbon atom aldehydes or ketones, five 2-enals and 1-hepta-2,4-dienal. There were some minor differences in the kinds of compounds isolated when cooking was conducted in an air stream, but the yields were very much greater. Acetoin is probably oxidized to yield diacetyl. Decadienal, and probably at least some of the other carbonyls, originate in the triglyceride or phospholipid fractions. Indirect evidence obtained by calculation of volatile and nonvolatile carbonyls in chicken broth indicates that there are sufficient amounts present to cause detectable taste effects, but direct evidence of this has yet to be obtained.

Kazeniac (13) attempted to divide various compounds in chicken broths contributing taste, aroma, body, and mouth satisfaction into groups corresponding to these classifications. Fat appeared to have little direct effect on aroma, other than could be attributed to "trapping" volatile compounds.

Skin distillates contained diacetyl, hydrogen sulfide, and ammonia and possessed a rather bitter flavor of carbonyl compounds as well as a slight chicken flavor. The nonvolatile residue possessed a weak chicken flavor also. Dark meat gave more sulfide, ammonia, and volatile carbonyls than did light meat, but less diacetyl. The broths from dark and light meats had characteristic flavor differences. When the pH was increased from 5.0 to 7.4, more diacetyl, ammonia, and sulfide were evolved from dark chicken meat. The amount of volatiles increased with heating temperatures of 65°, 85° and 100°C., the highest temperature giving the strongest typical chicken flavor.

Some 17 or 18 free amino acids occur in chicken broth and, since work had shown that several amino acids, including glutamic, arginine, lysine, α-alanine, and aspartic, improved chicken broth flavor, several of these were studied. The results showed that 0.02 to 0.05% of glutamate and 0.05 to 0.08% of lysine gave best over-all flavor and mouth satisfaction. The effect of other amino acids and of peptides such as carnosine and anserine is not as yet clear. Lactic acid, a major constituent of chicken broth, is believed to contribute to desirable flavor in the presence of certain amino acids.

Glucose, fructose, ribose, and inositol have been found in chicken meat extracts, and the reducing sugars may be responsible for browning under certain conditions but seem to be present in too small concentrations to contribute to sweetness. There is considerable evidence in support of the fact that sulfide is an important flavor constituent of chicken broth and that in the presence of a comparatively high level of ammonia, solutions acquire a sweet flavor. Addition of acetoin to fresh or heat-processed broths gave an improved buttery oil flavor, while diacetyl tended to give rather sour effects. Creatine, which is converted to creatinine on heating, may cause the somewhat bitter flavor sometimes noted in light meat extracts. Inosinic acid is present and is believed to contribute a pleasant meaty flavor, while hypoxanthine and inosine have a bitter taste.

Kazeniac investigated some probable precursors of chicken flavor. Dialyzates of raw and cooked meat broths showed minor differences in aroma on heating, neither giving typical fresh chicken broth aromas. A comparison showed that the dialyzable fraction of raw chicken meat had less diacetyl and ammonia than the residue, but that the residue had sulfide which was lacking in the dialyzate and also contained more carbonyl compounds.

While addition of glutathione prior to heating improved broth flavor, addition of cysteine and hemocysteine cause off-flavors, even though they caused an increase in sulfide. Additional studies, which cannot be recorded here, emphasized the complex situations which may arise because of interaction of certain of the substances that are naturally present in or are added to chicken broths. The results indicated that chicken flavor is due to a complex blend of different compounds. The desirability of further studies on precursors such as radioactive sulfur compounds, and on chicks raised on controlled rations with the hope of influencing muscle composition, was emphasized.

Red Meats

Yueh and Strong (23) refluxed ground beef in water for 3 hours and concentrated the steam distillate to between $1/3$ and $1/2$ its volume. The distillate on appropriate treatment yielded ammonia. 2,4-Dinitrophenylhydrazones prepared from the distillate yielded acetone, acetaldehyde, and diacetyl. Distillation of the extract at pH 1.0 yielded formate, acetate, propionate, butyrate, and isobutryrate, as well as hydrogen sulfide and a trace of dimethyl sulfide. Volatile esters and alcohols were absent. It was concluded that hydrogen sulfide, ammonia, diacetyl, and acetaldehyde are major components of cooked beef and are liberated from odorless precursors.

Hornstein, Crowe, and Sulzbacher (9) freeze-dried an ice-cold water extract of lean beef and subjected the resulting powder to pyrolysis under high vacuum at 100°C., after first determining that best results were obtained at this temperature. Carbonyls (less than 50 μg. of each per gram of dry powder), acetone, acetaldehyde, formaldehyde, and hydrogen sulfide (100 μg per gram) were present. About 1.7 mg. of ammonia per gram were also obtained. Excellent reproducibility was realized with different samples of beef.

Hornstein and Crowe (7) compared freeze-dried powders of lean beef and pork muscle extracts prepared as above. Pyrolysis was carried out at 100° in high vacuum so that two fractions were obtained, a comparatively volatile fraction and a less volatile fraction. The less volatile fraction was water-soluble, had a pleasant fruity odor that became meaty on exposure to air, and darkened rapidly on standing. The less volatile fractions from beef and pork had similar properties. The pH was 3.5 to 4.0 and the infrared spectra on rock salt plates were almost identical. This fraction contained about 87 to 90% of optically active lactic acid and an unknown compound absorbing strongly at 290 to 295 mμ and possibly being responsible for the meaty aroma. The nitrogen in this fraction was present in the form of ammonia. When a 3% aqueous extract was heated, a typical meaty aroma resulted. The "most volatile" fractions of lean beef and pork were similar, yielding acetaldehyde, acetone, formaldehyde, and some ammonia. Acidification and distillation resulted in liberating hydrogen sulfide and carbon dioxide.

The free fatty acids of beef and pork fats were extracted with petroleum ether and were obtained by absorption on an anion exchange column, conversion of the eluted fatty acids to their methyl esters, and identification of these by gas chromatography. They were determined prior to, and after heating at 100°C. in vacuo and in air.   Heating in air caused hydrolysis of the triglycerides by moisture present in the fat, and therefore the concentrations were much higher.   There were differences in the amounts and types of the approximately 11 free fatty acids in beef and pork fat.   Pork fat had a high linoleic and oleic acid content which was not observed in beef fat, while the latter contained heptadecaenoic, tetradecenoic, and pentadecanoic acids which appeared to be absent from pork fat.   Fatty acids tentatively identified in beef fat included linolenic, linoleic, oleic, stearic, heptadecenoic, palmitoleic, palmitic, pentadecanoic, tetradecenoic, myristic, and lauric.

The amounts of carbonyl compounds obtained by heating pork and beef fats under conditions similar to those used for identification of the fatty acids were very small when the fats were heated in vacuo.   The amounts obtained by heating in air were larger, presumably because of oxidation, and this technique was therefore used for identification purposes.   Heating the fats produced a much greater variation in odors than did heating the lean meat fractions, and the odors were far less reproducible.   The variety of compounds identified was much greater with pork than with beef.   Thus the volatile fraction from beef yielded only two identified alkanals (acetone and propanal) and one identified 2-enol (acetaldehyde).   A similar fraction from pork fat yielded five identified alkanals and seven identified 2-enals.   When steam distillation was employed, the differences between the two meats were not quite as marked.

In general, the results indicated that a similar basic meaty flavor arises on heating aqueous extracts of lean pork and beef, and that the flavor differences in these meats may be due to the lipid fractions and the compounds associated with these.

Much research on beef flavor was conducted at the American Meat Institute Foundation by Batzer, Doty, Schweigert, and their colleagues (2,3,5).   Their fractionation procedure involved preparation of an aqueous extract of ground raw beef that diffused into water contained in dialysis tubing and was called the diffuzate (fraction A).   This fraction was lyophilized and was then dialyzed in special batches of Visking sausage casing to yield two subfractions, a dialyzate (Aa) and a diffuzate (Ab).   These two fractions were further separated as indicated below.

Fraction Aa1 appeared to be a single protein according to ultracentrifuge data but gave two spots on application of zone electrophoresis. Fraction Aa2 (10 mg. per 1000 grams of beef) was a white fluffy material containing glucose.   When heated with fat, Aa2 gave an odor similar to that of broiled steak.   When Aa2 was mixed with small amounts of Ab1 and Ab2 and the mixture was heated in fat, the odor was equivalent to that of the original fraction A—i.e., a true cooked meat or broiled steak flavor and odor.   The natural and hydrogenated fats used in the heating also contributed to the desirable odor.   Mineral oil gave rather similar but

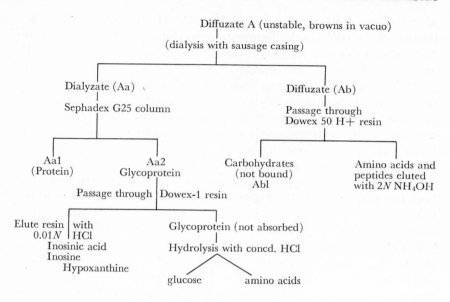

Diffuzate A (unstable, browns in vacuo)

(dialysis with sausage casing)

Dialyzate (Aa)

Sephadex G25 column

Diffuzate (Ab)

Passage through
Dowex 50 H+ resin

Aa1
(Protein)

Aa2
Glycoprotein

Passage through Dowex-1 resin

Carbohydrates
(not bound)
Abl

Amino acids and
peptides eluted
with 2N NH₄OH

Elute resin with 0.01N HCl
Inosinic acid
Inosine
Hypoxanthine

Glycoprotein (not absorbed)

Hydrolysis with concd. HCl

glucose   amino acids

apparently not identical effects. Aa2 isolated from chicken and pork muscle gave an odor similar to that of Aa2 from beef when heated with fat, but there were certain distinguishing characteristics. Aqueous solutions of Aa2 from all three sources had an ultraviolet absorption maximum at 248 mμ.

Aa2 was investigated in detail. It had a low molecular weight, yielded orthophosphate and eight amino acids on hydrolysis, and resembled a glycoprotein. The glycoprotein passed through a Dowex-1 resin column at alkaline pH, and the ultraviolet-absorbing material was absorbed and eluted with dilute HCl. The glycoprotein yielded glucose upon hydrolysis in 1N HCl at 100°C., and eight known amino acids following hydrolysis in strong HCl. Proline, isoleucine, leucine, α-alanine, β-alanine, serine, and valine, and traces of glycine and glutamic acid were identified positively. The original unhydrolyzed material did not give a positive ninhydrin reaction. Inosinic acid, inosine, and hypoxanthine were recovered from the Dowex-1 column eluate.

Heating a mixture of the glycoprotein, inosinic acid, and glucose in fat usually produced a broiled steak odor similar to that formed by the original extract A. However, the results were not always consistent. When Aa2 was added to freeze-dried veal, heating produced a steaklike flavor. It was concluded that the basic precursors of meat flavor had at least been generally identified but that much remained to be accomplished as in determination of the proportions and amounts of precursors and how these react with lipids to give desirable broiled steak aromas and flavors.

Hornstein and Crowe (8) studied lamb flavor. They prepared a cold water extract of the lean meat and subjected the powder obtained by freeze-drying this to pyrolysis at 100° in high vacuum. The total volatiles obtained by condensation in liquid nitrogen were permitted to distill over at room temperature, so that the most volatile fraction was again collected in liquid nitrogen and the residual material remained behind.

The most volatile fraction yielded 2.5 mg. of ammonia and only traces of hydrogen sulfide while in previous work with beef and pork the quantities had been 1.7 and 0.1 mg. per gram, respectively. Carbon dioxide was also present in this fraction. The least volatile fraction had a pleasant fruity aroma that slowly changed to a desirable meaty aroma. This fraction, as with beef and pork, contained 90% lactic acid, and its infrared spectrum was similar to that obtained in similar fractions from beef and pork.

Aqueous solutions of the dry powder had a pH of 6.0 as compared with 5.2 for similar solutions from pork and beef. The main carbonyl compound isolated was acetaldehyde. When a 25% solution of the powder was subjected to gel filtration using Sephadex G25 and $5 \times 10^{-3}M$ NaCl as eluent, two protein fractions were eluted: a comparatively high molecular weight brown powder and a low molecular weight white, fluffy material. These would appear to be similar to the protein and glycoprotein fractions isolated from beef at the American Meat Institute. Vacuum pyrolysis of the high molecular weight fraction gave no appreciable volatile compounds or aroma, while similar treatment of the low molecular weight material yielded the fractions and aromas characteristic of the starting powder.

Great difficulty was experienced in obtaining qualitative and quantitative data on carbonyl compounds in the lipid fraction of lamb. Though lamb fat heated 4 hours at 110° to 115° in a stream of purified air or nitrogen gave a muttonlike aroma, identifiable amounts of carbonyl compounds and free fatty acids were not obtained. Further work included refluxing the fat in the presence of water at 100°C. and distillation under high vacuum. This procedure, although increasing the intensity of the mutton odor, did not liberate significant amounts of carbonyl compounds. When the fat itself was treated by the Schwarz procedure for liberating bound carbonyl compounds, small amounts of comparatively nonvolatile C_6, C_{16}, and C_{18} saturated monocarbonyl compounds were isolated. It is doubtful if these contributed to the aroma. However, total carbonyls as measured by ultraviolet absorption were present in considerably greater amounts than those accounted for by the monocarbonyl fraction, and certain of these are presumably responsible for the mutton aroma. These results are in sharp contrast to those obtained with both beef and pork, where a variety of carbonyl compounds was isolated in each case.

Free fatty acids were detectable in the lamb fat itself before and after heating, but the amount (0.4%) as compared with beef fat (3.7%) and pork fat (5.5%) was very small. Oleic, stearic, and palmitic acids accounted for 99% of the free fatty acids in lamb fat. These saturated free fatty acids would presumably be much more resistant to oxidation than some of the unsaturated ones found in beef and pork fat, and this may explain the comparative absence of 2-enals and 2,4-dienals from heated lamb fat. These results show a similarity between other red meats and lamb as far as precursors of meaty flavor are concerned, but from the very outstanding differences in carbonyl compound and free fatty acid content of the fats, it would appear that trace amounts of carbonyl compounds may be responsible for the characteristic flavor of lamb.

A somewhat different approach to the lamb flavor problem was taken by Jacobson and Koehler (*10*). These investigators roasted lamb at 80° for 7 hours under 20 inches of vacuum, and condensed volatiles in ice-salt and dry ice–alcohol traps. Other lots were simmered in water and volatile carbonyls were collected by distillation.

Five prominent monocarbonyls were identified in such distillates—(1) *n*-hexaldehyde (or 4 to 10 carbon atom straight-chain aldehydes); (2) methyl isopropyl ketone (or methyl ketones of 5 to 10 carbon atoms); (3) methylcyclopentanone; (4) propionaldehyde; and (5) acetaldehyde. Polycarbonyls were present but not identified.

Dialyzates of ground raw and cooked lamb were prepared. Glucose, fructose, and inositol were identified in dialyzates of both raw and cooked lamb, as were 19 amino-containing components. No differences in different breeds of sheep were found. The authors suggest that, while the sugars and amino acids may contribute to the meaty flavor of lamb, the carbonyl compounds are probably responsible for typical lamb flavor.

Marine Flesh Foods

Much of the early work on fish flavor was carried out by Japanese investigators, and particularly by Obata and his colleagues. These and related studies have been reviewed by Bramstedt (*4*). The most recent review of this field was by Jones (*11*), who has referred to the contribution of 5′-inosinic acid to fish flavor in a recent article (*12*).

Fish flesh contains fairly variable amounts of free amino acids, the concentrations of which may alter with season or sexual maturity. These, specifically proline, may be important in contributing to the faint sweet flavor of really fresh fish, and of course each participates in Maillard reactions under certain conditions. Obata investigated certain degradation products of these amino acids, some of which appear to be present in or on fresh fish and others of which probably arise via bacterial degradation. Thus, pyridine, believed responsible for a proportion of the odor of fresh-caught fish, was found in the skin. It could be formed from lysine via pipyridine. α-Aminovaleric acid was also found in fish, and its possible routes of formation from proline or from arginine were outlined. It would seem that higher acids or aldehydes, such as isovaleric acid, may arise by degradation of certain amino acids, and are probably responsible for undesirable flavors.

It has been suggested that sugars and sugar phosphates, particularly ribose, glucose, and glucose 6-phosphate, which often occur in comparatively large amounts in fish flesh, may contribute to a desirable sweet flavor. As mentioned above, the combined effect of free amino acids, and particularly of histidine, aspartic, glutamic, and proline, may be to enhance sweetness. 5'-Inosinic acid, present in comparatively high concentrations in muscles of most fish post-mortem, almost certainly produces meaty flavor, while its degradation products, inosine, and more particularly hypoxanthine, probably occasion bitterness under some circumstances.

Though pure nonoxidized triglyceride oils are said to be flavorless, certain types of fish are considered in prime condition only when their muscle is rich in triglyceride depot fats. Recent work in these laboratories has indicated that volatile odoriferous compounds are responsible for the desirable flavors of red spring salmon. When fresh oil extracted by pressure from freshly baked salmon was incorporated into blended comparatively nonfatty, freshly cooked halibut flesh in an amount representing only one fifth that of the oil present in the salmon flesh (16%), the halibut assumed a salmon-like flavor (18). It was also demonstrated that a volatile fraction of the oil from baked spring salmon when examined by gas chromatography contained at least 13 different compounds which were not identified (19). Unfortunately the program had to be abandoned at this stage. Whether the oil contains bound carbonyl compounds or merely acts as a "carrier" of odorous substances is not known.

Other investigators have demonstrated the presence of a number of carbonyl and alcohol compounds in fresh raw or cooked fish, including acetaldehyde, methanol, ethanol, propionaldehyde, acetone, isobutyraldehyde, propionaldehyde, 2-methylbutyraldehyde, and small amounts of long-chain compounds. Volatile acids such as acetic, formic, propionic, and butyric may also be present. In recent work 13 different carbonyl compounds were identified in salted cod, but no attempt was made to determine the relation of any of these to flavor. Similar relative concentrations of volatile acids in this fish (formic, acetic, propionic, butyric, and valeric) suggested that monocarbonyls were their precursors. The carbonyl compounds probably arise by autoxidation of unsaturated lipids since this fish is stored under conditions which accelerate lipid oxidation (24). There is little doubt that these and other related volatile compounds are important contributors to aromas and flavors of fish, but positive information in this area is lacking. Since carbonyl compounds have frequently been associated with autoxidized fish oils, it would seem probable that these compounds may more frequently be associated with undesirable than desirable flavors and odors.

Organic nitrogenous compounds of low molecular weight are present in most sea foods. Thus betaines such as homarin, γ-butyrobetaine, glycinebetaine, trigonellin, and stachydrine, trimethylamine oxide, traces of mono-, di-, and trimethylamines, and urea are present in fresh edible sea fish and marine invertebrates. Many of these are known to possess characteristic flavors, but their comparative role in producing typical desirable flavors of various seafoods has never been accurately assessed.

Volatile sulfur compounds are present in marine products. Thus it has long been known that hydrogen sulfide is present in canned salmon, and traces of methylmercaptan have been found in fish. Recently interest has centered around the occurrence and role of dimethyl sulfide in odor and flavor production in marine products. Several years ago it was shown that small amounts of this compound were present in frozen haddock. Complaints of certain importers of frozen and canned Japanese and Canadian salmon regarding the limited occurrence of a "petroleum-like" aroma in the fish stimulated an exhaustive investigation of the problem. Briefly, it was discovered that a zooplankton, *Limacina helicina*, contained a comparatively large amount of dimethyl-2-carboxyethyl sulfonium chloride (dimethyl-β-propiothetin) and that chum salmon ingested this pteropod. As a result the livers, and eventually the flesh, became contaminated. On heating, as in canning, this compound degrades to yield dimethyl sulfide, which was considered to be responsible for the flavor defect (17).

$$(CH_3)_2 -SH - CH_2 - CH_2 - COOH \rightarrow (CH_3)_2S + CH_3 - CH_2 - COOH$$

More recently this compound has been found to be associated with a flavor problem in Labrador cod (1). Recently in our laboratories a study was made of the volatile sulfur compounds of fresh and staling Pacific oysters. In fresh oysters the only volatile compound present in significant amounts was dimethyl sulfide, and it was concluded that this compound is largely responsible for the characteristic desirable odor of these shellfish (20). The above would seem to constitute cases where a given compound produces desirable and undesirable aromas or flavors under different circumstances. There may be many similar situations.

Maillard reactions occur in dried and heated (canned) fish products under certain conditions, as was first demonstrated in our laboratories 15 years ago. These reactions usually occur between ribose or glucose and free amino acids and proteins, but carbonyl compounds arising via fatty acid oxidation are probably involved under certain conditions. Such browning is usually considered detrimental, in that it is usually associated with undesirable acrid and bitter flavors. Recent work from our laboratories, which will soon be published, has shown that these reactions proceed very slowly in freeze dried fish even at zero relative humidity under nitrogen and with most of the ribose and glucose removed if the fish is held at 35°C. When freeze-dried fish browns, it becomes extremely tough and gives off a most penetrating and unpleasant ammoniacal and acrid odor. This odor seems similar to that found for fraction A from beef, as mentioned previously.

Inosinic Acid and Related Compounds

This subject is being covered in detail in another presentation at this symposium. The subject has been reviewed recently by Wagner, Titus, and Schade (22), Kuninaka, Kibi, and Sakaguchi (15) and Shimazono (21). Since 5'-inosinic acid is frequently found in fish in comparatively large amounts (6), it is obvious that it must contribute to desirable flavor. Studies in our laboratories using radioactive adenosine triphosphate have shown that this compound is almost certainly the precursor of inosinic acid in fish muscle. It is further degraded to inosine, which is hydrolyzed by a nucleoside hydrolase to yield ribose and hypoxanthine. In certain fish such as salmon little hypoxanthine forms. Hypoxanthine itself has been reported to exert a bitter flavor. Recent work has implicated naturally occurring inosinic acid, guanylic acid, and glutamate as desirable flavoring components of ripe gonads of sea urchins, which are consumed in Japan (14).

Conclusions

The whole field of research into cause and control of desirable flavors in flesh foods offers great promise to interested chemists. In some ways it is surprising that so far such a small effort has been made in an area of research which would seem important to a multimillion dollar segment of the food industry.

Red meats, and perhaps chicken also, contain a glycoprotein fraction that, when heated in presence of inosinic acid and fats yields a pungent, meaty aroma and flavor. So far a similar fraction has not been identified in fish muscle. A volatile fraction containing lactic acid and a certain uncharacterized compound absorbing strongly at 290 to 295 mμ has also been isolated from meats. This fraction also seems to give a meaty aroma on heating. Certain fish, particularly tuna, have a high lactic acid content in their muscles post-mortem, and it would be interesting to determine whether these fish possess this fraction.

All flesh foods contain free amino acids and certain reducing sugars, and there is little doubt that Maillard reactions between these, and also between the sugars and certain proteins, affect flavor. Probably certain of these reactions affect flavor favorably, and others have an unfavorable effect. It seems certain that all flesh foods contain inosinic acid and that this either alone, or in combination with certain amino acids, exerts a "meaty" flavor.

The situation regarding free fatty acids and carbonyl compounds in flesh foods and their effect on flavors and aromas is undoubtedly important but is also extremely complex. All flesh foods appear to contain compounds such as formaldehyde, acetaldehyde, acetone, acetoin and/or diacetyl, and free fatty acids containing one to four carbon atoms. The contribution of long-chain and unsaturated carbonyl compounds to flavor and aromas is at present little understood.

Literature Cited

(1) Ackman, R. G., Sipos, J. C., *J. Fisheries Res. Board Can.* **21**, 423 (1964).
(2) Batzer, O. F., Santoro, A. T., Landmann, W. A., *J. Agr. Food Chem.* **10**, 94 (1962).
(3) Batzer, O. F., Santoro, A. T., Tan, M. C., Landmann, W. A., Schweigert, B. S., *Ibid.*, **8**, 498 (1960).
(4) Bramstedt, F., *Arch. Fischereiwissenschaft* **8**, 94 (1957).
(5) Doty, D. M., Batzer, O. F., Landmann, W. A., Santoro, A. T., Proceedings of Flavor Chemistry Symposium, Campbell Soup Co., Camden, N. J., p. 7 (1961).
(6) Fujita, T., Hashimoto, Y., *Bull. Japan Soc. Sci. Fisheries*, **26**, 907 (1960).
(7) Hornstein, I., Crowe, P. F., *J. Agr. Food Chem.* **8**, 494 (1960).
(8) *Ibid.*, **11**, 147 (1963).
(9) Hornstein, I., Crowe, P. F., Sulzbacher, W. L., *Ibid.*, **8**, 65 (1960).
(10) Jacobson, M., Koehler, H. H., *Ibid.*, **11**, 336 (1963).
(11) Jones, N. R., Proceedings of Flavor Chemistry Symposium, Campbell Soup Co., Camden, N. J., p. 61, 1961.
(12) Jones, N. R., Proceedings of 11th International Congress on Refrigeration, Munich, Germany, p. 917, 1963.
(13) Kazeniac, S. J., Proceedings of Flavor Chemistry Symposium, Campbell Soup Co., Camden, N. J., p. 37, 1961.
(14) Komata, Y., *Bull. Japan Soc Sci. Fisheries* **30**, 749 (1964).
(15) Kuninaka, A., Kibi, M., Sakaguchi, K., *Food Technol.* **18**, 287 (1964).
(16) Lineweaver, H., Pippen, E. L., Proceedings of Flavor Chemistry Symposium, Campbell Soup Co., Camden, N. J., p. 21, 1961.
(17) Motohiro, T., *Mem. Fac. Fisheries, Hokkaido Univ.* **10**, 1 (1962).
(18) Ronald, A. P., Thomson, W. A. B., Fisheries Research Board of Canada, Annual Report of Vancouver Station for 1961–62, p. 39, 1962.
(19) *Ibid., Vancouver Station* 1962–63, p. 54, 1963.
(20) Ronald, A. P., Thomson, W. A. B., *J. Fisheries Res. Board Can.* **21**, 1481 (1964).
(21) Shimazono, H., *Food Technol.* **18**, 294 (1964).
(22) Wagner, J. R., Titus, D. S., Schade, J. E., *Food Technol.* **17**, 730 (1963).
(23) Yueh, M. H., Strong, F. M., *J. Agr. Food Chem.* **8**, 491 (1960).
(24) Yurkowski, M., Bordeleau, M. A., *J. Fisheries Res. Board Can.* **22**, 27 (1965).

RECEIVED April 27, 1965.

Advances in Spice Flavor and Oleoresin Chemistry

J. A. ROGERS

Fritzsche Brothers, Inc., New York, N. Y.

The choice of spice materials has been based on human organoleptic selection since ancient times. Organic chemistry has been applied since its beginning to spice materials and their vital flavor components. Analysis, research, and production methods have provided flavor concentrates which are more representative of the dried spice. Three spice items have been chosen, capsicum, black pepper, and clove, which contain nonvolatile, volatile, or combination flavor components. A physical description of these spices, their origin, past and present import figures, a history of chemical investigations, some analytical methods, and instrumental curves identifying some components are presented. The value of organic analysis and research and their application to commercial products are discussed.

We are well aware of the complex nature of flavor and its chemical, physical, and physiological aspects. Various objective methods for evaluation have been presented, and any one (or a combination) may herald the discovery, correlating the mechanistic, chemical, or electronic characteristics of a flavor chemical or a compound, with the sensation observed subjectively by the human detectors. Admittedly, descriptive, reproducible flavor measurement of an objective nature could find ready application in the field of spice flavor chemistry.

A particular dualism further complicates the problem. We must consider that flavor is a combination of the senses of smell and taste, each contributing in varying proportions, each sense an independent entity, detecting different aspects of a flavor compound but combining to produce a unique sensation which we know as flavor. While one day, objective measurement may play a major role in flavor evaluation, the flavor industry at present operates from a position of subjective human sensation. Traditionally and empirically we are directed by odor and flavor experts, such as flavor chemists, perfumers, and tasters, by expert flavor panels, even by nonexpert panels. The most valuable quality control factor in a flavor company today is a person gifted with a unique sensitivity to a wide range of flavor; who has developed his senses of taste and smell by constant practice; and who possesses excellent sense memory or flavor recall. If he has imagination in the field, his quality control ability is overshadowed by his potential creativity, and he is valuable indeed.

Long before we had flavor experts, the strong pleasant odors of many natural products attracted ancient man, and he tasted them. Certain berries, fruits, roots, bark, and leaves also had pleasing aromas but were found to have little food value. They did, however, stimulate the senses, causing a noticeable increase in the flow of digestive juices, and thus they contributed to the better utilization of food. These materials are the spices of the flavor industry. Their main function is to impart flavor, and often the term spice is used as a synonym for flavor. Biological research may yet prove the metabolic utility of spices other than the simulatory and physiological effects brought about by sense satisfaction or the antiseptic, sedative, or healing properties of certain spices, such as clove oil. The prime purpose of spice and spice derivatives is to enhance the appeal of food, whether by flavor, eye appeal, and so on.

While food science has progressed rapidly and has kept pace with chemical and technological advances, flavor science has apparently lagged. The reason for this has been the esthetic nature of flavor itself, and the difficulty of measurement. Based on the unknown factors of human taste and odor perception, and the pure subjectivity of flavor, the development of scientific facts, numbers, classifications, and systems has been greatly limited. It is much too personally oriented at present to follow general rules which could then become the basis of a science. Even in those areas where physical science is equal to human sensation, as in the field of color evaluation, the flavor industry insists on the expression of a color entity in visual perception units of doubtful reproducibility, based on a nonequivalent standard when an accurate spectrophotometer value can be obtained (Figure 1). In such areas we find most subjective-objective discrepancies, some of which are being solved, but many remain to be solved before we may reasonably call the flavor industry scientifically controlled.

I have purposely emphasized the subjective nature of flavoring with spices to show that caution is necessary and also that you may not always find the direct scientific approach in flavor chemistry. Where only flavor is concerned, we must begin our application of chemical methods from a subjective evaluation. As an example, we know by taste that black pepper spice has a bite which is desirable. By the usual chemical or mechanical means we separate various components or fractions of the material and subjectively evaluate them for bite. Having eliminated extraneous mat-

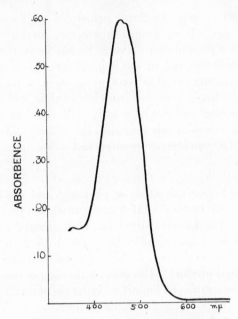

Figure 1. *Visible spectrophoto-*
metric curve of oleoresin paprika
Concentration 5 mg. per 100 ml. in acetone

ter, it becomes a chemical problem then to purify, confirm our flavor evaluation, and set about to identify the component. Since we are dealing with natural plant products, which are known to be complex mixtures of organic compounds, the chemistry of organic compounds has most application. Stereochemistry, optical isomerism, and the unique sensitivity of many of the chemicals encountered make a certain aspect of specialization necessary. Again, the focal point of the chemical applications has been the subjective sensation of human detectors to a chemical or group of chemicals.

The basic material from which spice flavor chemistry originates is the dried spice itself. Whether it is a fruit, berry, seed, bark, twig, leaf, or root, the dried spice contains the flavor components and extraneous plant matter. Such things as fixed oils (plant glycerides), tannins, resins, proteins, cellulose, pentosans, starch, pigments, alkaloids, and mineral elements, contribute little to flavor. The flavor components are volatile and nonvolatile organic compounds. For the most part, volatile oils are the vital flavor components. The essential oils of cinnamon bark, clove buds, and pimenta berries represent almost the total flavor in the dried spice. In red pepper or capsicum, the nonvolatile amides are responsible for the heat or flavor. In black pepper, a combination exists between nonvolatile piperine (an amide), which gives bite, and the essential oil of pepper, which gives flavor top note and odor character.

In those spices where the flavor principles are found in the volatile portion, the essential oils are a most satisfactory product to produce for a concentration of representative flavor. Steam or water distillation will codistill all the volatiles out of the ground spice, leaving the fixed oils, tannins, resins, proteins, cellulose, etc., in the flavor-exhausted still charge. The essential oils, being generally water-insoluble, will separate on condensation and cooling, and can be readily collected. In addition to steam distillation, some essential oils (notably the citrus) have also been produced by manual or machine expression, and some (notably the floral) by enfleurage (20).

The essential oils may be further processed by fractional distillation, crystallization, selective solvation, or chemical and mechanical isolation to concentrate even further vital flavor principles i.e., D-carvone from caraway oil or eugenol from clove oils. Organoleptic evaluation at one time determined the component to be isolated; modern chemical means can be used to detect, to control the reactions, to purify, and finally to produce the desired product. The odor evaluation of the finished product still remains, however, a most important criterion of quality.

In those spices where the flavor components are wholly or in part nonvolatile, the essential oil is not a representative concentration of the spice flavor. Another product must be developed, which incorporates the nonvolatile components as well. While tinctures and extracts may satisfy this requirement, the presence of solvents reduces the flavor concentration. Thus an oleoresin is manufactured, which is an extraction of the ground spice with a highly volatile selective solvent. The extract is then drained, leaving the insolubles, and transferred to a concentrator where the solvent is removed, leaving nonvolatiles, volatiles, and as little extraneous matter as possible. Depending on the polarity of the solvent and the moisture of the spice, certain nonflavor components may be carried along into the finished oleoresin. These may be removed to some extent by solubilization, filtration, or centrifugation and may include fixed oil, sugars, starches, tannins, resins, and pigments. Since overheating is detrimental to the flavor and solubility of the oleoresin, the concentration step is most critical. Reduced pressure is used to remove the solvent completely, quickly, and at a low pot temperature.

In both essential oil and oleoresin manufacture (20, 29), the selection of the raw spice material is based on quality, yield, cost, and availability, as well as flavor difference owing to origin. Grinding to the proper size for the particular spice is important: fine enough to release the flavor components but large enough to prevent channeling or carryover in the oil or necessitating filtration of fines from oleoresin. The flavor components of the spice determine whether dry or wet steam or water distillation is used for the essential oil, or whether one solvent is more efficient than another for extracting the oleoresin. Such solvents as methanol, ethanol, 2-propanol, hexane, heptane, benzene, ethylene dichloride, and methyl chloroform, as well as butane, Freons, and even carbon dioxide, have been used.

The various types of products we encounter in the flavor industry are:

Whole spice	Oleoresins	Spray-drys
Ground spice	Essential oils	Spray-cools
Tinctures	Isolates	Dry-solubles
Extracts	Synthetics	Freeze-drys

To demonstrate the importance of chemistry in the spice flavor field, we have selected three spice flavors of different types to discuss the improvements that have been made in these products because of chemical applications. We have chosen capsicum, where mainly nonvolatile components are responsible for the desirable flavor, and thus the oleoresin is the commercial concentrate; black pepper, where a combination of volatiles and nonvolatiles is most necessary for a representative flavor, and while an essential oil is produced, the oleoresin is most representative; and clove, where the essential oil is the most important flavor. In the trade, the pungency of capsicum is described as "heat"; in black pepper, it is described as "bite." To show the commercial interest of the raw materials, we look at the import figures for 1946, 1962, and 1965, the last are the most recent complete figures available.

United States Spice Imports (million of pounds)

	1946	*1962*	*1965*
Capsicum	8.9	8.8	10.1
Paprika	6.5	9.6	12.4
Black pepper	10.6	36.4	44.1
Cloves	4.8	2.7	2.8

Capsicum

Origins. Capsicum is the dried ripe fruit of a genus of Solanaceae. It was first discovered by the spice traders when Columbus and the Spaniards found it in the West Indies in 1492 and later throughout Central and South America. It had been cultivated by the Aztecs for a thousand years. It was brought back to Spain in 1514 and grown for decoration because of its bright red color (4). It rapidly became an important spice item because of its color and its bite as well. It spread throughout Italy, Greece, and Turkey. The Hungarians obtained it from Turkey and perfected the species along color lines. This development resulted in sweet red pepper called paprika and identified as *Capsicum annum* (L.). Similar strains were developed in Spain over the years, and work was started in California in 1931 to grow this domestically. The outbreak of World War II hastened this development. In addition, European immigrants brought seeds with them, and production was started to a small extent in Yakima Valley, Wash., and St. James Parish, La. (34). The first commercial production in the United States was the area of San Juan Capistrano, Calif., where 70 acres were grown in 1940 from the strains under development since 1931 (63). As the war halted the imports from Spain, Bulgaria, and Hungary, U. S. production increased significantly. In 1938–39, imports were 6 million pounds, 2.5 million from Hungary (28). In 1965, of the 12.4 million pounds imported, about 50% came from Spain. The Spanish strains have continued to produce the highest colored dry material, and now the oleoresin is produced in Spain as well. Since color is lost when the dried material is shipped, the larger part of the imports represent material destined for use as dried or ground spice, rather than extraction for oleoresin. The California product, while slightly lower in color, has also become a large commercial commodity. Since oleoresin capsicum is the more important flavor product, we will not discuss oleoresin paprika further at this time.

While capsicum for color developed toward perfection of the annum species, the smaller peppers, which had the greater bite as observed at the time of Columbus, were also selected and cross bred, and a few very hot pungent varieties have developed: *Capsicum frutescens* (L.), *baccutum* (L.), or *annum* var canoides Irish. These types have been developed in Mombassa, Congo, Zanzibar, India, Japan, and Mexico, and from these is derived oleoresin capsicum, which has been classified by the industry as "African" type chilies, of very high pungency. A second somewhat milder type is converted into oleoresin American red pepper, from *Capsicum annum* var. longum Sendt or Lousiana Sport hybrids. The product has medium to high pungency. Thus while innumerable varieties are grown for canning, pickling, and home use, the extremes of color and pungencies are the varieties of commercial importance. Of the 8.8 million pounds imported in 1963, 3.0 million came from Japan. A good deal of the African material is processed domestically for oleoresin (42).

Chemistry. In 1876 Thresh (57, 58) isolated the pungent principle from capsicum and called it capsaicin. Micko (31, 32) improved the method of Thresh in extracting capsaicin and obtained a crystalline substance of high pungency. The material melted at 63°C. and had the properties of a phenol. Micko found one hydroxyl and one methoxy group by the Zeisel method. On reaction with platinic chloride and HCl, he observed a vanilla-like odor. He also discovered a 20-fold increase in capsaicin available from frutescens over annum varieties.

Scoville (49) in 1912 developed an organoleptic threshold determination of heat. The extract or oleoresin was diluted until the solution failed to give a stinging sensation on the tongue. Based on an accurate weighing of initial product, the Scoville heat units were determined in large increments, such as 1 in 20,000, 1 in 30,000, etc. A modification of this test is used to the present day, and oleoresin capsicum (high pungency) has values above 1 million.

Nelson (*36*) contributed to the identification of capsicum by alkali hydrolysis of the methyl ether formed from the substance obtained by Micko's method, obtaining a nitrogenous material and an acid. The nitrogen-containing material was found to be a vanillylamine homolog, veratralamine, proved by synthesis via vanillin-oxime reduction and methylation, and the acid proved to be an isodecenoic acid. By reaction of vanillylamine and the acid, he reconstituted the pungent amide. In 1923, Nelson and Dawson (*37*) determined the location of the double bond in the acid by oxidation, forming adipic and isobutyric acid. The double bond is between the 6th and 7th carbon atoms. The saturated acid was synthesized, the natural acid saturated and proved identical. Thus the structure of the pungent principle was:

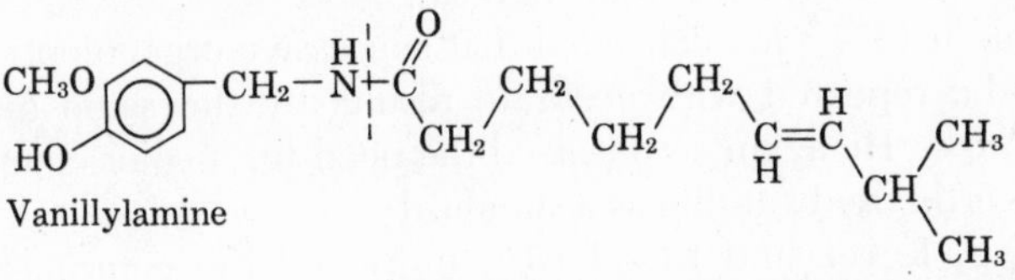

Vanillylamine

6–Isodecenoic acid

Nelson also established the fact that the double bond was not necessary for pungency.

Since most workers found the organoleptic control of capsaicin so difficult and nonreproducible, other methods were sought to determine capsaicin.

Tice in 1933 (*59*) developed a colorimetric method based on the work of Fodor (*18*), wherein capsaicin gave a blue color with vanadium oxytrichloride. Hayden and Jordan evaluated this method (*23*) and reported that the results were not very reliable. However, Tice's method has become the basis for a gravimetric separation still in use.

Dodge in 1941 (*12*) summarized the previous work and observed the similarity between the structures of capsaicin and one of the pungent principles of ginger, which is:

Zingerone

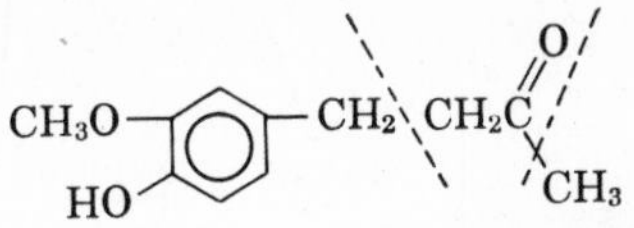

It is known that the heat intensity of the capsaicin amide is much greater than that of the ketones of ginger spices.

In 1946, Nakajima (*33*) undertook some syntheses and made vanillylamides, using acids from acetic to lauric. Organoleptically evaluating these products, he established that the most pungent material was the C-7 or heptanoic acid amine. The effect of chain branching or unsaturation close to the amide was not investigated. His postulation that dibasic acids, thus diamides, would be more pungent proved to be unfounded.

North (38) used the Folin-Denis reagent in the colorimetric analysis of capsaicin.

Folin and Denis in 1912 had used phosphotungstic-phosphomolybdic acid to determine vanillin in vanilla extracts. North, because of the similarity in structures, used vanillin as the standard in this method, and adjusted the results to the difference in molecular weights between capsaicin and vanillin. The sample preparation, however, was tedious since North attempted to reduce phenolic interference by selective solubility.

Schulte and Krüger (48) developed another colorimetric test, using diazobenzene sulfonic acid to form the color with the phenolic group. Again, the capsaicin had to be separated from interferences by column chromatography on alumina and charcoal.

Schenk in 1957 (46) conceded that successive organoleptic taste tests could not be repeated with accurate results by the same individual in under 3 hours. He again emphasized the need for a color comparison test and, like North, used vanillin as a standard.

Spanyar, Kevei, and Kiszel (51) improved the colorimetric test on the dry spice itself so that ascorbic acid, vanillin, phenol, and tannins did not interfere.

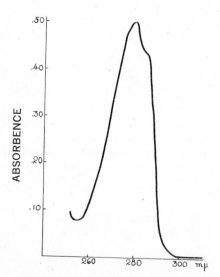

Figure 2.   Ultraviolet spectrophotometric curve of pure capsaicine

Concentration 50 mg. per 100 ml. in ethylene dichloride

In 1958, Borkowski, Gertig, and Olszak (5) tested drying methods on capsaicin and reported that the highest yield of capsaicin was from the fruit that was air dried with no light present.

Kosuge, Inagaki, and Uehara (26), using paper chromatography, separated two pungent principles in Japanese capsicum. These materials were in a ratio of 2.1 to 1.0 in weight. The molecular weights were calculated to be 302 and 315, respectively.

Four types of green peppers were examined for capsaicin by Samy, Kamat, and Pandya (45), and the extracts of the fresh green material showed capsaicin from 7.5 to 29.4 mg. per 100 grams. The authors state that ripening and sun drying reduced the amount of capsaicin.

Zitko and Durigova (64), using paper chromatography, identified hydroxycinnamic acid and four flavonoids in extracts of paprika. Another phenol was also separated as white crystals (m.p. 55.5°C.) which had no bite but had an ultraviolet maximum from 235 to 292 mμ. The identification of these items begins to indicate the reasons for the discrepancies in previous analyses.

In 1961, Datta and Susi (10) reported that it was possible to identify synthetic "capsaicin," since the unsaturated acid structure was not synthetically available. Thus an infrared peak at 970 cm.$^{-1}$, specific for trans double bonds, should indicate a natural product.

Todd and Perun (60) isolated the pungent principles from samples of oleoresin or ether extract, presumably from capsicum, and prepared the methyl ester of the fatty acid portion of the amides. These methyl esters were then separated by gas chromatography and compared with authentic capsicum samples treated in the same way. They detected two additional acids in natural crystallized capsaicin but did not identify them. The main unidentified acid increased in samples of annum species and was thought to be one carbon shorter than the isodecenoic. Infrared absorption at 970 cm.$^{-1}$ evidently confirms the presence of natural material of trans double-bonded acid but alone does not guarantee the complete authenticity of the product.

Ferns (17) evaluated solvents and found that acetone was the best solvent for extraction of capsicum.

The first ultraviolet method for capsaicin determination was suggested by Brauer and Schoen (6). After a column chromatographic separation, capsaicin is determined at 282 mμ (Figure 2).

Kosuge, Inagaki, and Ino (25) continued to investigate the two pungent principles. Infrared examination of the unknown showed no double bond, and the substance did not take up bromine. Reduction of the noneoic acid yielded a product identical with the unknown, which was thus shown to be 8-methylnonanoic acid.

Recently, Tandon, Dravid, and Siddappa (55) used North's method to determine capsaicin in local chilies in Mysore, India, variety acuminatum (*Capsicum annum*). They found that the pericarp, which is 40% of the whole chili, contains 89% of the capsaicin; the seeds, which are 54% of whole chili, contain 11% of total capsaicin. The finished oleoresin contained 2.0% capsaicin, and the order of solvent preference for capsaicin extraction was ether < hexane < chloroform < alcohol < acetone.

The foregoing reports bring us up to date and follow the advances in the chemistry of capsicum oleoresins from the beginning to the present day. Whether or not the flavor industry has made use of this information to produce commercial oleoresins can be determined by examining the products available. Uniformity and adherence to industry-wide standards indicate this fact. While not the final answer and while other industrial association specifications exist, the Essential Oil Association, a group composed of about 70 companies, many vitally concerned with flavoring materials, has published standards on both types of oleoresin capsicum ("African" chilies and American red pepper). These specifications define such items as botanical source, appearance and odor, method of determination and Scoville heat units, color value, residual solvent presence (according to Food, Drug and Cosmetic Act regulations), solubility, storage, and containers. Several aspects of the specifications, such as capsaicin content and color value, are still under investigation.

Black Pepper (Piper nigrum)

Black pepper spice is the small dried berry of a perennial vine, native to the East Indies. This is the most important of all the spices, being an article of value and commerce, as mentioned in the writings of the Romans and known in Greece from the Fourth Century B.C. It has continued to be produced in the greatest volume even to the present day. The fruit is borne on spikes 4 to 5 inches long, each carrying from 50 to 60 berries. Each berry contains a single seed enclosed in a pulpy layer within the pericarp. Black pepper is the whole berry while white pepper consists of the very ripe fruit from which the dark hull (outer and inner coating) has been removed by a soaking process during which some fermentation takes place. An important grade for processing for essential oils and oleoresins is the Lampong type, grown in an area centered in Southern Sumatra and extending into Indonesia. Another important type for processing, but at present produced more abundantly is Malabar, from India. The Malabar is slightly higher in oil and slightly lower in piperine (the pungent amide) than Lampong. Of the 36 million pounds imported in 1962, 21 million originated in India, and 12 million in Indonesia.

The dried pepper corn contains volatile oil, fixed oil, resin, alkaloids, proteins, cellulose, pentosans, starch, and mineral elements. The important flavor components are the volatile oil, which is present as 1 to 3% of the dried fruit, mainly in the seed covering. This essential oil is an almost colorless to slightly greenish liquid with the characteristic odor of pepper. The taste of the oil is mild and not at all pungent. The other vital flavor components are the nonvolatile alkaloids (present in from 6 to 10%) which are responsible for the pungent, biting taste. Oleoresin black pepper, which is the normal representative concentration of the spice flavor, is usually made by extraction with chlorinated solvents because piperine, the main pungent principle, is most soluble in such materials. Most oil and oleoresin used in this country are produced domestically. Fritzsche Brothers is collaborating in producing black pepper of the Malabar type in Jamaica, B.W.I.

Chemistry. Oersted (*39*), in 1820, first isolated a yellow crystalline material, which had a pungent taste, from extracts of black pepper. Though it was soluble in acetic acid, Pelletier (*43*) discovered that this material was not a base and was not the only pungent principle in piper nigrum.

Buchheim in 1876 (*8*) investigated the liquid portion of black pepper extract after the piperine was removed. He found a greater bite in this portion than he observed from crystalline piperine.

In 1877, Cazeneuve and Caillol (*9*) developed an extraction procedure for removal of piperine from the extract or oleoresin.

Rugheimer synthesized piperine from piperonyl chloride and piperidine (*44*).

Ladenbury and Scholtz (*27*) definitely established the structure of piperine by total synthesis.

STRUCTURE OF PIPERINE

In 1913, Dobbie and Fox (*11*) reported the infrared absorption spectrum of piperine.

Ott and Eichler in 1922 (*40*) confirmed the existence of other pungent principles in the oleoresin of pepper. It was found that they differ only in the structure of the acid component. They detected isochavicinic acid, which is the trans-cis isomer of piperic acid.

With Lüdemann (*41*), Ott discovered that chavicinic acid was also present. This is the cis-cis isomer and reportedly a more pungent material than piperine.

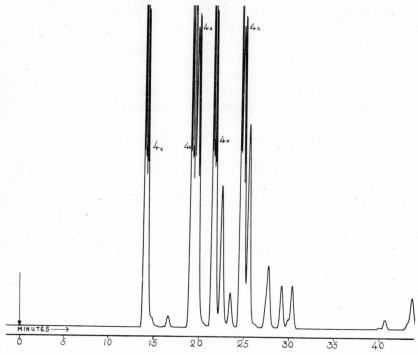

Figure 3. Gas chromatographic curve
Programmed temperature, flame detector,

In 1950, Spring and Stark (52) removed the piperine from extracts and found a second crystalline material (m.p. 146°C.). This was yellow rods with a pronounced green shade, giving a positive Labat test for menthene dioxy group. The ultraviolet maximum was 364 rather than 345 mμ for piperine. Hydrolysis yielded an acid which also gave the methylene dioxy test. This new material was called piperettine and identified as the homolog of piperine but with an additional ethylene linkage in the acid portion—that is, a C-7 instead of a C-5 side chain.

The first generally accepted method of analysis for piperine, still in effect in the flavor industry, is a Kjeldahl nitrogen determination (2).

In 1955, Fagen, Kolen, and Hussong (16) developed an ultraviolet spectrophotometric method, measuring piperine at about 345 mμ.

In 1956, Lee (30) developed a colorimetric method based on hydrolyzing the methylene dioxy group to formaldehyde and determining formaldehyde by chromatropic acid color development. Lee's method was based on the work done by Bricker and Johnson (7) and has been accepted by the American Spice Trade Association for determining piperine (1).

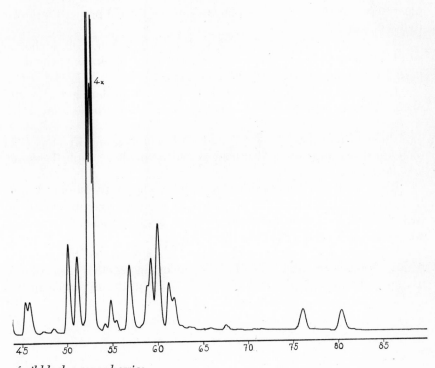

of oil black pepper berries
Carbowax 20M as liquid substrate

Tausig, Suzuki, and Morse (56), the following year, found certain discrepancies in the ultraviolet method and upon investigation reported that in the presence of light and in chlorinated solvents there is a loss of piperine as such, since the absorption maximum is reduced in intensity. We have observed this effect as well and have also noticed that this effect is more pronounced using chloroform, and in decreasing order, carbon tetrachloride, ethylene dichloride, and methylchloroform. It is our suggestion that this occurs because the amide interacts with trace hydrolysates of chlorinated solvents.

Most recently, Genest, Smith, and Chapman (19) reported a very thorough study on piperine in many different sources of black pepper by both colorimetric and spectrophotometric methods. Using column, paper, and thin-layer chromatography, they determined that piperittene was present in all black pepper samples and that there were no shorter side chain homologs than piperine. The authors used the ratio of piperine to piperittene to determine the geographical origin and in certain cases were successful; the Indian Malabar type has a ratio of from 5 to 9 piperine to 1 of piperittene; and the Indonesia Lampong type, 11 to 14 piperine to 1

piperittene. A single sample of Jamaica material gave properties similar
to the Indian type.

Oil of Black Pepper. In 1835 Dumas *(13)* and in 1840 Soubeiran
and Capitaine *(54)* examined the essential oil of black pepper and reported a minimum of oxygenated components.

Eberhardt in 1887 *(14)* treated the oil with alcohol and acid and
obtained terpin hydrate but could not determine the terpene from which
it came.

From 1890 Schimmel Co. *(3)* and 1901 Schreiner and Kremers *(47)*
found further components; identified were caryophyllene, 1-phellandrene,
and dipentene.

Little work was done on the oil until 1957, when Hasselstrom, Hewitt,
Konigsbacher, and Ritter *(22)* reported α- and β-pinene, piperonal, di-
hydrocarveol, β-caryophyllene and its oxide, cryptone, phenylacetic acid,
an azulene, and a series of unidentified alcohols.

Ikeda, Stanley, Vannier, and Spitler *(24)* investigated the monoterpene components present in oil of black pepper among other essential oils,
using gas chromatography, and found that 57.2% of the oil was composed

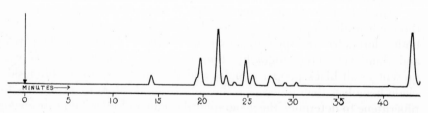

Figure 4. Gas chromatographic

Programmed temperature, flame detector,

of monoterpene components. The monoterpenes found and their per cent concentration in the terpene fraction were:

α-Pinene	9.4	α-Phellandrene	3.6
α-Thujene	2.9	α-Terpenene	0.3
Camphene	0.1	Myrcene	6.4
β-Pinene	13.1	d-Limonene	21.6
Sabinene	20.4	β-Phellandrene	4.1
Δ-3-Carene	15.1	γ-Terpene	1.0
		Terpinolene + p-cymene	2.5

Our gas chromatographic curve (Figure 3) supports the report of Ikeda *et al.* as well as the fact that few oxygenated components are found in oil of black pepper. The main components found in the oil below 30 minutes are monoterpenes α-pinene (14 minutes), β-pinene (8 minutes), sabinene (19 minutes), Δ-3-carene (22 minutes), and limonene (25 minutes). At the 50-minute mark, we are in the sesquiterpene range, and several sesquiterpenes are observed but are not identified. Infrared curves confirm the absence of hydroxyl, carbonyl, and ether bands, the normal oxygenated components of essential oils.

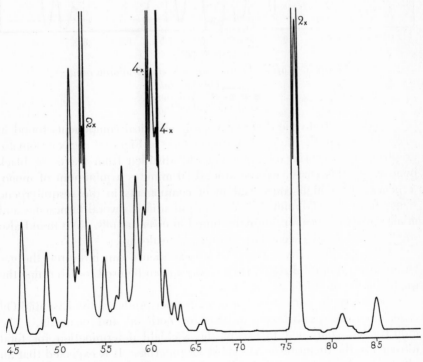

curve of oil black pepper leaves
Carbowax 20M as liquid substrate

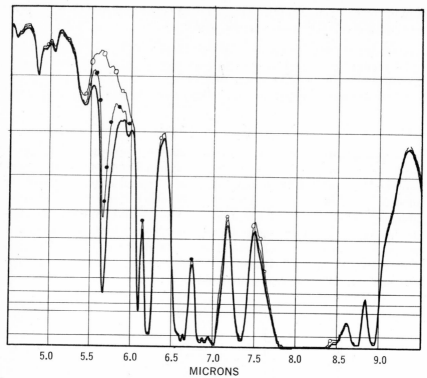

Figure 5. *Infrared curves for 5.0- to 6.5-micron range*
——— *Oil clove bud*
-●-●-●- *Oil clove stem*
O-O-O *Oil clove leaf*

To demonstrate the different volatile chemical components found in different parts of the same plant, we include in Figure 4 a gas chromatograph of the essential oil experimentally distilled from leaves of black pepper. In this curve, we see around 20 minutes a minimum of monoterpenes and a high concentration of components in the sesquiterpene range, from 45 to 60 minutes. We have identified several farnesenes and other sesquiterpenes not normally found in essential oils. We found also some nerolidol and a secondary sesquiterpene alcohol.

With the normal variations which experience can interpret, the gas chromatogram of oil distilled from oleoresin can be used to determine the quality of the product.

To ensure the consistency of black pepper products, the Essential Oil Association has published standards for both oil and oleoresin. The industry has continued to accept the Kjeldahl determination for total nitrogen as the quantitative standard for piperine. It is expected that an ultraviolet absorption method will be incorporated into these specifications in the near future.

Cloves

Clove spice is the dried unopened bud of an evergreen tree, which originated in the Molucca islands, now part of Indonesia. At present, most cloves are grown on the East African islands of Zanzibar and Madagascar. The clove is known by its characteristic nail-like shape, and the word itself is from the French "clou," or nail. References to this spice go back to IXth century Arabian writings.

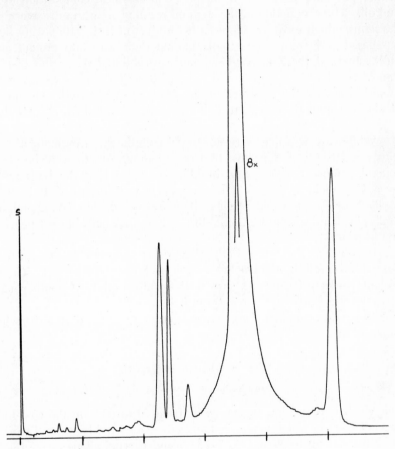

Figure 6.   Gas chromatogram of oil clove bud

250° isothermal, hot wire detector, Carbowax 20 M-DC-710 columns in series F & M Model 810
Column.   21-foot × 1/8-inch Carbowax 20M, 5% on CG-DMCS, plus 10-foot × 1/8-inch silicone DS-710, 20% on CW-HMDS
Carrier gas.   Helium, 40 ml. per minute at 110 p.s.i.
Oven temperature.   250° C. isothermal
Injection port.   230° C., packed with SE-39, 5% CW
Detector.   190-ma. at 285° C.
Sample size.   0.5 μl.
Minimum attenuation.   1 ×
Chart speed.   15 inches per hour

Clove buds contain about 15% volatile oil, some fixed oil, and the other extraneous materials associated with dried plant products. The essential oil of clove buds contains most of the major flavor components which are found in the dried spice.

In addition to the buds, other parts of the clove tree are valuable sources of flavor materials. The stems upon which the buds are found are dried together with the buds and later separated. The stems are steam-distilled, yielding an essential oil similar in chemical composition to the bud oil. The production of the stem oil resulted from the discovery that the stems, which were considered a by-product of little value, were being purchased and ground, eventually finding their way into ground clove buds. In 1936, the Zanzibar Government prohibited the export of clove stems. Stills were set up in the clove districts to process the stems for essential oil and a fair return on this by-product was realized. The normal yield of essential oil from stems in both Madagascar and Zanzibar is about 5%.

While care was necessary not to damage the trees permanently, the leaves and twigs of the clove tree were cut off and topping became a general practice. This forced budding and also kept the buds within reasonable picking range. The fragrant leaves and small twigs were distilled for essential oil, yielding about 2% of oil, rich in eugenol, and similar in chemical composition to the bud and stem oils but not nearly as fine in odor.

Chemistry. References to the chemical composition and chemistry of clove oils are few in number but stretch back at least 90 years. The important works prior to 1952 are well documented by Guenther (*21*). Several works bear repetition and emphasis.

The main components are eugenol, again a vanillyl derivative, whose structure is:

$$HO-\langle\bigcirc\rangle-CH_2-CH=CH_2$$
$$CH_3O$$

and which is found in concentrations from 70 to 90% in the free form; eugenol acetate, which is the phenol acetate, reported by several workers to be present up to 17% (*15, 50, 53*); and caryophyllene, according to Naves (*34*) present from 5 to 12% and of mixed alpha and beta isomers. The beta form predominates.

These three components make up approximately 99% of the oil. Smith, however (*50*), reminds us that a combination of these items cannot produce the fresh fruity character of a pure clove bud oil.

Vielitz (*62*) reported a levorotatory hydrocarbon in the high boiling fraction. Treibs in 1947 (*61*) separated and identified this material as caryophyllene oxide. Naves in 1948 (*35*) extracted clove buds with benzene and could not detect caryophyllene, and found only a trace of caryophyllene oxide in the extract. Boiling the benzene-insoluble portion with water, he produced a volatile oil, rich in caryophyllene, and concluded that the caryophyllene is chemically bound in the complex components of the clove spice and liberated only by hydrolysis. To liberate the essential oil and to attempt to improve the quality and yield of oil, some producers distilled with dilute mineral acid. This practice had varied results as far as the oil flavor and yield were concerned but did have a decided effect on metal distillation equipment.

To support certain of these reports with instrumental evidence, we have prepared both infrared and gas chromatographic curves of the various types of oils and offer them for evaluation.

Figure 5 compares the infrared curves of bud, leaf, and stem oils of clove. They are practically identical since eugenol, the main component

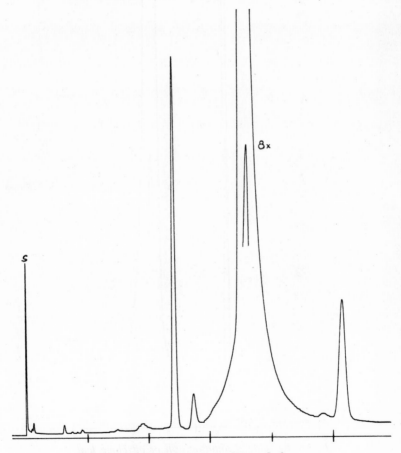

Figure 7.   Gas chromatograph of oil clove stem
Same instrumental conditions as Figure 6

of the three oils, is a very strong infrared absorber and interferes with most trace components. The only observable difference of note is in the carbonyl region at about 5.8 microns, where eugenyl acetate absorbs strongly, and the relative proportions of this ester can readily be seen. The strongest carbonyl band is found in the bud oil, stem oil is intermediate, and the leaf oil has negligible ester.

Figures 6, 7, and 8 are comparative gas chromatographic curves of bud, stem, and leaf oils run under identical conditions to emphasize the relative component percentages in these products. The main (8×) peak is eugenol at about 18.5 minutes since each scribe is 5 minutes. The peak at about 26 minutes is eugenyl acetate and the relative amounts in the three types of oils can be readily observed. The peak at 12 minutes is caryophyllene, and the relative order of concentration is leaf > stem >

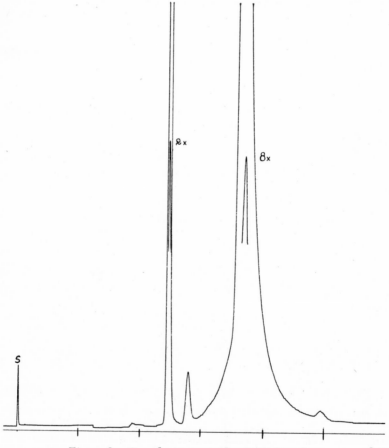

Figure 8.   Gas chromatograph of oil clove leaf
Same instrumental conditions as Figure 6

bud. The peak at 11.5 minutes in the bud oil is unique and distinguishes bud from the other oils.

Below 10 minutes are many flavor components found only in trace amounts, including terpenes. One can observe the larger number and quantity of these trace components in the bud oil, which are responsible for the decided odor and flavor preference of the bud oil.

Conclusions

While the flavor industry has and will continue to have a strong organoleptic background, advances in flavor chemistry have had a decided effect on commercial processing improvements. The new electronic age of detection, separation, and identification instrumentation has presented odors and combinations, as well as information, to the flavorist, to which he has never previously been exposed. The sensation–chemical structure interaction depends more and more on the organic chemist and analyst for direction. It is evident that a variety of chemical, biological, and physiological technical specialties can and must contribute if flavor chemistry is to advance.

Literature Cited

(1) American Spice Trade Association, "Official Analytical Methods," Methol. 13, p. 32, 1960.
(2) Association of Official Agricultural Chemists, Washington, D. C., "Methods of Analysis," 8th ed., p. 515, 1955.
(3) *Ber Schimmel & Co.*, A.G., **34**, 39 (October 1890).
(4) Bitting, A. W., *Phoenix Flame* **17** (6), 19 (1942).
(5) Borkowski, B., Gertig, H., Olszak, M., *Acta Polon. Pharm.* **15**, 39 (1958).
(6) Brauer, O., Schoen, W. J., *Angew. Botan.* **36**, 25 (1962).
(7) Bricker, C. E., Johnson, H. R., *Ind. Eng. Chem., Anal. Ed.* **17**, 400 (1945).
(8) Buchheim, R., *Arch. Exptl. Pathol. Pharmakol.* **5**, 455 (1876).
(9) Cazeneuve, P., Caillol, O., *Bull. Soc. Chim.* **27**, 199 (1877).
(10) Datta, P. R., Susi, Heino, *Anal. Chem.* **33**, 148 (1961).
(11) Dobbie, J. J., Fox, J. J., *J. Chem. Soc.* **103**, 1194 (1913).
(12) Dodge, F. D., *Drug Cosmetic Ind.* **45** (5), 516 (1941).
(13) Dumas, *Liebigs Ann.* **15**, 159 (1835).
(14) Eberhardt, L. A., *Arch. Pharm.* **225**, 515 (1887).
(15) Erdmann, E., *J. Prakt. Chem.* **56** (2), 143 (1897).
(16) Fagen, H. J., Kolen, E. P., Hussong, R. V., *J. Agr. Food Chem.* **3**, 860 (1955).
(17) Ferns, R. S., *Galencia Acta (Madrid)* **13**, 391 (1961).
(18) Fodor, K., *Z. Untersuch. Lebensm.* **61**, 94 (1933).
(19) Genest, Christiane, Smith, D. M., Chapman, D. G., *Ibid.*, **11**, 508 (1963).
(20) Guenther, E., "The Essential Oils," Vol. I, Chap. 3, Van Nostrand, New York, 1947.
(21) *Ibid.*, Vol. IV, p. 433.
(22) Hasselstrom, T., Hewitt, E. J., Konigsbacher, K. S., Ritter, J. J., *J. Agr. Food Chem.* **5**, 53 (1957).
(23) Hayden, A., Jordan, C. B., *J. Am. Pharm. Assoc.* **30**, 107 (1941).
(24) Ikeda, R. M., Stanley, W. L., Vannier, S. H., Spitler, E. M., *Food Sci.* **27** (5), 455 (1962).
(25) Kosuge, S., Inagaki, Y., Ino, T., *Nippon Nagei Kagaku Kaishi* **34**, 811 (1960).

(26) Kosuge, S., Inagaki, Y., Uehara, K., *Ibid.*, **32**, 578 (1958).
(27) Ladenburg, A., Scholtz, M., *Ber.* **27**, 1958 (1894).
(28) Landes, K. H., *Spice Mill*, p. 61 (December 1946).
(29) Langenau, E. E., *Am. Perfumer* **72** (4), 37 (1957).
(30) Lee, L. A., *Anal. Chem.* **28**, 1621 (1956).
(31) Micko, K., *Z. Nahr. Genussm.* **1**, 818 (1898).
(32) *Ibid.*, **2**, 411 (1899).
(33) Nakajima, M., *J. Pharm. Soc. Japan* **66**, 13 (1946).
(34) National Farm Chemurgic Council, Research Division, Rept. **693** (1904).
(35) Naves, Y. R., *Helv. Chim. Acta* **31**, 378 (1948).
(36) Nelson, E. K., *J. Am. Chem. Soc.* **41**, 1115 (1919).
(37) Nelson, E. K., Dawson, L. E., *Ibid.*, **45**, 2179 (1923).
(38) North, Horace, *Anal. Chem.* **21**, 394 (1949).
(39) Oersted, *Schweigers J. Chem. Phys.* **29**, 80 (1820).
(40) Ott, E., Eichler, F., *Ber.* **55 B**, 2653 (1922).
(41) Ott, E., Lüdemann, O., *Ibid.*, **57 B**, 214 (1924).
(42) Parry, J. W., "Spices," Chemical Publishing Co., New York, 1962.
(43) Pelletier, J., *Ann. Chim. (Paris)* **16**, 337 (1821).
(44) Rügheimer, L., *Ber.* **15**, 1390 (1882).
(45) Samy, T. S. A., Kamat, V. N., Pandya, H. G., *Current Sci. India* **29**, 271 (1960).
(46) Schenk, G., *Farmacognosia (Madrid)* **17**, 3 (1957).
(47) Schreiner, O., Kremers, E., *Pharm. Arch.* **4**, 61 (1901).
(48) Schülte, K. E., Kroger, H. M., *Z. Anal. Chem.* **147**, 266 (1955).
(49) Scoville, W. L., *J. Am. Pharm. Assoc.* **1**, 453 (1912).
(50) Smith, G. E., *Perfumery Essent. Oil Record* **37**, 144 (1946).
(51) Spanyar, Pal, Kevei, E., Kiszel, N., *Acta Chim. Acad. Sci. Hungary* **11**, 137 (1957).
(52) Spring, F. S., Stark, J., *J. Chem. Soc.* **1950**, 1177.
(53) Spurge, E. C., *Pharm. J.* **70**, 701–57 (1903).
(54) Soubeiran, E., Capitaine, H., *Liebigs Ann.* **34**, 326 (1840).
(55) Tandon, G. L., Dravid, S. V., Siddappa, G. S., *J. Food Sci.* **29** (1), 1 (1964).
(56) Tausig, F., Suzuki, J. I., Morse, R., *Food Technol.* **10**, 151 (1956).
(57) Thresh, J. C., *Pharm. J. Trans.* **7** (3), 21 (1876–77).
(58) *Ibid.*, **8** (3), 187 (1877–78).
(59) Tice, L. F., *Am. J. Pharm.* **105**, 320 (1933).
(60) Todd, P. H. Jr., Perun, C., *Food Technol.* **15** (5), 270 (1961).
(61) Treibs, W., *Chem. Ber.* **80** (1), 56 (1947).
(62) Vielitz, C., inaugural dissertation, Leipsig, 1912.
(63) White, McD., *Spice Mill*, p. 36 (1941).
(64) Zitko, V., Durigova, Z., *Chem. Svesti* **14**, 450 (1961).

RECEIVED May 8, 1965.

Irradiation Damage in Lipids

CHARLES MERRITT, Jr., PIO ANGELINI, M. L. BAZINET, and D. J. McADOO

Pioneering Research Division, U. S. Army Natick Laboratories, Natick, Mass.

Irradiation off-flavors in food fats are distinct and differ from other off-flavors. The degradation products of lipids due to irradiation damage are found by analysis employing gas chromatography and rapid scanning mass spectrometry. Studies show identification of compounds produced by irradiation, and the products formed in several animal fats and meats are compared as well as basic lipid substances such as fatty acid esters and triglycerides. The contribution of hydrocarbon compounds to irradiation off-odor is demonstrated, and the mechanism of their formation is discussed.

The undesirable odor and flavor produced in meat by irradiation has been a continuing problem in efforts to preserve food by irradiation. Studies of this problem have been in progress in many laboratories for several years in order to discover the nature of the off-flavor and how to prevent it.

It has been a basic assumption that the off-flavor may be related to the volatile compounds produced in meat upon irradiation, and moreover, that chemical analysis would show by comparison of irradiated with unirradiated meat that certain compounds might be responsible for the undesirable effects. Several groups of investigators (*1, 2, 5, 9, 11, 13, 14, 19*) have identified some of the volatile compounds isolated from irradiated meats. They have established the presence of several types of compounds, including carbonyls, alcohols, thiols, thiaalkanes, and esters. Early studies of irradiated beef by Merritt *et al.* (*3, 9*) showed an increase of several volatile carbonyl- and sulfur-containing compounds with increased irradiation dosage. Because of the lack of suitable separation techniques, however, most of the earlier studies were able to identify only a small number of the total compounds produced and failed to demonstrate any but a quantitative relationship between the presence of these compounds and irradiation dose. All the compounds were found to be present in unirradiated meat and their presence in greater amount in the irradiated product, while possibly contributing to the over-all "off-odor" sensation, could not, at least from the viewpoint of chemical composition, be described as peculiar to irradiation "off-odor."

Programmed, low temperature gas chromatography (10) greatly enhanced the ability to separate a mixture of compounds. By employing these techniques and trapping the separated gas chromatography eluates, Merritt et al. (11) identified 30 compounds from the combined carbon dioxide–center cut fraction of an irradiated beef sample. Fifteen of these compounds were hydrocarbons, many of which were also identified by Merritt et al. (11) in irradiated methyl oleate. In another investigation employing different techniques Wick (18) showed the presence of higher molecular weight hydrocarbons and methional in an extract of an aqueous distillate of an irradiated beef slurry.

The fact that homologous series of n-alkanes and n-alk-1-enes can be found in irradiated ground beef and that these hydrocarbons are not found in an unirradiated control sample has led to greater emphasis on the study of the mechanism involved. Accordingly, the investigations have been extended to include meats other than beef and several basic lipid substances related to meats. Moreover, the discovery of the widespread occurrence of hydrocarbons in irradiated lipids as well as in oxidized and thermally decomposed lipids (15, 16, 17) has also led to further detailed investigation to understand the various mechanisms involved in the oxidation and pyrolytic degradation of natural fats and oils. Only studies relating to irradiation damage are reported here.

The amount of information obtained on compounds produced by irradiation of meat has depended heavily on the analytical techniques available. Unfortunately, it has not been possible until recently to acquire enough good analytical data about the composition of the volatile compounds produced to relate this information to the mechanism involved. Now, however, improved methods of analysis are beginning to provide some of the needed data.

Experimental

Figure 1 shows a schematic diagram of a typical irradiation flask.

The meat, or a sample of fat or any other material to be irradiated, is placed in the 1-liter flask, and the top part with the breakseal is sealed on by the glass blower. (If the sample is contained only in the lower part of the flask, there is no danger of pyrolysis during the glassblowing operation.) If desired, the flask may then be evacuated or filled with an inert gas through the side arm and then sealed off. The contents are then irradiated in a 1.1-megacurie cobalt source.

High vacuum distillation is employed to collect the volatile components. Head space or noncondensable gases are trapped in an evacuated flash (4) by expansion when the breakseal is broken. The total con-

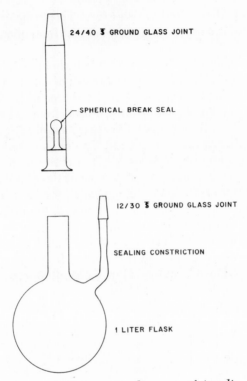

24/40 ⅌ GROUND GLASS JOINT

SPHERICAL BREAK SEAL

12/30 ⅌ GROUND GLASS JOINT

SEALING CONSTRICTION

1 LITER FLASK

*Figure 1. Schematic diagram of irradia-
tion flask*

densate is collected in a liquid nitrogen—cooled flask. The total condensate is then fractionated by low temperature—high vacuum distillation into
a carbon dioxide fraction, a water fraction, and a center cut—that is, the
material separated by vacuum distillation at temperatures between $-140°$
and $-80°$ C.

These procedures have been employed in this laboratory for many
years as a standard operating procedure for the preliminary separation of
a total condensate and have been described in detail by Merritt *et al.* (9).

Nearly all the previously reported results from this laboratory have
been based on the analysis of the center cut only. It is now possible to
carry out a complete analysis. Two principal developments in analytical
techniques have made complete analysis possible: the use of programmed cryogenic temperature gas chromatography (10) to separate
the mixtures of volatile compounds, and the use of a rapid scanning mass
spectrometer to identify the components as they are eluted from the gas
chromatograph (12).

The advantages of subambient programmed temperature operation
of the gas chromatographic column are now well known and have been

demonstrated by Merritt and Walsh (*10*). This technique has now been extended to permit temperature programming from about —180° to over 200° C. (*9*).

The remarkable effectiveness of this technique is demonstrated in Figure 2, in which it is applied to the analysis of a carbon dioxide fraction and a center cut from a sample of irradiated ground beef. The temperature program for both chromatograms ranged from —170° to 150° C. at 3° per minute. The chromatographic separation obtained when a carbon dioxide fraction—i. e., the vacuum distillate obtained below —140° C.— is programmed from —170° is seen in the chromatogram in the upper portion. In this case, although 99.9% plus of the sample is carbon dioxide, the separation of the trace components present is readily observed. Since a flame ionization detector was employed, the carbon dioxide peak does not appear on this chromatogram.

Only the most volatile materials of the initial sample are eluted in this separation since this fraction is separated by vacuum distillation at a temperature of —140° C. When a low temperature program such as this

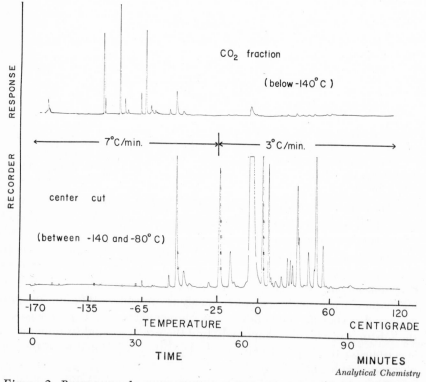

Analytical Chemistry

Figure 2. Programmed cryogenic temperature gas chromatograms of carbon dioxide and center cut fractions from irradiated beef volatiles

is employed, the components of the carbon dioxide fraction are all separated and eluted by the time the column temperature has reached —80°. On the other hand, in the lower portion of the graph, the chromatogram for the center cut fraction is seen. This fraction, when programmed from —170°, shows no components or very few components to be eluted before the column temperature rises to about —80°. The components of the center cut are separated and eluted to above 80°. Thus a very low temperature program is required to separate the components of the carbon dioxide fraction, but a program starting at —80° would satisfactorily separate the components of the center cut. The amount of overlap between these two chromatograms indicates the effectiveness of the preliminary separation by vacuum distillation. These chromatograms also show that wide range programming permits effective separation of the components of such a complicated mixture. Current practice in this

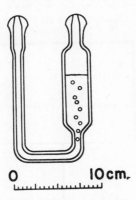

Figure 3. Schematic digram of ebullition tube used to introduce solvent extract to gas chromatography column

laboratory is to separate the water fraction from the total condensate by vacuum distillation at —80° C. and then separate the remainder of the sample—i. e., the combined carbon dioxide and center cut fractions—on a chromatographic column programmed from —180° C.

The volatile flavor compounds that may be present in very dilute concentration in the water fraction are isolated and separated by solvent extraction followed by programmed temperature gas chromatography. Figure 3 shows a schematic diagram of the sample trap used. This tube is used to contain the distilled concentrate of a volatile solvent extract of the components in a water fraction as described by Forss *et al.* (8). When filled, so that the solution occupies about 1/3 of the lower part of the expansion volume on the right, and when attached so that the carrier gas can bubble through, the solvent plus the extracted components are vaporized. The column temperature is appropriately chosen so that the solvent will be eluted, but the solutes will condense on the head of the column. The column is then temperature-programmed to achieve separation of the solutes.

The truly remarkable effectiveness of this technique can be appreciated only by consideration of its use in connection with a rapid scanning mass spectrometer, but before presentation of spectra, a brief description of the apparatus would be appropriate.

A block diagram of the combined gas chromatograph–mass spectrometer employed is shown in Figure 4 and a photograph of the apparatus is shown in Figure 5.

The gas chromatograph is a modified Barber-Colman Model 5060 column oven fitted with a 10-foot $\times$ $^1/_8$ inch o. d. coiled stainless steel column. Liquid nitrogen is used as the column chamber coolant, and

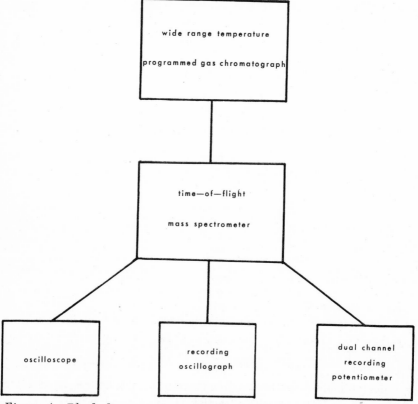

Figure 4. Block diagram of combined gas chromatograph–mass spectrometer

Figure 5. Photograph of apparatus

the programmer and heater are capable of providing temperature programs at rates varying from 1° to 40° C. per minute from −190° to over 200°. The inlet system has been modified by installing a rotary-type four-way valve, so that gaseous samples may be swept onto and condensed on the cold column with helium carrier gas. This method of sample introduction provides a uniform and very effective means of narrow band on column injection. Provision is also made for syringe injection of the sample if required. The column chamber with a front opening door is very convenient for changing columns without disturbing the connections to the mass spectrometer ion source. These connections, which require separate heating, are also conveniently located in what was originally the detector cell housing of the gas chromatograph.

The mass spectrometer used is a Bendix Model 14 time of flight mass spectrometer with modified pulse circuitry to permit continuous ion generation but operating with a spectrum scan rate of 10,000 spectra per second. The instantaneous spectrum can be viewed on the oscilloscope screen. With an analog gating system, a rapidly scanned strip chart recording of the spectrum is displayed on the high speed direct-writing oscillograph. A nominal scan speed of about 5 seconds is employed for a mass range of about 10 to 1—i.e., from mass 20 to 200. If required, mass resolution to higher than mass 200 can be achieved.

A second analog scanner is used to monitor a single spectrum peak to provide a chromatographic display. Thus, the cumulative peak 43, or any other common mass peak, is displayed on one channel of a dual-channel potentiometer recorder to register the chromatogram, while the column temperature is registered through a thermocouple on the other channel to provide a record of the temperature program. In another mode, with predynode gating of the helium ions, total ionization is displayed instead of peak 43 to register the chromatogram.

In practice the oscillograph record of the mass spectrum is made at the appropriate time by the operator who continuously monitors the spectrum display on the oscilloscope. Typical spectra of compounds isolated from an irradiated beef center cut have been published (*12*).

An example of the method applied to the volatiles from an irradiated beef sample can now be described. The noncondensable gases and the carbon dioxide center cut fraction are first separated from the water fraction by expansion and vacuum distillation at —80° C., respectively. The combined carbon dioxide–center cut is separated and analyzed directly. The residual water fraction is extracted with ether, which in turn is concentrated in volume to about 1 ml. at —80° C. on a vacuum manifold. The ether solution is then allowed to evaporate onto the column held isothermally at —10° C. The valve to the mass spectrometer is kept closed, and the ether solvent is bypassed through the auxiliary pumping system in order to prevent solvent contamination of the mass spectrometer ion source. After about 20 minutes the solvent is gone, the valve to the spectrometer ion source is opened, the temperature program is started, and the components are separated and identified.

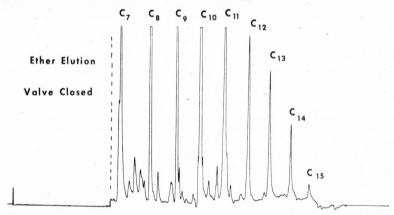

Figure 6. Gas chromatogram represented as m/e 43 peak intensity of separated components from ether extract of irradiated beef "water fraction"

Figure 6 is a chromatogram of an ether extract of an irradiated beef water fraction obtained by monitoring the 43 peak of the mass spectra. This sample gave a chromatogram whose major components were found to be the series of alkanes and alkenes typical of irradiation degradation of lipids.

Results and Discussion

The most significant single discovery resulting from the use of the gas chromatograph–mass spectrometer analysis system is the existence

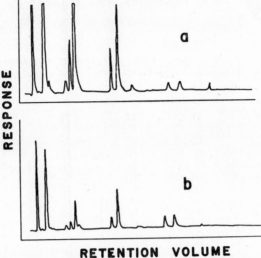

Figure 7. Gas chromatograms of center cuts of irradiated beef volatiles

a. Irradiated February 1960
b. Irradiated November 1960

of hydrocarbons as the major compounds produced in irradiated meat. This was first shown when cryogenic programming was used to separate the components of a center cut (*11*). The fact of hydrocarbon formation has since been well established by many repeated analyses of irradiated ground beef volatiles. In fact, the nature of the compounds found in irradiated meat is itself quite reproducible. Figure 7 shows two gas chromatograms of cryogenically programmed center cuts of irradiated ground beef volatiles isolated from two separate samples of meat, one irradiated in February 1960, the other in November 1960. The amount of sample and temperature program rates were slightly different in each case, but the over-all similarity of the sample composition is readily apparent.

Although beef has been studied extensively, very few, if any, significant analyses of other meats have been performed until recently. A comprehensive analysis of the volatiles from irradiated ground pork, mutton, lamb, and veal, as well as beef is shown in Table I. All of the samples included in this study were irradiated at a dose of 6 megarads and the complete analyses of the volatiles produced show the presence of more than 50 compounds, many in appreciable quantity. The controls, or unirradiated samples, showed the presence of only trace quantities of compounds except for expected metabolites such as ethanol, acetaldehyde, or acetone.

Table I. Volatiles from Irradiated Meats

L. Large   S. Small
M. Moderate   T. Trace

	Beef		Veal		Mutton		Lamb		Pork	
	Control	Irrad.	Control	Irrad.	Control	Irrad.	Control	Irrad.	Control	Irrad.
Alkanes										
Methane		M		M		M		M		M
Ethane		L		L		L		L		L
Propane		L	T	L		L		L		L
Butane	S	L		L		L		L		L
Pentane	M	L		L	S	L	M	L	S	L
Hexane	S	L		L	S	L		L		L
Heptane	S	L		L	M	L		L	T	L
Octane	S	L		L	M	L		L	T	L
Nonane		L		L	T	L		L		L
Decane		L		L		L		L		L
Undecane		L		L		L		L		L
Dodecane		L		L		L		L		L
Tridecane		L		L		L		L		L
Tetradecane		M		M		M		M		M
Pentadecane		S		S		S		S		S
Alkenes										
Ethene		M		M		M		M		M
Propene		M		M		M		M		M
Butene		M		M		M		M		M
Pentene		M		M		M		M		M
Hexene		M		M		M		M		M
Heptene		M		M		M		M		M
Octene		M		M		M		M		M
Nonene		M		M		M		M		M
Decene		M		M		M		M		M
Undecene		M		M		M		M		M
Dodecene		M		M		M		M		M
Tridecene		S		S		S		S		S
Tetradecene		S		S		S		S		S
Alkynes										
Decyne		S				S				S
Undecyne		T								
Aromatic hydrocarbons										
Benzene	T	S	T	T		T	T	T		T
Toluene	T	S	T	S	T	T	T	S	T	S
Ethylbenzene		S	T	T	T	T	T	T		S
Propylbenzene		T	T	T	T			T	T	T
Alcohols										
Ethanol	L	L	L	L	L	L	L	L	S	S
Propanol		M	M	M		M	M	L	T	T
Butanol		M		M	S	S	S	S	T	S
Pentanol		M		M		M	S	S	T	
Hexanol		S								
Ketones										
Acetone	L	M		S	S	M	L	L	M	L
Butanone		S		M		M		L		L
Acetoin			L	S		T		T	T	T

Table I. Continued

	L. Large M. Moderate						S. Small T. Trace			
	Beef		Veal		Mutton		Lamb		Pork	
	Con-trol	Ir-rad.	Con-trol	Ir-rad.	Con-trol.	Ir-rad.	Con-trol	Ir-rad.	Con-trol	Ir-rad.
Aldehydes										
Pentanal		M	T		T		T	S	T	
Hexanal		M	S	S		S	T	S	S	L
Heptanal		S								
Octanal		T								
Esters										
Ethyl acetate		T	S	T	T	T	T	S	T	T
Sulfur compounds										
Sulfur dioxide										T
Carbonyl sulfide										T
Dimethyl sulfide		S		T	S			T		T
Dimethyl disulfide		M		M	S			S		M
Methyl ethyl sulfide										T
Diethyl disulfide		S	S	S	T	M		T	T	T
Ethyl butyl sulfide		S		T	T					T
Methional		S			T					T

Small amounts of the hydrocarbons are found in some of the unirradiated controls. In view of our work with butterfat, and that of Buttery, Day, and others (6, 7), the traces of hydrocarbons found in the control are probably due to oxidation of the meat fat during storage.

A distribution of normal alk-1-enes corresponding to the normal alkanes but in smaller quantity was found to exist uniformly in all the irradiated samples. The olefin compounds are about 20% as abundant as the alkanes but together with the alkanes constitute approximately 90% of the total composition of the total volatile constituents isolated, discounting water and carbon dioxide.

It seems evident that the hydrocarbons found in the irradiated meats can come only from the lipid. This hypothesis was verified in early studies (11) when the volatiles from irradiated methyl oleate were found also to contain appreciable quantities of alkanes and alkenes. This has been demonstrated more recently in a comparison of the volatiles produced in irradiated and oxidized butter fat. The relative abundances of *n*-alkanes and *n*-alkanals found in a sample of butter fat irradiated at 6 megarads and an aliquot of the same butter fat autoxidized for one week in the presence of a copper catalyst are shown in Figure 8. In accordance with the generally accepted mechanism for fat oxidation, the usual high concentration of carbonyl compounds is found in the oxidized sample. Small amounts of hydrocarbons are also found, however, probably due to occasional recombination or hydrogen termination of alkyl free radicals.

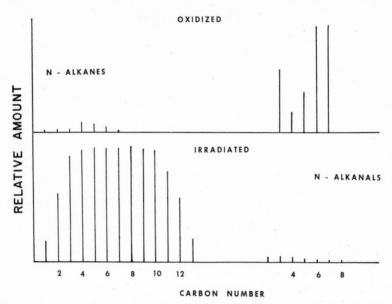

Figure 8. Distribution of hydrocarbon and carbonyl compounds among irradiated and oxidized butter fat volatiles

The presence of large amounts of hydrocarbons and the relative lack of carbonyl compounds even in the presence of air show that the mechanism for irradiation production of volatiles is different from the mechanism for autoxidation. The sensory response is likewise different. Whereas the oxidized fat is typically rancid, the irradiated fat is not but has what we have come to recognize as a characteristic fat irradiation odor.

The mechanism of irradiation damage in lipids now seems clear and relatively simple. It appears that radiation-induced, direct bond cleavage to form primarily alkyl free radicals can account for nearly all of the components detected upon analysis. If the glycerol stearate depicted here is considered as an example, with scission of the bonds at all points of the chain with recombination or hydrogen termination of the resulting

alkyl free radicals, all the *n*-alkanes from methane to heptadecane could be formed.   Alkanes to pentadecane are found in good yield.   Moreover, if secondary collisions, extracting a second electron, occur—a similar homologous series of alkenes is predicted and these also are detected in quantity.   If the fatty acid were oleic or linoleic, increased quantities of olefins might be expected; and this, in fact, proves to be the case.

Of even greater significance, however, is the study of the radiation products induced in methyl oleate and methyl stearate.   Table II shows the principal products to be alkanes, alkenes, and a homologous series of methyl esters.   The highest member of the alkane series found in irradiated methyl oleate is n-nonane and the highest methyl ester is methyl caprylate—i. e., the C_8 acid.   The series of unsaturated hydrocarbons goes up to C_{10} or higher.   These compounds can arise from methyl oleate by the mechanism described for tristearin, as follows:

$$CH_3CH_2CH_2CH_2CH_2CH_2CH_2CH_2CH = CHCH_2CH_2CH_2CH_2CH_2CH_2CH_2COOCH_3$$

$+$

CH_3

n-Nonane

Methyl acetate

Methyl propionate

Methyl butyrate

Methyl caprylate

Table II.   Radiation Products Induced in Methyl Stearate, Methyl Oleate and Tristearin

	Methyl Stearate	*Methyl Oleate*	*Tristearin*
n-Alkanes	$C_1 \rightarrow C_{13}$	$C_1 \rightarrow C_9$	$C_1 \rightarrow C_{13}$
n-Alkenes	$C_2 \rightarrow C_9$	$C_2 \rightarrow C_{10}$	$C_2 \rightarrow C_{10}$
Methyl esters	$C_2 \rightarrow C_{10}$	$C_2 \rightarrow C_9$	
			Acetone

Another important observation is the fact that no methyl esters have been detected among the radiation products in tristearin, but acetone is a major component.   All the data thus far obtained support the simple hypothesis that radiation products are primarily the result of direct bond cleavage.   Most of the other products found in irradiated meat volatiles may also be accounted for by mechanisms associated with alkyl free radical formation in the fat.

Since the water content of meat is fairly high, averaging more than 60% in the meats analyzed in this study, the formation of alcohols is readily predicted by direct reaction of the alkyl fre radical with water. This mechanism is suported by the fact that only traces of alcohols are found in irradiated dry butter fat were undetected in irradiated triglycerides or methyl esters of fatty acids.   The carbonyl compounds, on the other hand, are probably produced by an indirect route which is most likely similar to that involved in autoxidation of a fat.   The alkyl free radical can absorb oxygen, form a hydroperoxide, and then follow the many decomposition paths which are familiar in the oxidation chemistry of fats.

Figure 9 shows the relative abundance of the alcohols and carbonyl compounds in various irradiated meats. The oxygenated compounds are far less abundant than the hydrocarbons, but nevertheless, appreciable amounts are found of the members of a homologous series of *n*-aliphatic alcohols up to hexanol. Of these, only ethanol is detected in the unirradiated controls. The aldehydes and ketones are least abundant of all the compounds which may be considered as derived from the fat. The more abundant aldehydes found are unsaturated, which is in further agreement with the hypothesis that they are derived from the decomposition of hydroperoxides. Studies of butter fat irradiated in the absence of air have shown that carbonyl compounds are essentially absent.

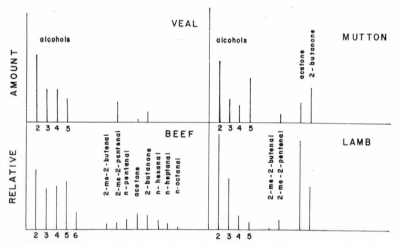

Figure 9. Distribution of oxygenated compounds among volatile compounds isolated from irradiated meat

At present, the role of carbonyl compounds in irradiation off-odor seems to be uncertain. Chemical evidence shows them to be absent or in low concentration in samples which are irradiated in the absence of air, yet the irradiation odor of these samples is very definite and unmistakable. The importance of the hydrocarbons in terms of chemical composition is very great, yet their role as odorants is not clear. Irradiation odor in butterfat is not a hydrocarbon odor, yet it is unmistakably characteristic. There are no sulfur compounds present. On the other hand, irradiation odor in meat is also characteristic; it is the same for all meats studied here—i. e., veal, beef, lamb, mutton, and pork—and the chemical composition of the volatiles is practically the same for all. Yet irradiated meat odor is not the same as irradiated butterfat odor.

In meats, of course, components arise from the protein which cannot be present in the products from pure fats. Table III shows some of the sulfur compounds and aromatic compounds which are also found in irradiated meats. Many of these can be postulated as arising from direct bond cleavage of amino acid moieties. Benzene and toluene may come

Table III. Sulfur and Aromatic Compounds from Irradiated Meats

Sulfur Compounds	*Aromatic Compounds*
Sulfur dioxide	Benzene
Carbonyl sulfide	Toluene
Dimethyl sulfide	Ethylbenzene
Dimethyl disulfide	Propylbenzene
Methyl ethyl sulfide	
Diethyl disulfide	
Ethyl butyl sulfide	

from phenylalanine and phenol and *p*-cresol from tyrosine. Some of the sulfides, disulfides, and mercaptans can derive directly from cystine or methionine, but those containing more than two carbon atoms in a chain require more than a superficial explanation. Hexyl mercaptan or ethyl butyl disulfide perhaps comes from free radicals originating in part in the protein and in part in the lipid portions of the meat. Although the current work has seemingly provided greater insight into the mechanisms of irradiation damage in meat, it has also raised more questions. Studies are now being conducted to try to relate the effects of irradiation on proteins, and ultimately model systems of fat and protein substances will be investigated in an attempt to clarify some of the questions of interaction.

Literature Cited

(1) Batzer, O. F., Doty, D. M., *J. Agr. Food Chem.* 3, 64 (1955).
(2) Batzer, O. F., Scribney, M., Doty, D. M., Schweigert, B. S., *Ibid.,* 5, 700 (1957).
(3) Bazinet, M. L., Merritt, C., Jr., *Anal Chem.* 34, 1143 (1962).
(4) Bazinet, M. L., Walsh, J. T., *Rev. Sci. Instr.* 31, 346 (1960).
(5) Burks, R. E., Baker, E. B., Clark, P., Esslinger, J., Lacey, J. C., Jr., *J. Agr. Food Chem.* 7, 778 (1959).
(6) Buttery, R., Hendel, C. E., Boggs, M. M., *Ibid.,* 9, 245 (1961).
(7) Day, E. A., Papaioannou, S. E., *J. Dairy Sci.* 46, 1201 (1963).
(8) Forss, D. A., Bazinet, M. L., Swift, S. M., *J. Gas Chromatog.* 2, 134 (1964).
(9) Merritt, C., Jr., Bresnick, S. R., Bazinet, M. L., Walsh, J. T., Angelini, Pio, *J. Agr. Food Chem.* 7, 784 (1959).
(10) Merritt, C., Jr., Walsh, J. T., *Anal. Chem.* 35, 110 (1963).
(11) Merritt, C., Jr., Walsh, J. T., Bazinet, M. L., Kramer, R. E., Bresnick, S. R. *J. Am. Oil Chemists Soc.* 42, 57 (1965).
(12) Merritt, C., Jr., Walsh, J. T., Forss, D. A., Angelini, Pio Swift, S. M. *Anal. Chem.* 36, 1502 (1964).
(13) Monty, J. J., Tappel, A. L., Groninger, H. S., *J. Agr. Food Chem.* 9, 55 (1961).

(14) Scribney, M., Lewis, U. J., Schweigert, B. S., *Ibid.*, **3**, 958 (1955).
(15) Toi, B., Ota, S., Iwata, N., *J. Japan Oil Chemists, Soc.* **10**, 536 (1961).
(16) *Ibid.*, **11**, 504 (1962).
(17) *Ibid.*, **11**, 508.
(18) Wick, E. L., "Explorations in Future Food Processing Techniques," S. A. Goldblith, ed., Chap. 2, p. 5, M.I.T. Press, Cambridge, Mass., 1963.
(19) Wick, E. L., Yamanishi, Tei, Westheimer, L. C., Hoff, J. E., Proctor, B. E.. Goldblith, S. A., *J. Agr. Food Chem.* **9**, 289 (1961).

RECEIVED June 1, 1965.

14

Flavor and Biochemistry of Volatile Banana Components

EMILY L. WICK, ALICE I. McCARTHY[1], MARSHALL MYERS, EDWINA MURRAY, HARRY NURSTEN[2], and PHILLIP ISSENBERG

Department of Nutrition and Food 'Science, Massachusetts Institute of Technology, Cambridge, Mass.

Existing knowledge of the nature of volatile banana constituents, their production during ripening, and their contribution to sensory quality is reviewed. Characterization and identification of components employed infrared spectrophotometry and mass spectrometry. The increase in volatile constituents observed as ripening progresses and flavor develops suggests a fundamental interrelationship between these substances and biochemical processes occurring in the fruit. Knowledge of these processes is reviewed.

Bananas are a particularly advantageous system for a basic study of the chemistry of flavor and of flavor changes which occur during ripening, storage, or processing. They can be obtained in large quantity, of known variety, maturity, and history, and the nature and quantity of their volatile components may be relatively easily investigated. In addition, bananas can be ripened under controlled conditions. Knowledge of the qualitative and quantitative differences in volatile constituents and their correlation with odor and taste quality at these stages may give insight into their relationship to the metabolism of the fruit, the mechanisms of producing the volatiles, and the identity of their precursors. Establishment of these mechanisms is the ultimate goal of basic flavor research and should contribute significantly to man's ability to measure and control this important biological but nonnutritive property of all foods. This paper describes work carried out on the volatile constituents of ripe bananas. It reviews related work of other groups and offers preliminary consideration of the biochemistry of banana aroma component production.

[1] Present address, Corn Products Food Technology Institute, Waltham, Mass.
[2] Present address, The University, Leeds, England.

Early investigations of bananas have been reviewed by Hultin and Proctor (*10*), who studied changes in volatile constituents during ripening, storage, and processing. Their results, obtained before the general availability of gas chromatography, are summarized in Table I. Derivative formation of volatile components from 150-gram batches of fruit followed by paper chromatography and direct study of individual components was the basis of the identifications made. Their study showed that 2-hexenal and ethyl and methyl acetate were lost, and an unidentified alcohol and an unknown carbonyl compound were formed in preparation of heat-processed puree.

Table I. Volatile Banana Constituents (*10*)

Known before 1950	Ripe Banana (Gros Michel)	Heat-Processed Puree (Gros Michel)
Methanol	Methanol	Methanol
Ethanol	Ethanol	Ethanol
Amyl acetate	Isoamyl alcohol	Isoamyl alcohol
Amyl isovalerate	Ethyl acetate	Unknown alcohol
Amyl butyrate	Methyl acetate	Methyl acetate
Acetaldehyde	Isoamyl acetate	2-Pentanone
Acetoin	2-Hexenal	2-Octanone
	2-Pentanone	Unknown carbonyl
	2-Octanone	
	Acetic acid	

Table II. Yield of Banana Odor Concentrates

Variety	Batch, Kg.	Weight (Ether-Free Basis), Mg.	Yield from Banana Pulp, p.p.m.
Gros Michel	10	121	12.1
	10	121	12.1
	10	180	18.0
	10	150	15.0
Valery	2.28	158	69.3
	4.48	291	65.0
	2.7	247	91.6
	2.7	276	102.1

Initial work (*14*) in our laboratory was concerned with ripe Gros Michel fruit. A reduced pressure (25 to 35 mm.) flash distillation procedure at 24° to 30°C. was developed, which allowed isolation, in reproducible yield (10 to 20 p.p.m.), of banana odor concentrates from a 1 to 1 aqueous homogenate of approximately 10 kg. of fruit. Recent investigations with Valery fruit have resulted in significantly higher yields. Simple lyophilization of an aqueous homogenate afforded the quantities shown in Table II. Although the distillation methods used for the two varieties differ, the increased yields shown may be due to the fruit itself and not the procedures used. Observed variations in yields from the Valery fruit reflect its degree of ripeness at the time of lyophilization.

General qualitative and quantitative differences between Gros Michel and Valery fruit at various stages of ripeness are graphically illustrated in Figure 1. These chromatograms (*18*) show the distribution of volatile constituents over a single banana. In all cases Valery fruit contained greater quantities of volatiles in the head space vapor. Thus larger amounts of odor concentrate were expected and obtained with this variety.

Odor concentrates were obtained from the initial aqueous condensates by saturation with sodium chloride, diethyl ether extraction, and concentration of the ether extract by careful distillation to a minimum volume (150 to 300 μl.). Sensory evaluation at all stages of isolation indicated the presence of characteristic banana odor in the concentrates. Objective support for this subjective evidence was obtained by gas chromatographic determination of the distribution (*14*) of volatile components of Gros Michel fruit throughout the isolative procedures. Figure 2 shows that preparation of an aqueous banana homogenate caused no significant detectable change in the characteristic chromatogram of the vapor over crushed banana pulp. Although the relative quantities of certain components appeared altered, these differences were no greater than those obtained from two different bananas taken from the same batch. Only traces of volatiles were detected in the head gas over stripped pulp, consistent with its almost complete lack of odor.

Further evidence that undue loss of major volatile components did not occur is provided by Figure 3. Comparison of the vapor over the total aqueous distillate (Figure 3, *a*) with vapor over banana pulp (Figure 2, *a*) and homogenate (Figure 2, *b*) showed that the same components were present in each at similar concentrations. In like manner vapor over the odor concentrate itself was found to be very similar in composition to that over crushed pulp. On the basis of this evidence and sensory evaluation, isolation of odor concentrates from aqueous distillates in the manner described has been accepted as reliable and successful. Thus, these procedures were employed in all subsequent work.

Chromatography of a Gros Michel concentrate on a 20% Ucon 50HB-2000 on Chromosorb (48 to 60-mesh) column at 85°C. gave the separation (*14*) shown in Figure 4. Individual fractions were trapped, and evidence of their identity was obtained from infrared spectra and relative retention volumes. The purity of each fraction was assessed by its separation on a 1% Ucon column in an instrument fitted with an ionization detector. On the basis of such evidence the fractions were found to contain the substances listed in Table III.

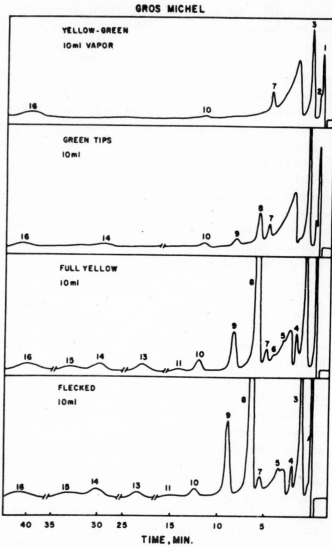

Figure 1. *Distribution of constituents in head space during*
5% Ucon 50HB 2000 column

To determine the contribution of these substances to banana odor, all the peaks shown in Figure 4 were collected in a single trap, and the odor was evaluated. Many of the notes of banana odor were present, but components which provide the characteristic full-bodied mellow aroma were absent. Subsequent investigations have therefore been directed toward isolating and identifying components having higher boiling points than those already discussed.

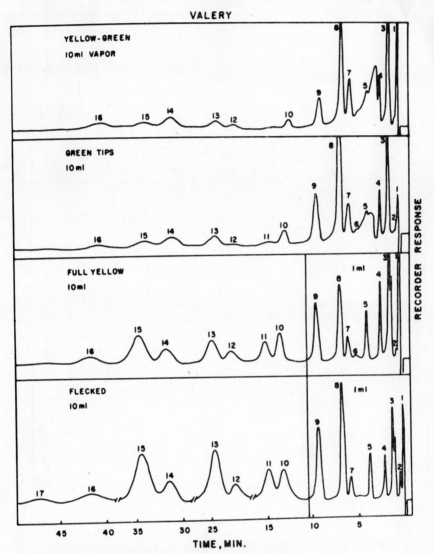

ripening of Gros Michel and Valery banana fruit
at 55°C., Sr⁹⁰ detector (18)

Excellent correlation of the major head space components of both Gros Michel and Valery fruit with banana aroma has been achieved by McCarthy *et al* (18). Figure 5 summarizes their results and indicates components which contribute to fruity, banana-like, and woody, green, or musty notes. Identifications shown were based on retention data and represent the major component of each peak. Using retention volume constants (21), McCarthy, Wyman, and Palmer (19) proposed the

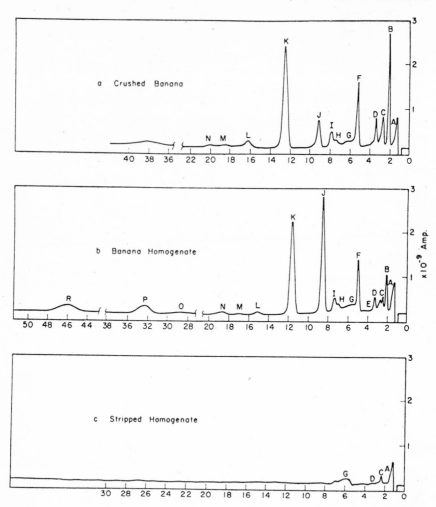

Figure 2. Distribution of constituents during preparation of an odor concentrate

1% Ucon 50HB 2000 column at 32–36°C., argon detector (14)

presence of acetaldehyde, methyl acetate, 2-propanol, and 1-propanol, in addition to the substances shown in Figure 5.

Banana odor concentrates were further studied to isolate and identify constituents boiling higher than those discussed. Separation obtained on an Apiezon N column is shown in Figure 6. Peak 14 is isoamyl butyrate. Thus, all the compounds previously described were eluted before peak 14 and at least 10 higher boiling banana constituents were detected.

The individual fractions shown were trapped and their infrared spectra determined. The spectrum of fraction 22 was identical with that of an authentic sample of eugenol (I). Spectra of fractions 19, 21, 23, and 24 indicated that they were structurally related to eugenol. An authentic sample of *O*-methyleugenol (II) was prepared (*15*). Its infrared spectrum was like that of fraction 23, although absorption bands due to eugenol itself were also present. Retention data for authentic *O*-methyleugenol were in agreement with those of fraction 23. Thus it was concluded that *O*-methyleugenol as well as eugenol was present in the banana concentrate, and that peak 24 must contain a substance such as myristicin (IV) or elemicin (VI) (*13*), since its spectrum contained bands typical of methoxy or methylenedioxy groups (*4*).

This hypothesis has been confirmed by isolation of authentic samples of myristicin (IV), apiole (V), and 1-allyl-2,3,4,5-tetramethoxybenzene from parsley seed oil (*8, 25*), and elemicin (VI) from elemi oil. Parsley oil was separated on a 20% Silicone DC 550 on Fluorpak column at 206°C. Three fractions having appropriate retention times for the compounds of interest were trapped. Apiole (V) was isolated directly as shown by its infrared spectrum. Rechromatography of the other two fractions on an Apiezon N column yielded pure myristicin (IV) (*25*) and pure 1-allyl-2,3,4,5-tetramethoxybenzene as shown by their infrared spectra. Neither compound was the one found in fraction 24 of banana concentrate. Elemicin (VI) could not be obtained in pure form from parsley oil, but it was isolated from elemi oil. The ether-soluble extract of gum elemi was distilled. The fraction boiling above 257°C. was separated on the Apiezon N column and rechromatographed on Silicone DC 550. Its elemental analysis (Found: C, 69.21; H, 7.79. Calculated: C, 69.21; H, 7.74) and infrared spectrum were in agreement with those of elemicin. The spectrum was identical with that of peak 24. The identity of peaks 19 and 21 has not been absolutely proved, but their infrared spectra indicate that they are very closely related to veratrole (1,2-dimethoxybenzene) and safrole (III), respectively.

a   Total Distillate

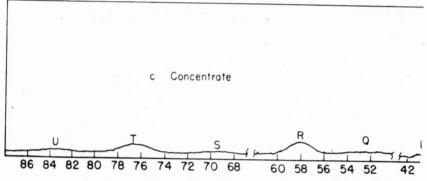

c   Concentrate

| U | | | T | | S | | R | | Q | | |
86 84 82 80 78 76 74 72 70 68   60 58 56 54 52   42

Figure 3.   Distribution of constituents during
1% Ucon 50HB 2000 column

Banana constituents of intermediate volatility—i.e., less volatile than isoamyl butyrate and more volatile than eugenol—were separated by chromatography of banana concentrates at 101°C. on a 20% Silicone DC 550 column. The composition of Gros Michel and Valery concentrates is compared in Figure 7. Knowledge of these components is summarized in Table IV. Conclusions were based on the infrared spectrum of each trapped fraction, on retention data, and on a study of the products of hydrolysis of each fraction. Rechromatography in an instrument fitted with a flame ionization detector, of each fraction before and after hydrolysis, provided information about the alcohol moiety of the esters. As observed previously, Valery fruit contains greater quantities of volatile components than Gros Michel. No evidence has yet been obtained that qualitative differences exist between the two varieties.

Chromatogram *c* in Figure 7 illustrates a poor separation of additional high boiling constituents which are minor components. Each peak shown could be expected to contain numerous substances if separated

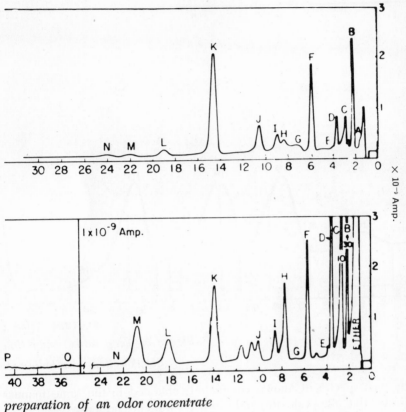

preparation of an odor concentrate

at 32–36°C., argon detector (14)

under conditions affording good resolution. On the basis of infrared spectra of fractions, the major components present are believed to be esters.

The possible contribution of substances appearing in Figure 7 to banana aroma was checked by sensory evaluation of single traps in which fractions A through R, S through Z, and A through Z were collected. The total mixture of A to Z was most banana-like in aroma. The other mixtures represented parts of the aroma.

Fractions S to Z were investigated by separating each of the individual trapped fractions on a 5% Carbowax 20M column programmed from 50° to 110°C. at 2° per minute. Mass spectra of the column effluent were obtained on a modified Model 14 Bendix Time-of-Flight mass spectrometer. Electron energy was set at 70 e.v., and spectra were scanned from m/e 14 to 200 in 6 seconds. Examples of chromatograms thus obtained and recorded in terms of the ionization at m/e 43 are shown in Figure 8. Interpretation of the resulting spectra and comparison

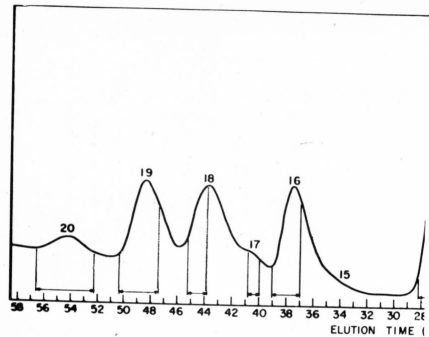

Figure 4. Preparative separation

Fractions trapped as indicated.

with mass spectra of known compounds obtained in the same manner indicated that alkyl valerates and caproates were not present.

Comparison of spectra obtained from fractions S to V (Figure 8) at similar elution temperatures showed that overlap of components between traps occurred in only two cases. A trace of the major component of S was found in T, and a trace of the two poorly resolved substances in T was found in U. All other components differed. Although tentative structures could be proposed for many of the substances detected, the probability that unexpected modes of decomposition and rearrangement had occurred makes such proposals unwise until authentic samples can be obtained and examined. It is believed that most of the unknown substances are esters.

High boiling banana constituents have been further studied by separating odor concentrates on preparative and analytical scale Carbowax 20M-TPA (terminated with terephthalic acid) columns. An analytical separation is illustrated in Figure 9. Retention data indicate that peak 24 may be elemicin, 22 may be eugenol, and 18 may be O-methyleugenol. Peaks 17, 13, 9, 8, 5, and 3 may be C_7 to C_4 normal and isocarboxylic acids. Evidence supporting the presence of isovaleric acid was obtained from an infrared spectrum of a fraction from a preparative separation. How-

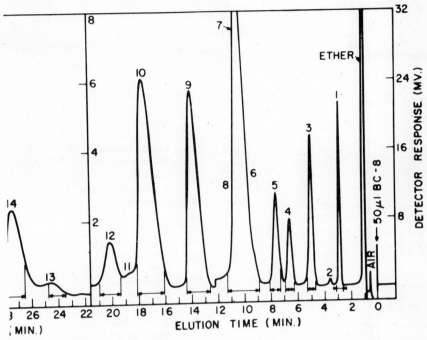

of banana odor concentrate

20% 50HB 2000 Ucon column at 85°C. (14)

ever, confirmation of the presence of acids is needed. Separation of a mixture of fractions R to Z at the conditions shown indicate that their constituents are present in peaks up to 18 in Figure 9.

Thus far only the chemistry of banana odor has been discussed. What of its biochemistry? The increase in volatile constituents observed (Figure 1) as ripening progresses and flavor develops (*17, 18*) leaves little doubt that a fundamental interrelationship must exist between these substances and the biochemical processes occurring in the fruit. Soon after bananas (and certain other fruits) are harvested and stored, greatly increased respiration occurs. Carbon dioxide evolution reaches a peak, the "climacteric," and then decreases. In Valery bananas production of volatiles begins during the climacteric. They increase rapidly in complexity and amount within 12 to 24 hours after the climacteric peak, when peel color is yellow-green. Gros Michel fruit, however, shows no significant production of volatiles until the late postclimacteric period and then relatively smaller quantities of volatiles are found (*17*).

The climacteric, and definition of the mechanism by which it occurs, have been the subject of many investigations. Millerd *et al.* (*22*) proposed that increased carbon dioxide evolution in avocados was due to a native uncoupling agent which released respiration from the control of

Table III.   Volatile Banana Constituents (Gros Michel)
(20% Ucon 50HB 2000 column at 85°C.)

Fraction		
(Fig. 4)	(Figs. 2 and 3)	Identification
1	B	Ethyl acetate[a]
—	C	Ethanol[a]
2	—	2-Butanone[b]
3	D	2-Pentanone[a]
—	—	1-Propanol[a]
4	F	Isobutyl acetate[a]
5	H	2-Butanol[a]
6	I	n-Butyl acetate
7	J	2-Pentanol acetate[c]
—	—	2-Pentanol[c]
8	—	1-Butanol[a]
9	K	Isoamyl acetate[a]
10	L	Isoamyl alcohol[a]
11	M	n-Amyl acetate
12	N	trans-2-Hexenal[a]
13	O	An octenone[b]
14	P	2-Pentanol butyrate
15	Q	n-Hexyl acetate
16	R	Isoamyl butyrate[a]
17	—	2-Hexanol[b]
18	—	1-Hexanol and an acetate
19–20	—	Unknown

[a] (14).
[b] Tentative identification.
[c] (13).

oxidative phosphorylation.   Marks (20), using P[32], demonstrated in tomatoes that phosphorylation did occur, and that ripening did not proceed normally without it.   In studies with apples Pearson and Robertson (24) suggested that the climacteric resulted from a greater than normal turnover of the phosphorylation cycle.   The mechanism controlling the climacteric is, in fact, unknown.   It is noteworthy that not all fruits—e.g., citrus—exhibit a climacteric.

Certain metabolic events have been observed during the climacteric. Carboxylase and aldolase activities in bananas were shown (29) to increase.   This was in agreement with previous evidence (28) that the pentose phosphate pathway was operative in the preclimacteric banana, and that the Embden-Meyerhof-Parnas (EMP) pathway predominated near the beginning of the climacteric.   If nicotinamide adenine dinucleotide phosphate produced by the pentose phosphate pathway were used for synthetic reductions, the shift from this pathway to the EMP scheme of metabolism might reflect a change from anabolic to catabolic reactions near or at the climacteric.   This is, at present, pure speculation.

GROS MICHEL
FULL YELLOW

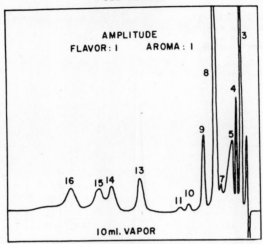

AMPLITUDE
FLAVOR: 1   AROMA: 1

10ml. VAPOR

VALERY
FULL YELLOW

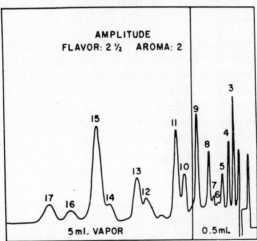

AMPLITUDE
FLAVOR: 2 ½   AROMA: 2

5ml. VAPOR   0.5mL.

*Figure 5. Correlation of head space constituents with
sensory evaluation*

Banana-like	Fruity	Green, Woody, or Musty
9. Isoamyl acetate	5–7. Butyl acetate	2. Metyl acetate
11. Amyl acetate	12. Butyl butyrate	4. Pentanone
13. Amyl propionate	14. Hexyl acetate	8. Butyl alcohol
15–17. Amyl butyrate	15–17. Amyl butyrate	10. Amyl alcohol
		16. Hexyl alcohol

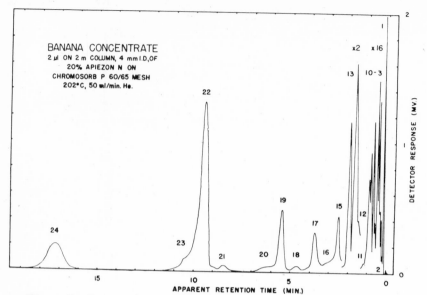

Figure 6. Separation of high boiling constituents of banana odor concentrate, Gros Michel variety

Increased membrane permeability in banana (*2*, *26*) and avocado (*26*) has been shown to occur during the climacteric, and extensive cellular disorganization has been observed (*1*) during the ripening of pears. Lyons and Pratt (*16*) showed that ethylene, a natural product of most mature fleshy fruits which may hasten the onset of the climacteric, causes a limited change in membrane permeability. It has been suggested (*1*, *2*, *16*, *26*) that increased membrane permeability may cause higher levels of respiration since metabolites would become more available and transport would not be a limiting factor. The breakdown of starch and protopectin as well as of other cellular constituents at or near the climacteric (*3*) might also provide substrates needed to bring about the respiration levels observed.

Palmer's group, with the United Fruit Co., has made several biochemical studies related to flavor research—example, the nonvolatile organic acids were determined in banana pulp (Gros Michel) at various stages of ripening (*31*). The results, presented in relationship to climacteric carbon dioxide evolution and peel color, are summarized in Table V. Malic acid, and "citric acid," which included an organic phosphate and some inorganic phosphate, increased markedly during early stages of ripening and then tended to remain constant or to increase slowly. Oxalic acid, the major acid in green fruit, decreased to about 60% of its original amount. An over-all increase in acidity occurred during ripening, with malic acid the major acidic component of ripe fruit. The

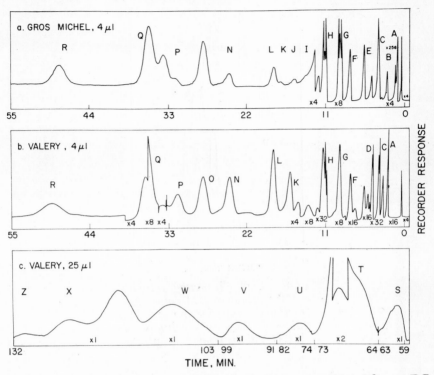

Figure 7. Separation of banana odor concentrates on a 20% Silicone DC 550 column at 101°C.

Table IV.   Volatile Banana Constituents

20% Silicone DC 550 column at 101°C.

Fraction (Fig. 7)	Identification
H	Isoamyl acetate
I	*trans*-2-Hexenal
J	*n*-Amyl acetate
K	An acetate
L	Isobutyl butyrate
M	An acetate
N	*n*-Butyl butyrate
O	2-Pentanol butyrate
P	*n*-Hexyl acetate
—	1-Octanol[a]
Q	Isoamyl butyrate
R	*n*-Amyl butyrate
S–Z	Unknown esters

[a] Tentative identity.

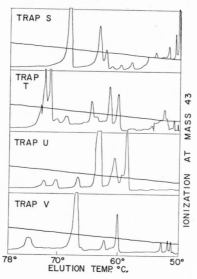

Figure 8. Rechromatography on
a 5% Carbowax 20M column of
fractions trapped from a 20%
Silicone DC 550 column at
101°C Valery odor concentrate

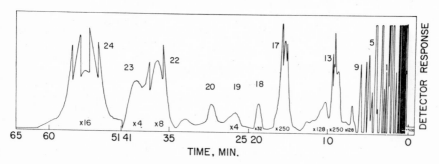

*Figure 9. Separation of banana odor concentrate (Valery, 05. μl.) on a
5% Carbowax 20M-TPA column at 125°C.*

Flame ionization detector

"other acids" at all ripeness stages consisted of trace amounts of glutamic,
aspartic, glutaric, quinic, glyceric, glycolic, and succinic acids in addition
to pyruvic, α-ketoglutaric, oxalacetic, glyoxylic, and four other keto acids.
Each of these acids showed little or no change in quantity (0.005 to 0.1
meq. per 100 grams). The authors (*31*) pointed out that too little is known
about fruit ripening to discuss their results in meaningful biochemical or
physiological terms, but that the absence (or very small amounts noted)
of many acids of the tricarboxylic acid cycle was noteworthy. They sug-

gested that either a very rapid turnover of these acids occurs or that certain of the Krebs cycle reactions are not operative. Similarly, the amino acids were studied (Table VI) during the ripening of banana fruit (5), and a correlation in time was found between the quantitative changes in certain amino acids and the production of volatile constituents. In particular, the rapid accumulation of valine and leucine was simultaneous with the first appearance and rapid increase in evolution of isobutyl and isoamyl alcohols and their acetates. These investigators have also developed a technique for introducing radioactive compounds into single slices of banana fruit and subsequently measuring the radioactivity in the evolved volatiles (30). Preliminary results with this technique suggest that valine, leucine, and isoleucine are precursors for a number of alcohols and esters (6, 9, 12).

Table V. CO_2 Production, Peel Color, and Organic Acid Content of Bananas during Ripening

	Stages of Ripening		
	Preclimacteric	Climacteric	Postclimacteric
CO_2 production, mg./100 g. fr. wt. × hr.	2.0–4.0 (steady)	10.0–17.5 (rising)	9.0–11.0 (erratic fluctuations)
Peel colors	Green	Yellow-green through yellow with green tips	Fully yellow through yellow flecked with brown
Organic acids, meg./ 100 g. fr. wt.			
Malic	1.36[a]	5.37	6.20
"Citric peak"	0.68	1.70	2.17
Oxalic	2.33	1.32	1.37
Other acids	0.19	0.16	0.17
Total organic acidity[b]	4.43	8.74	10.90

[a] Mean values for at least six samples from three independent experiments.
[b] Includes phosphate of peak VIII (31).

Relatively little information is available on banana lipid. It is a minor constituent (about 0.5% dry weight) of the fruit (7). Palmitic, stearic, and linoleic acids have been reported to be the major acids present although trace amounts of C_6 to C_{24} acids have been detected. Of particular interest was the observation that unsaturated fatty acids, palmitoleic acid in particular, decreased in quantity during ripening. However, additional knowledge is needed before any significance can be assigned to this change.

Fatty acids have been implicated as precursors of volatile banana constituents by Hultin's (11) observation that banana aroma was intensi-

Table VI. Amino Acids in Banana Pulp (5)

(Mmoles per gram fresh weight)

Stage	Days after Cutting	Valine	Leucine	Isoleucine
Green	3	0.01	0.13	0.06
	7	0.37	0.51	0.28
	10	0.33	0.49	0.22
Ripening	11	0.37	0.61	0.23
	12	0.59	0.86	0.20
Flavor development	13	0.95	1.60	0.21
	14	1.22	2.17	0.23
Maximum flavor	15	1.62	2.68	0.24
	16	0.72	1.86	0.17
	17	1.44	2.41	0.18
Overripe	21	0.97	1.52	0.11

fied when oleic acid and a crude banana enzyme extract were added to heat-processed banana puree. Selection of oleic acid as a possible precursor was based on the work of Nye and Spoehr (23), who showed it to be a possible precursor of 2-hexenal in leaves. Valine and pyruvic acid also were shown, on the basis of sensory evaluation, to be odor precursors in banana puree (11).

Work directed toward determining whether fatty acids may act as precursors of volatile banana constituents is being initiated in our laboratory. A careful study of the change in volatile organic acid content in both Valery and Gros Michel fruit during ripening should yield much interesting information for consideration in relationship to existing knowledge (27, 32) of the pathways and site of synthesis and degradation of plant fatty acids.

Conclusions

In view of the great amount of quantitative information still needed about possible precursors or key metabolic compounds which may be present in banana fruit during ripening, it is not now possible to suggest biochemical mechanisms of flavor or odor production. However, accumulation of information necessary for compilation of a "balance sheet" of such substances should be encouraged. Such a balance sheet can, of course, represent only states of equilibrium between synthesis and breakdown at various stages during ripening. Subsequent use of labeled compounds will lead to real knowledge of mechanisms for volatile constituent production.

It is hoped that continued investigations of volatile banana constituents and of their precursors will contribute significantly toward an understanding of the mechanisms of flavor production and of the ripening process in general.

Acknowledgment

The authors express their appreciation to Charles Merritt, Head, Analytical Laboratory, U.S. Army Natick Laboratories, for use of the Time-of-Flight mass spectrometer in these investigations.

Literature Cited

(1) Bain, J. M., Mercer, F. V., *Australian J. Biol. Sci.* **17**, 78 (1964).
(2) Ben-Yehoshua, S., *Physiol. Plant.* **17**, 71 (1964).
(3) Biale, J. B., Young, R. E., *Endeavor* **21**, 164 (1962).
(4) Briggs, L. H., Colebrook, L. D., Fales, H. M., Wildman, W. C., *Anal. Chem.* **29**, 904 (1957).
(5) Buckley, E. H., Lukow, B. J., Sullivan, W. A., United Fruit Co. Central Research Laboratory, Norwood, Mass., personal communication, 1965.
(6) Buckley, E. H., Wyman, H., McCarthy, A. I., United Fruit Co. Central Research Laboratory, personal communication, 1965.
(7) Grosbois, M., Mazliak, P., *Fruits* **19**, 55 (1964).
(8) Guenther, E., "The Essential Oils," Vol. IV, p. 656, Van Nostrand, New York, 1950.
(9) Guymon, J. F., Ingraham, J. L., Crowell, E. A., *Arch. Biochem. Biophys.* **95**, 163 (1961).
(10) Hultin, H. O., Proctor, B. E., *Food Technol.* **15**, 440 (1961).
(11) *Ibid.,* **16**, 108 (1962).
(12) Ingraham, J. L., Guymon, J. F., Crowell, E. A., *Arch. Biochem. Biophys.* **95**, 169 (1961).
(13) Issenberg, P., Nursten, H. E., Wick, E. L., Proceedings of First International Congress of Food Sciences and Technology, Gordon and Breach, New York, 1964.
(14) Issenberg, P., Wick, E. L., *J. Agr. Food Chem.* **11**, 2 (1963).
(15) Luff, B. D. W., Perkin, W. H., Jr., Robinson, R., *J. Chem. Soc.* **97**, 1131 (1910).
(16) Lyons, J. M., Pratt, H. K., *Arch Biochem. Biophys.* **104**, 318 (1964).
(17) McCarthy, A. I., Palmer, J. K., Proceedings of First International Congress of Food Science and Technology, Gordon and Breach, New York, 1964.
(18) McCarthy, A. I., Palmer, J. K., Shaw, C. P., Anderson, E. E., *J. Food Sci.* **28**, 279 (1963).
(19) McCarthy, A. I., Wyman, H., Palmer, J. K., *J. Gas Chromatog.* **2**, 121 (1964).
(20) Marks, J. D., Bernlohr, R. W., Varner, J. E., *Plant Physiol.* **32**, 259 (1957).
(21) Merritt, C., Walsh, J. T., *Anal. Chem.* **34**, 903 (1963).
(22) Millerd, A., Bonner, J., Biale, J. B., *Plant Physiol.* **28**, 521 (1953).
(23) Nye, W., Spoehr, H. H., *Arch. Biochem.* **2**, 23 (1943).
(24) Pearson, J. A., Robertson, R. N., *Australian J. Biol. Sci.* **7**, 1 (1954).
(25) Privett, O. S., Nadenicek, J. D., Weber, R. P., Pusch, F. J., *J. Am. Oil Chemists, Soc.* **40**, 28 (1963).
(26) Sacher, J. A., *Nature* **195**, 577 (1962).
(27) Stumpf, P. K., Bradbeer, C., *Ann. Rev. Plant Physiol.* **10**, 197 (1959).

(28) Tager, J. M., S. *African J. Sci.* **53**, 167 (1956).
(29) Tager, J. M., Biale, J. B., *Physiol. Plant* **10**, 79 (1957).
(30) Wyman, H., McCarthy, A. I., Buckley, E. H., Palmer, J. K., United States Fruit Co. Central Research Laboratory, personal communication, 1965.
(31) Wyman, H., Palmer, J. K., *Plant Physiol.* **39**, 630 (1964).
(32) Zill, L. P., Cheniae, G. M., *Ann. Rev. Plant Physiol.* **13**, 225 (1962).

RECEIVED May 25, 1965. Investigations supported in part by Public Health and Food Protection, and a grant-in-aid from the United Fruit Co. Publication No. 694 from the Department of Nutrition and Food Science.

Recent Studies of 5′-Nucleotides as New Flavor Enhancers

AKIRA KUNINAKA[1]

Microbial Laboratory, Yamasa Shoyu Co., Ltd., Choshi, Japan

Among the three isomers of inosinic acid, only 5′-inosinic acid has flavor activity. Disodium 5′-guanylate is 3.8 times as active as disodium 5′-inosinate although the qualitative effects of these nucleotides are virtually identical. There is a synergistic action between 5′-nucleotide and monosodium L-glutamate, tricholomic acid, or ibotenic acid. In the synergistic action, tricholomic or ibotenic acid is about 5 times as active as monosodium L-glutamate. Synergistic action can be also confirmed from the neurophysiological point of view. The 5′-nucleotides are beneficial as flavor enhancers in soups, gravies, bouillons, and other foods at very low levels and can be used to replace beef extract. The 5′-nucleotides are now produced by enzymatic degradation of ribonucleic acid or by chemical phosphorylation of inosine that is produced fermentatively.

Since 1909 only monosodium L-glutamate has been used widely as a pure organic compound to enhance the flavor of natural food products. Recently, however, we found that several 5′-nucleotides, especially 5′-inosinate and 5′-guanylate, were also capable of enhancing flavor. Furthermore, they have specific flavor activities which are not provided by monosodium L-glutamate. Food additive petitions for the use of disodium 5′-inosinate and disodium 5′-guanylate have been approved in both Japan and the United States (Table I). In this paper, recent developments in the study of the 5′-nucleotides as new flavor enhancers are reviewed.

---

[1] Present address, Division of Biochemistry, Department of Biology, Massachusetts Institute of Technology, Cambridge, Mass.

Table I. Specifications for 5'-Nucleotides

| | Disodium 5'-Inosinate | | Disodium 5'-Guanylate | |
	Japan Sept. 1960	U. S. A. July 1962	Japan June 1961	U. S. A. Dec. 1962
N range, %[a]	14.0–14.6	14.01–14.59	16.2–17.2	16.8–17.5
P range, %[a]	7.6–8.2	7.58–8.22	7.3–7.9	7.3–7.9
Loss on drying, %	Max. 26.5[b]	Max. 26.5	Max. 8[b]	Max. 15
pH, 5%	7.0–8.5	7.0–8.5	7.0–8.5	7.0–8.5

[a] Dry Basis.
[b] In 1964, loss on drying was revised in Japan as follows; Disodium 5'-inosinate, max. 28.5%. Disodium 5'-guanylate, max. 25%. Disodium 5'-inosinate and disodium 5'-guanylate standardized according to original Japanese specifications were used in our laboratory.

Monosodium L-glutamate and Inosinic Acid as Flavor Enhancers

The introduction of monosodium L-glutamate and disodium 5'-inosinate as flavor-enhancing compounds arose from studies on flavor components of typical Japanese foods.

In 1909, a flavor component of sea tangle, a kind of sea weed, was reported to be monosodium L-glutamate (7). Almost immediately, commercial production of monosodium L-glutamate started.

Only a few years later, a flavor component of dried bonito, a kind of fish, was reported to be the histidine salt of inosinic acid (10). Unfortunately, this compound could not be produced economically and therefore was not used commercially as a flavor enhancer. Inosinate began to be used about 50 years later, together with guanylate, when we elucidated the relationship between chemical structure and flavor activity of the nucleotide and developed a process for preparing 5'-nucleotides from ribonucleic acid (15, 17). Why was the commercial use of 5'-nucleotides so long delayed? One reason was the existence of isomers of inosinic acid.

Chemical Structure Necessary for Flavoring Action of Nucleotide

There are three types of inosinic acid—2'-, 3'-, and 5'-isomers—and the relationship between isomerism and flavoring action of inosinic acid had never been reported. To solve the problem, we prepared the disodium salts of these isomers and compared their flavor effects (13, 15, 17). The conclusion was that of the three inosinates only the 5'-isomer had flavor activity.   Histidine was found not to be necessary.   We also confirmed that hypoxanthine, inosine, and ribose 5-phosphate had no flavor activity.   Both ribosidic and 5'-phosphomonoester linkages are essential for the flavoring action of inosinate.   Furthermore, in the structure of 5'-inosinate, the hydroxyl group at the 6-position was confirmed to be essential for flavor activity.   If the hydroxyl group is replaced by an amino group, for example, flavor activity decreases sharply.

On the other hand, hydrogen at the 2-position could be replaced by another group such as a hydroxyl or an amino group without much change in flavor activity.   Especially, an amino group increased the flavor activity.   In other words, not only 5'-inosinate but also 5'-guanylate and 5'-xanthylate were found to have flavor activity.   The qualitative flavor effects of these nucleotides are virtually identical, and an additive relationship exists between them.   The general structure of the nucleotides which have flavor activity is:

X = H, NH$_2$, (or OH)

In addition, we found that *Asperigillus* ribosidase specifically attacked 5'-inosinate, 5'-guanylate, and 5'-xanthylate as well as their nucleosides (*11, 12, 14*).   An analogy between sensory specificity and enzyme specificity may be suggested.   The fact is that the study of the specificity of the ribosidase enzyme action on the nucleotides led us to the discovery of the specific flavor activities of 5'-guanylate and 5'-xanthylate.

The flavor activity of 5'-xanthylate is weaker than that of 5'-guanylate or 5'-inosinate.   Therefore, 5'-xanthylate has not been produced commercially, although it can be produced by deaminating 5'-guanylate.

Effects of Chemical Modifications of 5'-Inosinate or 5'-Guanylate

Several Japanese researchers have further elucidated the relationship between flavor activity and the chemical structure of the nucleotide.

The first problem is whether or not the 2'- and 3'- OH groups of 5'-inosinate or 5'-guanylate are necessary for flavoring action. The second problem is how chemical modifications of the phosphate moiety of 5'-inosinate or 5'-guanylate affect their flavoring action.

Regarding the first point, Nakao and Ogata (20) disclosed that 5'-deoxyinosinate and 5'-deoxyguanylate also had flavor activity. Therefore the 2'-OH can be replaced by H without total loss of flavor activity. Furthermore, Honjo and coworkers (6) reported that the flavor activity of 5'-inosinate or 5'-guanylate could be detected in 2'-, 3'-O-isopropylidene inosine 5'-monophosphate, inosine 2'(3'), 5'-diphosphate, and guanosine 2'(3'), 5'-diphosphate, although the activity was weaker (Table II, A). In these cases the hydrogen in the 2'- and/or 3'-OH groups was replaced by another group. On the other hand, 9-(4'-hydroxybutyl)-6-hydroxypurine 4'-monophosphate, a compound having a straight-chain aliphatic primary alcohol instead of the ribose of 5'-inosinic acid, had no flavor activity (Table II, B). These results indicate that the hydrogen atoms of the 2'- and 3'-hydroxyl groups are not necessarily essential for flavor activity although the principal part of the ribose molecule is essential.

In regard to the second point, Honjo and coworkers (6) found that the sodium salts of the methyl ester of 5'-inosinic acid, the ethyl ester of 5'-inosinic or 5'-guanylic acid, diinosine 5'-pyrophosphate, diguanosine 5'-pyrophosphate, inosine 3', 5'-cyclic phosphate, polyinosinic acid, the amidate of 5'-inosinic or 5'-guanylic acid, inosine 5'-monosulfate, and guanosine 5'-monosulfate had no flavor activity, while the trisodium salt of inosine 5'-diphosphate had flavor activity (Table II, C). These results indicate that both hydroxyls of the phosphate group are essential and that both primary and secondary dissociations are probably necessary for flavor activity.

Although none of the synthesized compounds had stronger flavor activity than 5'-inosinate or 5'-guanylate, further research on the modification of the purine moiety may result in discovery of structures with high flavor activity.

Synergistic Action between Monosodium L-glutamate and 5'-Nucleotides

The 5'-nucleotides have several specific flavor-enhancing properties. The most important and the most basic property is their synergistic action with monosodium L-glutamate.

Table II. Effects of Chemical Modifications of 5'-Inosinate or 5'-Guanylate on Flavor Activity

[Based on results reported by Honjo *et al.* (*5, 6*)]

Compound	Part of Structure	Flavor Activity
	A. MODIFICATION OF RIBOSE MOIETY	

5'-Inosinate
5'-Guanylate   ++++

5'-Deoxyinosinate
5'-Deoxyguanylate   +++

2',3'-*O*-Isopropylidene-inosine
5'-monophosphate   +

Inosine 2'(3'),5'-diphosphate   +

Guanosine 2'(3'),5'-diphosphate   +~++

B. REPLACEMENT OF RIBOSE WITH *n*-BUTYL ALCOHOL

5'-Inosinate   ++++

9-(4'-Hydroxybutyl)-6-
hydroxypurine 4'-monophosphate   −

Table II. Continued

Compound	Part of Structure	*Flavor Activity*
C. MODIFICATION OF PHOSPHATE MOIETY		

5′-Inosinate

5′-Guanylate

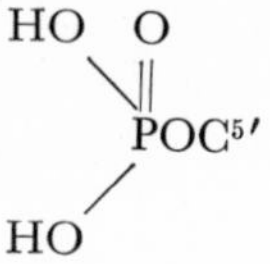

$$\begin{array}{c} HO \quad O \\ \diagdown \parallel \\ POC^{5'} \\ \diagup \\ HO \end{array}$$

++++

Inosine 5′-diphosphate

$$\begin{array}{c} O \qquad O \\ \parallel \qquad \parallel \\ HO\!-\!P\!-\!O\!-\!POC^{5'} \\ \mid \qquad \mid \\ OH \qquad OH \end{array}$$

+++

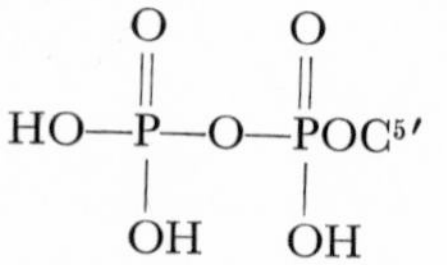

Methyl ester of 5′-inosinic acid

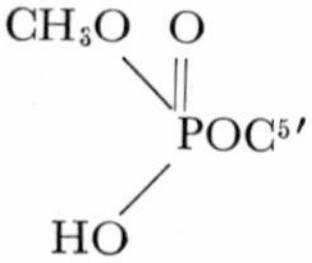

$$\begin{array}{c} CH_3O \quad O \\ \diagdown \parallel \\ POC^{5'} \\ \diagup \\ HO \end{array}$$

—

Ethyl ester of 5′-inosinic or 5′-guanylic acid

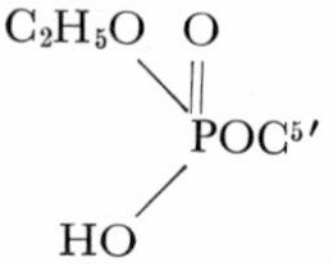

$$\begin{array}{c} C_2H_5O \quad O \\ \diagdown \parallel \\ POC^{5'} \\ \diagup \\ HO \end{array}$$

—

Diinosine 5′-pyrophosphate

Diguanosine 5′-pyrophosphate

$$\begin{array}{c} O \qquad O \\ \parallel \qquad \parallel \\ C^{5'}O\!-\!P\!-\!O\!-\!P\!-\!OC^{5'} \\ \mid \qquad \mid \\ OH \qquad OH \end{array}$$

—

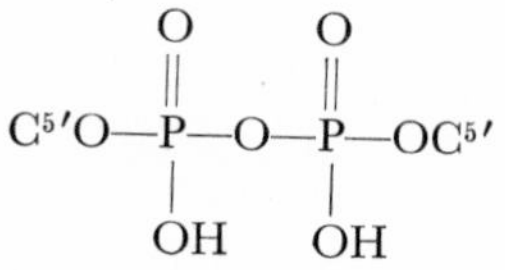

Inosine 3′,5′-cyclic phosphate

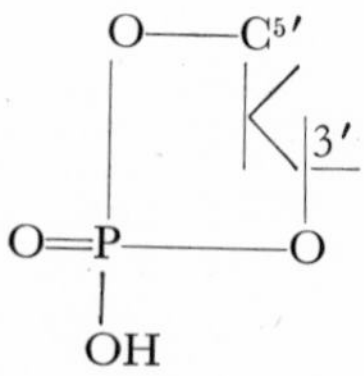

$$\begin{array}{c} O\!\!-\!\!-C^{5'} \\ \mid \qquad \diagdown 3' \\ O\!\!=\!\!P\!\!-\!\!-\!\!-O \\ \mid \\ OH \end{array}$$

—

Polyinosinic acid

$$\begin{array}{c} O \\ \parallel \\ C^{3'}O\!-\!P\!-\!OC^{5'} \\ \mid \\ OH \end{array}$$

—

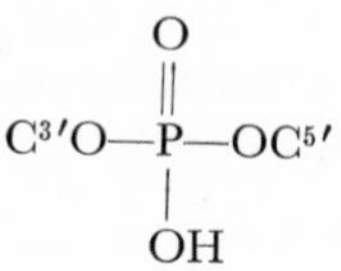

Table II. Continued

Compound	Part of Structure	Flavor Activity
Amidate of 5'-inosinic or 5'-guanylic acid	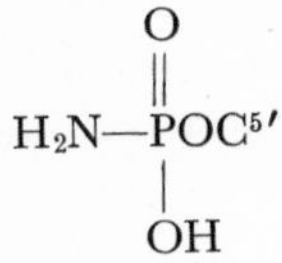 $\begin{array}{c} O \\ \parallel \\ H_2N—POC^{5'} \\ \mid \\ OH \end{array}$	—
Inosine 5'-monosulfate	$\begin{array}{c} O \\ \parallel \\ O{=}SOC^{5'} \\ \mid \\ OH \end{array}$	—
Guanosine 5'-monosulfate		

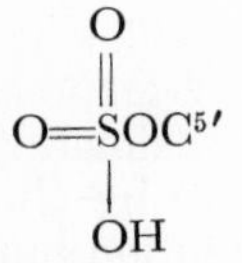

At first, we found that the latent flavor level of disodium 5'-inosinate or disodium 5'-guanylate was detectable when monosodium L-glutamate solution was employed as a medium. The latent flavor level of monosodium L-gultanate was also detectable when the 5'-nucleotide solution was employed as a medium (*13, 15*).

Synergistic action also can be demonstrated by studying the mutual effects of these compounds in reducing their individual threshold levels. As shown in Table III, the threshold level of disodium 5'-inosinate or disodium 5'-guanylate is reduced sharply in a solution of monosodium L-glutamate, and the threshold level of monosodium L-glutamate is reduced sharply in a solution of 5'-nucleotide.

Table III. Threshold Levels of Flavor Enhancers

	Threshold Level, %		
Solvent	Disodium 5'-Inosinate[a]	Disodium 5'-Guanylate[a]	Monosodium L-Glutamate[b]
Water	0.012	0.0035	0.03
0.1% monosodium L-glutamate	0.00010	0.000030	—
0.01% disodium 5'-inosinate	—	—	0.002

[a] Based on results reported by Fujita *et al.* (*4*).
[b] Based on results reported by Toi *et al.* (*32*).

Synergistic action was further elucidated by studying the relative flavor activity of a mixture of 5'-nucleotide and monosodium L-glutamate, changing the ratio of mixing as shown in Table IV. The data revealed three facts:

As the ratio of 5'-nucleotide to monosodium L-glutamate is lowered, the flavor activity of the resulting mixture is reduced.

However, this relationship is not linear. Thus, at lower relative concentration the relative effectiveness of the nucleotide is much greater.

In other words, the relative replacing effect of nucleotide for monosodium L-glutamate in a mixture of monosodium L-glutamate and nucleotide is greater at a lower relative concentration of nucleotide. For instance, in flavor activity, a mixture of 1 gram of disodium 5′-guanylate and 10 grams of monosodium L-glutamate corresponds to 209 grams of monosodium L-glutamate alone, and a mixture of 1 gram of disodium 5′-guanylate and 100 grams of monosodium L-glutamate corresponds to 556 grams of monosodium L-glutamate. In the former case, 1 gram of guanylate replaces 199 grams of glutamate, while in the latter case, 1 gram of guanylate replaces 456 grams of glutamate (15).

5′-Guanylate was more efficient than 5′-inosinate. The relative weight efficacy of disodium 5′-guanylate and disodium 5′-inosinate has been demonstrated to be approximately 3.8 to 1 (17). On an anhydrous basis, the ratio is calculated to be about 3 to 1. This relationship was confirmed not only in pure solution but also in liquid food products such as chicken soup and in solid products such as sausage.

Table IV. Flavor Activity of Mixture of Monosodium L-Glutamate and 5′-Nucleotide (16)

| Ratio of Mixing | | Relative Flavor Activity per Unit Weight of Mixture | |
Monosodium L-Glutamate	5′-Nucleotide	A[a]	B[b]
1	0	1.0	1.0
1	1	7.5	30.0
10	1	5.0	19.0
20	1	3.4	12.4
50	1	2.5	6.4
100	1	2.0	5.5

[a] A. Disodium 5′-inosinate was used as nucleotide components.
[d] B. Disodium 5′-guanylate was used as nucleotide component.

Neurophysiological Studies of 5′-Nucleotides

Lately, in Japan, the neurophysiological effect of nucleotides has been studied. Adachi (1) and Kawamura et al. (9) placed a test solution on the dorsum of the tongue of a cat and analyzed the electrical response of the chorda tympani nerve.

Some of the single nerve fibers of the taste nerve which responded to pure sucrose or sodium chloride solutions responded to monosodium L-glutamate and disodium 5′-inosinate solutions, although some differences were noted in the response patterns of each solution. Some types of fibers specifically responded to monosodium L-glutamate or disodium 5′-inosinate.

The response to $0.05M$ monosodium L-glutamate solution or to $0.005M$ disodium 5′-inosinate solution was less than the response to a mixed solution of $0.05 M$ L-glutamate and $0.005 M$ 5′-inosinate. Also the latter response is greater than the sum of the individual responses (Table V). Even if the concentrations of 5′-inosinate and L-glutamate are at less than threshold level, a mixture at these concentrations induces significant response. Thus, synergistic action between L-glutamate and 5'-inosinate was observed from a neurophysiological point of view.

Table V. Influence of 5'-Inosinate or L-Glutamate on Integrated Response of Whole Chorda Tympani Nerve of Cat to Taste Compounds

	Response Coefficient[a]		
		Mixed Solution with	
Compound	Pure Solution	0.005M Disodium 5'-Inosinate	0.05M Monosodium L-Glutamate
—	0	17	17
0.005M disodium 5'-inosinate	17	—	45
0.05M monosodium L-glutamate	17	45	—
0.5M sodium chloride	40	53	53
0.2M acetic acid	100	100	100
0.005M quinine	28	20	20
1M sucrose	40	20	20

[a] Based on results reported by Kawamura *et al.* (*9*).

In addition, the relationship between 5'-inosinate or L-glutamate and sodium chloride, acetic acid, quinine, or sucrose was studied. The response to 0.5M sodium chloride solution increased slightly when 0.005M disodium 5'-inosinate or 0.05M monosodium L-glutamate was added to the solution. The responses to 0.005M quinine and 1M sucrose solutions decreased on the addition of 0.005M 5'-inosinate or 0.05M L-glutamate. It is interesting that 5'-inosinate and L-glutamate had similar effects on the responses to these compounds. (Table V).

Independently, Sato and coworkers (*22*) compared the response of rat chorda tympani to four kinds of nucleotides. In this work, disodium 5'-guanylate and disodium 5'-inosinate showed more response than disodium 5'-uridylate and disodium 5'-cytidylate (5'-guanylate > 5'-inosinate ≫ 5'-uridylate > 5'-cytidylate). They also confirmed that there was synergistic action between L-glutamate and each 5'-nucleotide. In the synergistic action, 5'-guanylate and 5'-inosinate were much more active than 5'-cytidylate and 5'-uridylate. The synergistic action between L-glutamate and 5'-inosinate in the chorda tympani response was more remarkable in a rat than in a cat. It is of special interest that in the synergistic action in rat chorda tympani disodium 5'-guanylate was about three times as active as disodium 5'-inosinate. The results of the above neurophysiological studies are essentially consistent with the results of our sensory tests. In addition, the influence of temperature on response was studied by Sato and coworkers (*22*). The responses of rat chorda tympani to 0.03% 5'-guanylate and 0.03% 5'-inosinate were maximum at about 30°C., while those to 0.1% 5'-uridylate, 0.1% 5'-cytidylate, 0.3% L-glutamate, and 0.1% sodium chloride decreased with a rise in temperature. The synergistic effect of 5'-nucleotide on the response to monosodium L-glutamate was negligible at 10°C., but increased sharply with a rise in temperature.

Relationship between 5'-Nucleotides and Two New Amino Acids

Recently Takemoto and coworkers (25–29) isolated two new amino acids, tricholomic acid and ibotenic acid, from the Japanese fungi, *Tricholoma muscarium* and *Amanita strobiliformis*.

$$H_2C\text{------}CHCHCOOH$$
$$| \quad | \quad NH_2$$
$$O=C \quad O$$
$$\diagdown N \diagup$$
$$H$$

Tricholomic acid

$$HC=\!\!\!=\!\!\!=C\text{------}CHCOOH$$
$$| \quad | \quad NH_2$$
$$O=C \quad O$$
$$\diagdown N \diagup \quad \cdot H_2O$$
$$H$$

Ibotenic acid

It has been known in Japan that such fungi are effective in killing the housefly, and this work was undertaken to elucidate the specific insecticidal compounds in the fungi. Having isolated these two amino acids, these workers also reported that they had good flavor activity. In addition, ibotenic acid was readily decarboxylated in water by heating (28), and the pyro-product of ibotenic acid had neither flavor activity nor insecticidal activity (24).

According to Takemoto (24), the threshold level of tricholomic or ibotenic acid is 0.001 to 0.003%, and there is a synergistic action between these amino acids and 5'-nucleotides. The threshold levels is much less than that of monosodium L-glutamate [0.02% (24) to 0.03% (32)] or disodium 5'-inosinate [0.01% (13, 17, 24), 0.012% (4), 0.02% (33) or 0.025% (32)]

The flavor activity of these amino acids was further studied in our laboratory in Japan (34). The flavor properties of tricholomic and ibotenic acid were qualitatively similar to that of monosodium L-glutamate. There was no synergistic action between the former and the latter—for example, in flavor activity,

$$(0.02\% \text{ MSG}, 0.005\% \text{ Ibo}) \cong (0.02\% \text{ MSG},$$
$$0.005\% \text{ Tri}) \cong (0.025\% \text{ MSG})$$

where MSG = monosodium L-glutamate, Ibo = ibotenic acid, and Tri = tricholomic acid.

On the other hand, synergistic action between tricholomic or ibotenic acid and 5'-inosinate or 5'-guanylate easily could be confirmed; the mixed solution at the threshold level of tricholomic or ibotenic acid and at the threshold level of disodium 5'-inosinate or disodium 5'-guanylate had remarkable flavor activity. We concluded from repeated sensory tests that tricholomic and ibotenic acid were about five times or more active than monosodium L-glutamate in respect to synergistic action with 5'-nucleotides—for example, in flavor activity,

   A. $(0.1\%$ IMP, 0.02% MSG$) \geqq (0.1\%$ IMP, 0.002% Ibo$) \geqq (0.1\%$ IMP, 0.002% Tri$) \cong (0.1\%$ IMP, 0.01% MSG$)$
   B. $(0.1\%$ GMP, 0.02% MSG$) > (0.1\%$ GMP, 0.002% Ibo$) \cong (0.1\%$ GMP, 0.002% Tri$) \cong (0.1\%$ GMP, 0.01% MSG$)$
   C. $(0.01\%$ IMP, 0.1% MSG$) > (0.01\%$ IMP, 0.01% Ibo$) \cong (0.01\%$ IMP, 0.01% Tri$) > (0.01\%$ IMP, 0.05% MSG$)$
   D. $(0.005\%$ GMP, 0.1% MSG$) > (0.005\%$ GMP, 0.01% Ibo$) \cong (0.005\%$ GMP, 0.01% Tri$) > (0.005\%$ GMP, 0.05% MSG$)$
where IMP = disodium 5'-inosinate and GMP = diosodium 5'-guanylate.

We also concluded that disodium 5'-guanylate was about four times more active than disodium 5'-inosinate in respect to its synergistic action with tricholomic or ibotenic acid as well as with monosodium L-glutamate—for example, in flavor activity,

$$(0.1\% \text{ IMP}, 0.002\% \text{ Ibo}) \geqq (0.025\% \text{ GMP}, 0.002\% \text{ Ibo})$$
$$(0.1\% \text{ IMP}, 0.002\% \text{ Tri}) \cong (0.025\% \text{ GMP}, 0.002\% \text{ Tri})$$

It is now clear that 5'-inosinate and 5'-guanylate have the same kind of flavor-enhancing activity and an additive relationship exists between them. Monosodium L-glutamate, tricholomic acid, and ibotenic acid have a different kind of flavor-enhancing activity, and an additive relationship exists between them. Synergistic action in regard to flavor exists between the above two groups.

Recent Studies of 5'-Nucleotides in United States

5'-Nucleotides were first used in Japan as new flavor enhancers. Since 1961, however, the use of disodium 5'-inosinate and disodium 5'-guanylate as flavor enhancers has also been studied actively in the United States, mainly by the Titus (*30, 31, 33*) and Sjöström groups (*3, 19*).

At first, they screened the 5'-nucleotides in a variety of foods, using profile panel techniques. As a result, the profile panel recommended the use of 5'-nucleotides in soups, gravies, bouillons, certain canned meats, fish, certain vegetables, tomato juice, and instant coffee. The recommended use levels in soups varied from product to product but usually fell in the range of 50 to 200 p.p.m. of disodium 5'-inosinate.

They also found that the 5'-nucleotides consistently altered certain flavor characteristics, regardless of the foods to which they were added. The nucleotides enhance the following flavor notes: meaty, brothy, monosodium L-glutamate, mouth-filling, dryness, astringency, and sensation of viscosity. Buttery and sweet flavors were usually not affected by nucleotides, but in some cases they were enhanced. On the other hand, the nucleotides suppress sulfide-like flavor notes and the flavor note of hydrolyzed vegetable protein. Flavor notes such as sour, fatty and oily, starchy, burnt, and herb-spice complexes were usually not affected by the nucleotides, but in some cases they were suppressed.

Caul and Raymond (3) conducted a consumer home-use test using a dried noodle soup as a control, and the same soup containing 0.01% disodium 5'-inosinate. As the result, 44 out of 86 families accurately described an improvement in the flavor of the soup containing inosinate.

Titus and Klis (31) evaluated 5'-nucleotides as replacements for beef extract in bouillon. Replacement of beef extract by 1/10 as much disodium 5'-inosinate resulted in a product significantly more acceptable than the standard bouillon. We also confirmed that 24 grams of beef extract could be replaced by 1 gram of a 50 : 50 mixture of disodium 5'-inosinate and disodium 5'-guanylate in a bouillon. Thus, the flavor activity ratio in bouillon may be summarized as follows:

Beef extract : IMP : GMP : (50 : 50 mixture of IMP/GMP) = 1 : 10 : 38 : 24

Methods for Producing 5'-Nucleotides

There are several methods for producing 5'-inosinic and 5'-guanylic acid (17). At present, in Japan, two methods are employed industrially.

Degradation of Ribonucleic Acid. Since nucleotides are the building blocks of ribonucleic acid, they can be produced by degrading ribonucleic acid. However, most of the ribonucleic acid–degrading enzymes that were known split the molecule at the 3'-phosphodiester linkages, giving rise to nucleotides which have no flavor activity. Therefore, the key was to find the microorganism which would produce 5'-phosphodiesterase to split the ribonucleic acid molecule efficiently at the 5'-phosphodiester linkages, giving rise to 5'-nucleotides.

Fortunately, we found such an enzyme in *Penicillium* strains (16, 18) and Ogata and coworkers found the same type of enzyme in *Streptomyces* strains (21). Since the microbial 5'-phosphodiesterase can be obtained in large amounts, it was possible to produce four 5'-nucleotides—5'-adenylic, guanylic, cytidylic, and uridylic acid—industrially from yeast ribonucleic acid. 5'-Inosinic acid could then be easily obtained by deaminating 5'-adenylic acid.

Combination of Fermentation and Chemical Synthesis. It is rather difficult today to produce 5'-nucleotides directly by fermentation in good yield. Economical, total chemical synthesis of 5'-nucleotides is also difficult. However, fermentative production of nucleosides, particularly inosine, is rather easy (2, 17). Inosine can then be chemically phosphorylated to 5'-inosinic acid in good yield (8). Thus, the following process was established industrially in 1963.

Culture medium $\xrightarrow[\text{mutant}]{\substack{\text{B. subtilis}\\ \text{adenine-requiring}}}$ Inosine $\xrightarrow{\text{Acetone}}$
(C source,
  N source, etc.)

2',3'-O-isopropylidene inosine $\xrightarrow{\text{POCl}_3}$

2',3'-O-isopropylidene inosine 5'-monophosphoric acid

$\xrightarrow[\text{70°C. 20 min.}]{\text{pH 1.5}}$ 5'-inosinic acid $\xrightarrow{\text{NaOH}}$ disodium 5'-inosinate

Distribution, application, physical properties, and assay method of 5'-nucleotides were excellently reviewed by Shimazono (23).

Acknowledgment

I thank T. Takemoto, professor at Tohoku University, for gifts of tricholomic and ibotenic acids. This paper is based on many contributions by members of the Laboratory of Yamasa Shoyu Co., Ltd., Choshi, Japan. Their help is acknowledged, too.

Literature Cited

(1) Adachi, A., *J. Physiol. Soc. Japan* **24**, 607 (1962).
(2) Aoki, R., Momose, H., Muramatsu, N., Kondo, Y., Tsuchiya, Y., *Sym. Amino Acid Nucleic Acid* **8**, 127 (1963).
(3) Caul, J. F., Raymond, S. A., *Food Technol.* **18**, 353 (1964).
(4) Fujita, E., Yasumatsu, K., Bichu, S., Uda, Y., Annual Meeting, Agricultural Chemical Society of Japan, Fukuoka, April 1, 1961.
(5) Honjo, M., Takeda Research Laboratories, Osaka, Japan, private communication.
(6) Honjo, M., Imai, K., Furukawa, Y., Moriyama, H., Yasumatsu, K., Imada, A., *Ann. Rept. Takeda Res. Lab.* **22**, 47 (1963).
(7) Ikeda, K., *J. Tokyo Chem. Soc.* **30**, 820 (1909).
(8) Kato, T., Mori, H., Muramatsu, N., Meguro, T., Yoshikawa, M., Ichikawa, T., Takenishi, T., Tsuchiya, Y., Annual Meeting, Agricultural Chemical Society of Japan, Tokyo, April 1, 1963.
(9) Kawamura, Y., Adachi, A., Ohara, M., Ikeda, S., *Sym. Amino Acid Nucleic Acid* **10**, 168 (1964).
(10) Kodama, S., *J. Tokyo Chem. Soc.* **34**, 751 (1913).
(11) Kuninaka, A., *Bull. Agr. Chem. Soc. Japan* **23**, 281 (1959).
(12) Kuninaka, A., *J. Agr. Chem. Soc. Japan* **30**, 583 (1956).
(13) *Ibid.*, **34**, 489 (1960).
(14) Kuninaka, A., *J. Gen. Appl. Microbiol.* **3**, 55 (1957).
(15) Kuninaka, A., "Symposium on Flavor Potentiation," p. 4, Arthur D. Little, Inc., Cambridge, Mass., 1964.

(16) Kuninaka, A., Kibi, M., Yoshino, H., Sakaguchi, K., *Agr. Biol. Chem.* 25, 693 (1961).
(17) Kuninaka, A., Kibi, M., Sakaguchi, K., *Food Technol.* 18, 287 (1964).
(18) Kuninaka, A., Otsuka, S., Kobayashi, Y., Sakaguchi, K., *Bull. Agr. Chem. Soc. Japan* 23, 239 (1959).
(19) Kurtzman, C. H., Sjöström, L. B., *Food Technol.* 18, 22 (1964).
(20) Nakao, Y., Ogata, K., Meeting of Kanto Division, Agricultural Chemical Society of Japan, Tokyo, Nov. 12, 1960.
(21) Ogata, K., Nakao, Y., Igarashi, S., Omura, E., Sugino, Y., Yoneda, M., Suhara, I., *Agr. Biol. Chem.* 27, 110 (1963).
(22) Sato, M., Akaike, N., Yamashita, S., *Sym. Amino Acid Nucleic Acid* 11, 53 (1965).
(23) Shimazono, H., *Food Technol.* 18, 294 (1964).
(24) Takemoto, T., Pharmaceutical Institute, Tohoku University School of Medicine, Sendai, Japan, private communication.
(25) Takemoto, T., Nakajima, T., *Yakugaku Zasshi* 84, 1183 (1964).
(26) *Ibid.*, p. 1230.
(27) Takemoto, T., Nakajima, T., Sakuma, R., *Ibid.*, 84, 1233 (1964).
(28) Takemoto, T., Nakajima, T., Yokobe, T., *Ibid.*, 84, 1232 (1964).
(29) Takemoto, T., Yokobe, T., Nakajima, T., *Ibid.*, 84, 1186 (1964).
(30) Titus, D. S., "Symposium on Flavor Potentiation," p. 10, Arthur D. Little, Inc., Cambridge, Mass., 1964.
(31) Titus, D. S., Klis, J. B., *Food Process.* 24 (5), 150 (1963).
(32) Toi, B., Maeda, S., Ikeda, S., Furukawa, H., Meeting of Kanto Division, Agricultural Chemical Society of Japan, Tokyo, Nov. 12, 1960.
(33) Wagner, J. R., Titus, D. S., Schade, J. E., *Food Technol.* 17, 730 (1963).
(34) Yoshino, H., Suzuki, M., Yamasa Shoyu Co., Ltd. Choshi, Japan, private communication.

RECEIVED May 4, 1965.

INDEX

A

Acetylcholine 55
Acids in breads, organic...........157
Ascorbigen 178
Adaptation, odor.................45
5'-Adenylic acid.................272
Adsorption and odor············37
Alcohols in Blue Cheese, secondary..102
Alcohols in bread.................158
Alcohols, odors of secondary......104
Aldehyde oxidation..............110
Aldehydes from lipid autoxidation...107
Allium 135
Amadori rearrangement............167
Amino acids in banana pulp.......258
Analysis of variance..............69
Anomers of mannose..............11
Appearance properties of foods......65
Apples 126
Aromagram technique.............155
Aromatic compounds from irradiated
    meats 239
Aspergillus ribosidase..............263
Autoxidation 107–110

B

Bacterium linens..................102
Banana
  climacteric 251
  components, flavor and biochemis-
    try of volatile.................241
  constituents, volatile....242, 252, 255
  metabolism during climacteric....252
  odor concentrate
    chromatogram of.........246, 248
    high boiling constituents of.....254
    separation of........250, 255, 256
    yield of......................242
  pulp, amino acids in............258
Banana ripening volatiles, chromato-
    gram of......................244
Bananas, ripening of..............257
Bartlett pears.....................125
Beans 151
Beef 194
  extract, 5'-nucleotides as replace-
    ment for....................272
  hydrocarbons in
    irradiated..........226, 233, 235
  volatiles, gas chromatogram of....228
Beer 188
Behavior, odor and................16
Benzaldehyde autoxidation.........110
Beverage flavors..................174

Biochemistry of volatile banana com-
    ponents 241
Biogenesis 175
Bitter principle of grapefruit.......128
Black pepper......................212
  monoterpenes in oil of..........217
  oil of.........................216
Black tea........................185
Blends, odor.....................44
Blue cheese
  methyl ketones in...............101
  secondary alcohols in...........102
Bread
  alcohols in.....................158
  carbonyl compounds in......160–165
  flavor 153
    fermentation and..............165
    oven browning and............166
Breakdown flavors.................184
Butter
  ketones in.....................99
  oil stabilization.................116
  volatiles, carbonyl compounds in
    irradiated 236

C

Capsaicin 209
Capsicum 207
Carbonyl compounds in bread..160–165
Carbonyl compounds in irradiated
    butter volatiles................236
Carrots 146
Celery 145
Chalcone 129
Cheddar cheese
  fruity flavor defect of............105
  methyl ketones in...............101
Cheese
  esters in......................104
  fruity flavor defect of Cheddar....105
Chemical excitation of taste and odor
    receptors 1
Chemical senses..................30
Chromatogram of banana ripening
    volatiles 244
Climacteric, banana...............251
Clove oil........................220
Cloves 219
Cocoa 184
Coffee 184
Compound beverage flavors........187
Cooked vegetables................150
Cookie color.....................170
Cordials 183
Cucumbers 148

5'-Cytidylate 269
5'-Cytidylic acid..................272

D

Dairy products, flavor of...........94
n-Decanal autoxidation............110
Descriptive testing of foods........67
Difference tests for foods..........67
Disodium 5'-inosinate..............262
Distilled spirits...................186
δ-dodecalactone 106
Doughs
 carbonyl compounds in......160–165
 organic acids in.................157
Dynamic area of odorivector molecule 37

E

Electrical properties of taste cells......6
Electrochemical approach to odor....65
Emulsion, inversion of............55
Enzyme theory of odor...........47
Esters in bread..................165
Esters in cheese.................104
Evaporated milk, ketones in........99

F

Falling film flash evaporator........73
Fast-scan mass spectrometer.......122
Fat, irradiated...................236
Fat, oxidized....................236
Fatigue, odor....................44
Fatty acids, free...............95, 97
Fatty acids, β-oxidation of.........101
Fatty esters, radiation products induced in....................237
Fermentation and bread flavor......165
Fermentation flavors..............185
Fish 198
Flavor
 activity of flavor enhancers.......268
 analysis 70
 components 70
  synergistic interaction of......100
 defect of Cheddar cheese, fruity...105
 defects, lactones in.............107
 enhancers
  flavor activity of.............268
  5'-nucleotides as.............261
  threshold levels of...........267
 -enchancing compounds........262
 and information theory...........3
 in meat, undesirable............225
 profiles 32
 vs. structure of 5'-inosinate and 5'-guanylate 265
 vs. structure of nucleotide.......262
Flavors by aging.................187
Flesh foods.....................190
Food acceptance.................25
Food flavor, sensory evaluation of....64

Foods
 appearance properties of.........65
 descriptive testing of............67
 difference tests for.............67
Free fatty acids...............95, 97
 flavor of.......................98
Fruit flavor.....................121
Fruity flavor defect of Cheddar cheese 105
Fusel oils.......................180

G

Garlic 139
Gas chromatograph-mass spectrometer 230
Gas chromatography..............74
 mass spectrometry with.......86–89
Gas chromatogram of beef volatiles..228
Geotricum candidum..............102
Gin 183
Glucobrassicin 178
Grapefruit aroma................128
Grapefruit, bitter principle of......128
Green tea.......................183
5'-Guanylate
 chemical modifications of........264
 flavor vs. structure of...........265
5'-Guanylic acid.................272

H

Headspace analysis................75
Headspace gas analysis...........155
Hedonic scale....................68
Hemolysis and odor...............40
Hydrocarbons in irradiated beef...
 ....226, 233, 235
Hydroperoxides.............109, 110

I

Ibotenic acid....................270
3-Indolacetonitrile 178
Inhibitors, taste...................13
5'-Inosinate
 chemical modifications of........264
 flavor vs. structure of...........265
Inosinic acid....................201
Inversion of emulsions............55
Ion binding to proteins............59
Irradiated fat....................236
Irradiated meats
 sulfur and aromatic compounds from 239
 volatiles, oxygenated compounds in 238
Irradiation damage in lipids.......225
Irradiation of milk fat............113
Isomers, taste of................11
Isopulegol..................123, 126

K

β-Keto esters....................99

Ketone formation................99
Ketones in butter................99
Ketones in evaporated milk.........99
Kinesthetics 64

L

Lachrymatory principle............144
Lactones in flavor defects.........107
Lactones from milk fat............106
Lamb 197
Latin square....................68
Lettuce 146
Lime oil.......................128
Lipid autoxidation, aldehydes from..107
Lipid bound aldehydes...........113
Lipids, irradiation damage in.......225
Lipids, milk.....................94
Liqueurs 183

M

Maillard-type browning............166
Mandarin peel oil................128
Mannose anomers................11
Marine flesh foods...............198
Mass spectrometer, gas chromato-
    graph-.....................230
Mass spectrometry with gas chroma-
    tography 86–89
Meat 190
    sulfur and aromatic compounds...239
    undesirable odor and flavor in.....225
    volatiles from irradiated.........234
    volatiles, oxygenated compounds
        in irradiated..............238
Mechanism of receptor stimulation....7
Membrane puncturing theory of odors.34
Metabolism during climacteric, ba-
    nana 252
Methional and furfural.......82, 90–91
Methyl ketones...................99
    in Blue cheese................101
    in Cheddar cheese.............101
    reduction of..................102
Milk 183
    fat, lactones from..............106
    ketones in evaporated...........99
    lipids 94
    rancid 96
Mixed beverage flavors...........187
Molecular properties, odor and......20
Molecular shape and odors.........33
Monosodium ʟ-glutamate...........262
Monosodium glutamate and 5′-nu-
    cleotides, synergism...........264
Monoterpenes in oil of black pepper..217
Mycoderma 104

N

Naringin 128
Natural beverage flavors...........182
Nerve cell membranes, structure and
    composition of...............54

Nerve sheath, phospholipids in......55
Neurophysiological studies of 5′-nu-
    cleotides 268
Nitrotoluidine taste...............10
Nootkatone...................71, 128
Nose, analogs of the..............59
Nucleotide, flavor *vs.* structure of....262
5′-Nucleotides
    as flavor enhancers.............261
    methods for producing..........272
    and monosodium glutamate, syn-
        ergism of..................264
    neurophysiological studies of.....268
    as replacements for beef extract...272
    specifications of...............262

O

Odor
    adaptation 45
    and adsorption.................37
    and behavior..................16
    blends 44
    classifications 31
    concentrates
        chromatogram of banana...246, 248
        separation of banana..250, 255, 256
        yield of banana.............242
    electrochemical approach to......65
    emotional content of............25
    enzyme theory of..............47
    fatigue 44
    flow rate.....................19
    and food acceptance............25
    and hemolysis.................40
    and interfacial adsorptivity.......39
    measurement 53
    in meat, undesirable............225
    membrane puncturing theory of...34
    and molecular properties......20, 31
    and molecular shape............33
    pigment theory of..............46
    primary 22
    quality classification............22
    quantitative measurement of......18
    receptors 42
        chemical excitation of..........1
    of secondary alcohols...........104
    sensing state.................42
    and solubility.................38
    and spectra...................35
    stereochemical theory of........32
    theories 29
    thresholds 37
    types 31
    vibrational theory of...........34
Odorivector molecule, dynamic area
    of 37
Odorivectors 30
Odorous molecules................15
Off-flavor in meat................225
Oil of black pepper...............216
    monoterpenes in...............217
Oleoresin chemistry...............203
Olfaction 29
    measurement of...............53

Olfaction (*Continued*)
  mechanisms 45
  theories of.....................56
Olfactory receptor sensitivity.......19
Olfactory receptor sites.............23
Olfactory sensors, passive...........48
Onion flavor.....................135
Orange blossom odor..............177
Orange oil.............123–125, 128
Organic acids in bread.............157
Osmophile 61
Osmophoric groups................32
Oven browning and bread flavor....166
Oven vapors, alcohols in...........158
Oxidation of aldehydes............110
β-Oxidation of fatty acids..........101
Oxidized fat.....................236
Oxygenated compounds in irradiated
  meat volatiles................238

P

Peas 149
Penicillium roqueforti.............102
5′-Phosphodiesterase 272
Phospholipids in nerve sheath.......55
Pigment theory of odor............46
Piperettine 214
Piperine 213
Potato chromatograms..77, 84–85, 88–89
Potatoes 149
Potassium ions....................54
Potentiators, taste.................13
Poultry 191
Pre-ferments
  alcohols in.....................158
  carbonyl compounds in......160–165
  esters in.......................165
  organic acids in................157
Processed beverage flavors..........184
Profile functional group theory......32
Proteins, ion binding to............59

R

Radiation products induced in fatty
  esters 237
Rancid milk.......................96
Receptor stimulation, mechanism of....7
Red meats........................194
Regression equation................66
Ribonucleic acid, degradation of....272
Ripening of bananas..............257
Rutabaga 148

S

Saccharin, substitutions in........9, 10
Sandlewood 123
Sauerkraut 147
Sea foods........................198
Secondary alcohols in Blue cheese...102
Secondary alcohols, odors of........104
Sensing state, odor................42
Sensory evaluation of food flavor.....64
Sodium ions......................54

Solubility and odor.................38
Solubility parameter................38
Spectra and odors..................35
Spice
  flavor 203
  imports 207
  products 207
Stepwise multiple regression.........66
Stereochemical theory of odors......32
Stereoisomers, taste of.............11
Stimulation, mechanism of..........23
Strawberry oil....................122
Streptococcus diacelilactis..........106
Streptococcus lactis...............106
String beans......................177
Structure *vs.* flavor of
  5′-inosinate and 5′-guanylate.....265
  nucleotide 262
Sulfur compounds from irradiated
  meats 239
Synergism of monosodium L-gluta-
  mate and 5′-nucleotides........264

T

Taste
  categories 2
  genetics of.....................12
  inhibitors and potentiators........13
  messages 4
  molecules, properties of...........9
  of nitrotoluidine................10
  odor, and food acceptance........25
  of stereoisomers................11
  panels 67
  primary 2
  qualities 1
  receptors, chemical excitation of.....1
Terpenes in oil of black pepper,
  mono- 217
Threshold levels of flavor enhancers..267
Thresholds, odor..................37
Tomato chromatograms......76, 84–87
Tomatoes 150
Torulopsis sphaerica..............102
Tricholomic acid.................270

U

Undesirable odor and flavor in meat.225
5′-Uridylate 269
5′-Uridylic acid..................272

V

Variance, analysis of................69
Vegetables, cooked................150
Vegetables, flavor components of....131
Vibrational theory of odors..........34
Volatile banana components, flavor
  and biochemistry of...........241
Volatiles from irradiated meat.......234

W

Wines 186

Z

Zingerone 209